BECKONING TRAILS

THE CLOWN WAS SPEAKING TO BUDDY NONAME

BECKONING TRAILS

BY
MADELINE YOUNG
LORNE PIERCE

THE RYERSON PRESS
THE MACMILLANS IN CANADA

ACKNOWLEDGMENTS

For permission to use copyrighted material, grateful acknowledgment is made to the following:
D. Appleton-Century Company Inc. for "Well Sung, Master Skylark!" from *Master Skylark*, by
John Bennett; Greta Briggs for "Other Lights Keep Burning"; The British Admiralty for "Submarine Epic," from *His Majesty's Submarines*, also published in *The Daily Telegraph* (London,
Eng.), by "Naval Eyewitness"; Canadian Broadcasting Corporation, McLaren Advertising
Agency and the Imperial Oil Co. for "He Shoots! He Scores!" by Foster Hewitt and Wes McKnight;
Century Company and the author for "The Education of Helen Keller," from *The World I Live In*,
by Helen Keller; Mary Ellen Chase for "A Library of One's Own"; Wm. Collins Sons & Co. Ltd.
for "The Adventure of the *Altmark*," from *Steady as You Go*, by "Bartimeus"; Ralph Connor for
"The Spelling Match"; Alberta W. Constant for "Bookworms Don't Have to Bite," by Alberta
W. Constant, from *Twenty-five Non-royalty Plays*; Alban Dobson and Humphrey Milford for "The
Song of the Sea Wind," by Austin Dobson; Doubleday & Company Inc. for "One Minute Longer,"
from *Buff a Collie*, by Albert Payson Terhune, copyright 1921 by Doubleday & Company Inc.,
"The House with Nobody in It," from *Trees and Other Poems*, by Joyce Kilmer, copyright 1914 by
Doubleday & Company Inc.; Doubleday, Doran and Company Inc. for "Trees" from *Trees and
Other Poems* by Joyce Kilmer, and "The Wild Geese of Wyndygoul" and "Coaly-Bay," from *Wild
Animal Ways*, by Ernest Thompson Seton, copyright 1916; Mrs. May Harvey Drummond for
"Johnnie Courteau," by W. H. Drummond; Arthur Heming for "Holidaying in the Woods," from
The Living Forest; William Heyliger for "Bean Ball Bill"; Henry Holt and Company, Inc. for
"The Staggit Eve," from *Understood Betsy*, by Dorothy Canfield, copyright 1917, 1946 by Henry
Holt and Company, Inc.; Houghton Mifflin Company for "The Campfire," from *Camp Ken-
Jockety*, by Ethel Hume Bennett, "Robinson Crusoe's Story," from *Davy and the Goblin*, by C. E.
Carryl and "The House and the Road," from *The Singing Leaves*, by Josephine Preston Peabody;
Hutchinson & Co. Ltd. for "Amy Johnson Reaches Australia," from *Fifty-two Thrilling Stories
for Girls*, by Ethel Talbot; Rudyard Kipling and The Macmillan Company of Canada Limited for
"If" and "Moti Guj"; Little Brown & Company for "The Thunder Storm," from *Poems of Emily
Dickinson* edited by Martha Dickinson Bianchi and Alfred Leete Hampson, and "Dorothy's
Daffodils," by Frances Avery Faunce; Longmans, Green & Company for "Winter," from *The
Unknown Country*, by Bruce Hutchison; Isobel Ecclestone Mackay for "The Merchants";
The Macmillan Company of Canada Limited for "The Browns," from *A Dryad in Nanaimo*, by
Audrey Alexandra Brown, "The House of McGinnis," by Grey Owl and "Chapdelaine Makes
Land," from *Maria Chapdelaine*, by Louis Hémon, translated by W. H. Blake; Macmillan & Co.
Ltd. and The Macmillan Company of Canada Limited for "The Escape from the Press Gang,"
from *The Trumpet Major*, by Thomas Hardy and "Weathers," from *Collected Poems* of Thomas
Hardy; The Macmillan Company for "Gypsies," from *The Pointed People*, by Rachel Field,
copyright 1924 and 1930 by The Macmillan Company, "The Story of Keesh," by Jack London,
"The Fox Hunt," from *Reynard the Fox*, by John Masefield and "Roads of the Air," from
North America, by Lucy Mitchell; McClelland and Stewart Limited for "The Bear Hunt,"
from *Glengarry School Days*, by Ralph Connor, "Now the Lilac Tree's in Bud," "Ships of Yule"
and "Vagabond Song," by Bliss Carman, "Leetle Bateese," by William Henry Drummond, "How
We Kept Mother's Day," from *Laugh with Leacock*, by Stephen Leacock, "The King's Breakfast,"
by A. A. Milne and "Tom Thomson," from *Adventure of Canadian Painting*, by R. S. Lambert;
Jack Miner for "Love Among the Birds," from *Jack Miner and the Birds*; The Musson Book
Company for "The Song My Paddle Sings," from *Flint and Feather*, by Pauline Johnson; Thomas
Nelson and Sons Limited for "Christmas at Fort Norman," from *Sixty Below*, by Tony Onraet;
the author's estate for "The Fighting *Temeraire*" and "Gillespie," from *Poems New and Old*, by
Sir Henry Newbolt, published by Messrs. John Murray; Alfred Noyes, A. P. Watt & Sons and the
publishers for "Old Grey Squirrel," from *Collected Poems of Alfred Noyes*, published by Wm.
Blackwood & Sons Ltd. and "Eagles of Freedom," from *Shadows on the Down*, by Alfred Noyes,
published by Hutchinson & Co. Ltd.; Martha Ostenso for "The Tramp"; John Oxenham for "The
High Way," from *The King's Highway*; Hesketh Pearson for "The Magic of Books," from *Conan
Doyle, His Life and Art*; J. B. Priestley and the Proprietors of *Punch* for "The Carrip"; The
Ryerson Press for "After School" and "Trees," from *Pipes of Pan*, by Bliss Carman, "The
Mounties," from *The Mounties*, by Anne I. Grierson, "Marie Hébert: A Mother of New France,"
by Julia Jarvis, "Heat" and "A Thunderstorm," from *Selected Poems* of Archibald Lamp-
man, "Love among the Birds," by Jack Miner, "In Flanders Fields," by John McCrae, "The
Evening Hour at Kingscroft," from *A Book of Roberts*, by Lloyd Roberts, "The Bear that Thought
He Was a Dog," from *Hoof and Claw*, by Sir Charles G. D. Roberts, "The Yak," from *Leaves in
the Wind*, by Virna Sheard, "A Pioneer Home," by Catharine Parr Trail, and "The Great
Physician," from *Men Who Played the Game* and "He Gave Wings to Words," from *Heroes of Peace*,
both by Archer Wallace; Gordon V. Thomson Ltd. and the author's estate for "O Canada," by
R. Stanley Weir; Percy Westerman for "The Stopgap"; E. M. Wilkie for "Rain"; and John C.
Wilson for "Lie in the Dark and Listen," by Noel Coward, reprinted from *The Atlantic Monthly*.
Mrs. Charles Edward Brown for a selection from *Paul Bunyan and Tony Beaver Tales*, by C. E.
Brown; Doubleday & Co. for a selection from *Paul Bunyan and His Great Blue Ox*; Houghton
Mifflin Company for a version of "Pyramus and Thisbe," by Josephine Peabody from *Old Greek
Folk Stories Told Anew*; The Macmillan Company of Canada Limited for "Whoso Loseth His
Life," from *Men of Valour*, by Mabel Tinkiss Good.

Every reasonable care has been taken to trace ownership of copyright material. Information
will be welcome which will enable the publishers to rectify any reference or credit in subsequent
editions.

PRINTED AND BOUND IN CANADA
BY THE RYERSON PRESS, TORONTO

CONTENTS

I

THE WONDERFUL COUNTRY OF BOOKS

II

TRAILS TO ADVENTURE

III

OFF TO THE GAME

*A starred selection is a poem. Canadian authors are in italics.

CONTENTS

IV

OUTDOORS CALLING

V

ACTORS ALL

VI

HOME IS BEST

VII

SCHOOL DAYS

VIII

SKYWAYS OF FREEDOM

IX

HIGH WAYS OF PEACE

X

WITH GLOWING HEARTS

CONTENTS

Beckoning Trails

I

The Wonderful Country of Books

COUNTRY OF BOOKS

This workaday world is so trying at times,
  Folks chatter and squabble like rooks!
So the wise flee away to the best of all climes,
Which you enter through History, Memoirs, or Rhymes,
  That most wonderful Country of Books.

And griefs are forgotten.   You go on a tour
  More wondrous than any of "Cook's";
It costs you but little—your welcome is sure—
Your spirits revive in the atmosphere pure
  Of the wonderful Country of Books.

Your friends rally round you.   You shake by the hand
  Philosophers, soldiers, and spooks!
Adventurers, heroes, and all the bright band
Of poets and sages are yours to command
  In that wonderful Country of Books.

New heights are explored; and new banners unfurled;
  New joys found in all sorts of nooks—
From the work-weary brain misgivings are hurled—
You come back refreshed to this workaday world
  From that wonderful Country of Books.

—Author Unknown

STUDY AND ENJOYMENT

1. Write down a list of six characters whom you have met in books. Exchange
   lists with another member of your class, and give the title and author of
   the book in which each character appears.

"WELL SUNG, MASTER SKYLARK!"

Nicholas Attwood, a young lad of Stratford-on-Avon, runs away from home to see the Lord Admiral's company of players from London at Coventry. There he becomes acquainted with Gaston Carew, the leading player, and meets the Admiral's company at the Blue Boar Inn. Master Carew discovers that Nicholas has remarkable talent, and so it all comes about that young Nicholas Attwood "joins" the High Admiral's company and becomes Master Skylark. You should read the book. It is a wonderfully interesting story of Shakespeare's day.

It was past high noon, and they had long since left Warwick Castle far behind. "Nicholas," said the master-player, in the middle of a stream of amazing stories of life in London town, "there is Blacklow knoll." He pointed to a little hill off to the left.

Nick stared; he knew the tale: how grim old Guy de Beauchamp had Piers Gaveston's[1] head upon that hill for calling him the Black Hound of Arden.

"Ah!" said Carew, "times have changed since then, boy, when thou couldst have a man's head off for calling thee a name. But, Nicholas, hast anything to eat?"

"Nothing at all, sir."

Master Carew pulled from his pouch some barley-cakes and half a small Banbury cheese, yellow as gold and with a keen, sharp savour. "'Tis enough for both of us," said he, as they came to a shady little wood with a clear, mossy-bottomed spring running down into a green meadow with a mild noise, murmuring among the stones. "Come along, Nicholas; we'll eat it under the trees."

He had a small flask of wine, but Nick drank no wine, and went down to the spring instead. There was a wild bird singing in a bush there, and as he trotted down the slope it hushed its wandering tune. Nick took the sound up softly, and stood by the wet stones a little while, imitating the bird's trilling note, and laughing to hear it answer

[1]Pronounce: Guy dĕ Bē'chăm; Găv'ĕs-tŭnz.

NICK STOOD BY THE WET STONES A LITTLE WHILE, IMITATING THE BIRD'S
TRILLING NOTE

timidly, as if it took him for some great new bird without wings. Cocking its shy head and watching him shrewdly with its beady eye, it sat, almost persuaded that it was only size which made them different, until Nick clapped his cap upon his head and strolled back, singing as he went.

It was only the thread of an old-fashioned madrigal which he had often heard his mother sing, with quaint words long since gone out of style and hardly to be understood, and between the staves a warbling, wordless refrain which he had learned out on the hills and in the fields, picked up from a bird's glad-throated morning-song.

He had always sung the plain-tunes in church without taking any particular thought about it; and he sang easily, with a clear young voice which had a full, flute-like note in it like the high, sweet song of a thrush singing in deep woods.

Gaston Carew, the master-player, was sitting with his back against an oak, placidly munching the last of the cheese, when Nick began to sing. He started, straightening up as if some one had called him suddenly out of a sound sleep, and, turning his head, listened eagerly.

Nick mocked the wild bird, called again with a mellow, warbling trill, and then struck up the quaint old madrigal with the bird's song running through it. Carew leaped to his feet, with a flash in his dark eyes. "My soul! my soul!" he exclaimed in an excited undertone. "It is not— nay, it cannot be—why, 'tis—it is the boy! Upon my heart, he hath a skylark prisoned in his throat! *Well sung, well sung, Master Skylark!*" he cried, clapping his hands in real delight, as Nick came singing up the bank. "Why, lad, I vow I thought thou wert up in the sky somewhere, with wings to thy back! Where didst thou learn that wonder-song?"

Nick coloured up, quite taken aback. "I do na know, sir," said he; "mother learned[1] me part, and the rest just came, I think, sir."

[1]*Learned*, meaning *taught*, was correct then, but is never used now, except, very rarely, by poets.

The master-player, his whole face alive and eager, now stared at Nicholas Attwood as fixedly as Nick had stared at him.

It was a hearty little English lad he saw, about eleven years of age, tall, slender, trimly built, and fair. A grey cloth cap clung to the side of his curly yellow head, and he wore a sleeveless jerkin of dark-blue serge, grey home-spun hose, and heelless shoes of russet leather. The white sleeves of his linen shirt were open to the elbow, and his arms were lithe and brown. His eyes were frankly clear and blue, and his red mouth had a trick of smiling that went straight to a body's heart.

"Why, lad, lad," cried Carew, breathlessly, "thou hast a very fortune in thy throat!"

Nick looked up in great surprise; and at that the master-player broke off suddenly and said no more, though such a strange light came creeping into his eyes that Nick, after meeting his fixed stare for a moment, asked uneasily if they would not better be going on.

Without a word the master-player started. Something had come into his head which seemed to more than fill his mind; for as he strode along he whistled under his breath and laughed softly to himself. Then again he snapped his fingers and took a dancing step or two across the road, and at last fell to talking aloud to himself, though Nick could not make out a single word he said, for it was in some foreign language.

"Nicholas," he said suddenly, as they passed the winding lane that leads away to Kenilworth—"Nicholas, dost know any other songs like that?"

"Not just like that, sir," answered Nick, not knowing what to make of his companion's strange new mood; "but I know Master Will Shakespeare's 'Then nightly sings the staring owl, tu-who, to-whit, tu-who!' and 'The ousel-cock so black of hue, with orange-tawny bill,'[1] and then, too, I know the throstle's song that goes with it."

[1]See "The Comedy of Pyramus and Thisbe," page 215.

"Why, to be sure—to be sure thou knowest old Nick Bottom's song,[1] for isn't thy name Nick? Well met, both song and singer—well met, I say ! Nay," he said hastily, seeing Nick about to speak; "I do not care to hear thee talk. Sing me all thy songs. I am hungry as a wolf for songs. Why, Nicholas, I must have songs! Come, lift up that honeyed throat of thine and sing another song. Be not so backward; surely I love thee, Nick, and thou wilt sing all of thy songs for me."

He laid his hand on Nick's shoulder in his kindly way, and kept step with him like a bosom friend, so that Nick's heart beat high with pride, and he sang all the songs he knew as they walked along.

Carew listened intently, and sometimes with a fierce eagerness that almost frightened the boy; and sometimes he frowned, and said under his breath, "Tut, tut, that will not do!" but oftener he laughed without a sound, nodding his head in time to the lilting tune, and seeming vastly pleased with Nick, the singing, and last, but not least, with himself.

And when Nick had ended, the master-player had not a word to say, but for half a mile gnawed his moustache in nervous silence, and looked Nick all over with a long and earnest look.

Then suddenly he slapped his thigh, and tossed his head back boldly. "I'll do it," he said; "I'll do it if I dance on air for it! I'll have it out of Master Stubbes and canting Stratford town, or may I never thrive! My soul! It is the very thing. His eyes are like twin holidays, and he breathes the breath of spring. Nicholas, Nicholas Skylark,—Master Skylark,—why, it is a good name, in sooth, a very good name! I'll do it—I will, upon my word, and on the remnant of mine honour!"

"Did ye speak to me, sir?" asked Nick, timidly.

[1]You meet Bottom on page 217.

"Nay, Nicholas; I was talking to the moon."

"Why, sir, the moon has not come yet," said Nick, staring into the western sky.

"To be sure," replied Master Carew, with a queer laugh. "Well, the silvery loafer has missed the first act."

"Oh," cried Nick, reminded of the purpose of his long walk, "what will ye play for the Mayor's play, sir?"

"I don't know," replied Carew, carelessly; "it will all be done before I come. They will have had the free play this afternoon, so as to catch the pence of all the May-day crowd tomorrow."

Nick stopped in the road, and his eyes filled up with tears, so quick and bitter was the disappointment. "Why," he cried, with a tremble in his tired voice, "I thought the free play would be on the morrow—and now I have not a farthing to go in!"

"Tut, tut, thou silly lad!" laughed Carew, frankly; "am I thy friend for naught? What! let thee walk all the way to Coventry, and never see the play? Nay, on my soul! Why, Nick, I love thee, lad; and I'll do for thee in the twinkling of an eye. Canst thou speak lines by heart? Well, then, say these few after me, and bear them in thy mind."

And thereupon he hastily repeated some half a dozen disconnected lines in a high, reciting tone.

"Why, sir," cried Nick, bewildered, "it is a part!"

"To be sure," said Carew, laughing, "it is a part—and a part of a very good whole, too—a comedy by young Tom Heywood, that would make a graven image split its sides with laughing; and do thou just learn that part, good Master Skylark, and thou shalt say it in tomorrow's play."

"What, Master Carew!" gasped Nick. "I—truly? With the Lord Admiral's players?"

"Why, to be sure!" cried the master-player, in great glee, clapping him upon the back. "Thou art just the very fellow for the part—my lady's page should be a pretty lad, and, soul o' me, thou art that same! And, Nick, thou

shalt sing Tom Heywood's newest song. It is a pretty
song; it is a lark-song like thine own."

Nick could hardly believe his ears. To act with the
Lord Admiral's company! To sing with them before all
Coventry! It passed the wildest dream that he had ever
dreamed. What would the boys in Stratford say? Aha!
They would laugh on the other side of their mouths now!

"But will they have me, sir?" he asked doubtfully.

"Have thee?" said Master Carew, haughtily. "If I
say go, thou shalt go. I am master here. And I tell thee,
Nick, that thou shalt see the play, and be the play, in part,
and—well, we shall see what we shall see."

With that he fell to humming and chuckling to himself,
as if he had swallowed a water-mill, while Nick turned
ecstatic cart-wheels along the grass beside the road, until
presently Coventry came in sight.   —*John Bennett*

From *Master Skylark*

"THE STAGGIT EVE"

Elizabeth Ann, "Betsy" for short, has left the home of two aunts in
the city to live in the country with Aunt Abigail, Uncle Henry and Cousin
Ann. Betsy notices a great change. Her aunts in the city have fussed
over her, protected her, and regarded her as a sensitive child to be "understood." Her country relatives are pleasant, matter-of-fact people, who
expect her to stand on her own feet. You may read more of the story in
Understood Betsy, by Dorothy Canfield.

After supper was over and the dishes washed and wiped,
Betsy helping with the putting away, the four gathered
around the big lamp on the table with the red cover.
Cousin Ann was making some buttonholes in the shirt-
waist she had constructed that afternoon, Aunt Abigail was
darning socks, and Uncle Henry was mending a piece of
harness. Shep lay on the couch and snored until he got so
noisy they couldn't stand it, and Cousin Ann poked him in
the ribs and he woke up snorting and gurgling and looking
around very sheepishly. Every time this happened it made

Betsy laugh. She held Eleanor, who didn't snore at all, but made the prettiest little tea-kettle-singing purr deep in her throat, and opened and sheathed her needle-like claws in Betsy's dress.

"Well, how'd you get on at school?" asked Uncle Henry.

"I'm *awfully* mixed up!" said Betsy, complainingly. "I don't know what I am! I'm second-grade arithmetic and third-grade spelling and seventh-grade reading and I don't know what in writing or composition. We didn't have those."

Nobody seemed to think this very remarkable, or even very interesting. Uncle Henry, indeed, noted it only to say, "Seventh-grade reading!" He turned to Aunt Abigail. "Oh, Mother, don't you suppose she could read aloud to us evenings?"

Aunt Abigail and Cousin Ann both laid down their sewing to laugh! "Yes, yes, Father, and play checkers with you too, like as not!" They explained to Betsy: "Your Uncle Henry is just daft on being read aloud to when he's got something to do in the evening, and when he hasn't he's as fidgety as a broody hen if he can't play checkers. Ann hates checkers and I haven't got the time, often."

"Oh, I *love* to play checkers!" said Betsy.

"Well, *now* . . ." said Uncle Henry, rising instantly and dropping his half-mended harness on the table. "Let's have a game."

"Oh, Father!" said Cousin Ann, in the tone she used for Shep. "How about that piece of breeching! You know that's not safe. Why don't you finish that up first?"

Uncle Henry sat down again, looking as Shep did when Cousin Ann told him to get up on the couch, and took up his needle and awl.

"But I could read something aloud," said Betsy, feeling very sorry for him. "At least I think I could. I never did, except at school."

"What shall we have, Mother?" asked Uncle Henry eagerly.

"Oh, I don't know.   What have we got in this book-case?" said Aunt Abigail.   "It's pretty cold to go into the parlour to the other one."   She leaned forward, ran her fat fore-finger over the worn old volumes, and took out a battered, blue-covered book.   ".Scott?"

"Yes, yes!" said Uncle Henry, his eyes shining.   "The staggit eve!"

At least that was the way it sounded to Betsy, but when she took the book and looked where Aunt Abigail pointed she read it correctly, though in a timid, uncertain voice. She was very proud to think she could please a grown-up so much as she was evidently pleasing Uncle Henry, but the idea of reading aloud for people to hear, not for a teacher to correct, was unheard-of.

> The Stag at eve had drunk his fill
> Where danced the moon on Monan's rill,

she began, and it was as though she had stepped into a boat and was swept off by a strong current.   She did not know what all the words meant, and she could not pronounce a good many of the names, but nobody interrupted to correct her, and she read on and on, steadied by the. strongly-marked rhythm, drawn forward swiftly from one clanging, sonorous rhyme to another.   Uncle Henry nodded his head in time to the rise and fall of her voice and now and then stopped his work to look at her with bright, eager, old eyes.   He knew some of the places by heart evidently, for once in a while his voice would join the little girl's for a couplet or two.   They chanted together thus:

> A moment listened to the cry
> That thickened as the chase drew nigh,
> Then, as the headmost foes appeared,
> With one brave bound, the copse he cleared.

At the last line Uncle Henry flung his arm out wide, and the child felt as though the deer had made his great leap there, before her eyes.

SHE READ ON AND ON—

"I've seen 'em jump just like that," broke in Uncle Henry. "A two-three-hundred-pound stag go up over a four-foot fence just like a piece of thistledown in the wind."

"Uncle Henry," asked Elizabeth Ann, "what is a copse?"

"I don't know," said Uncle Henry indifferently. "Something in the woods, must be. Underbrush most likely. You can always tell words you don't know by the sense of the whole thing. Go on."

And stretching forward, free and far,

The child's voice took up the chant again. She read faster and faster as it got more exciting. Uncle Henry joined in on

For, jaded now and spent with toil,
Embossed with foam and dark with soil,
While every gasp with sobs he drew,
The labouring stag strained full in view.

The little girl's heart beat fast. She fled along through the next lines, stumbling desperately over the hard words but seeing the headlong chase through them clearly as through tree-trunks in a forest. Uncle Henry broke in in a triumphant shout:

> The wily quarry shunned the shock
> And *turned* him from the opposing rock;
> Then dashing down a darksome glen,
> Soon lost to hound and hunter's ken,
> In the deep Trossach's wildest nook
> His solitary refuge took.

"Oh *my*!" cried Elizabeth Ann, laying down the book. "He got away, didn't he? I was *so* afraid he wouldn't!"

"I can just hear those dogs yelping, can't you?" said Uncle Henry.

"Sometimes you hear 'em that way up on the slope of Hemlock Mountain back of us, when they get to running a deer."

"What say we have some pop-corn?" suggested Aunt Abigail. "Betsy, don't you want to pop us some?"

"I never *did*," said the little girl, but in a less doubtful tone than she had ever used with that phrase so familiar to her. A dim notion was growing up in her mind that the fact that she had never done a thing was no proof that she couldn't.

"I'll show you," said Uncle Henry. He reached down a couple of ears from a big yellow cluster hanging on the wall, and he and Betsy shelled them into the popper, popped it full of snowy kernels, buttered it, salted it, and took it back to the table.

—*Dorothy Canfield*
From *Understood Betsy*

STUDY AND ENJOYMENT

1. Betsy was learning to do her share in her new home. What three actions show this?
2. Betsy stumbled over the hard words, yet she enjoyed reading the poem. Why did she like it?

3. Uncle Henry said: "You can always tell words you don't know by the sense of the whole thing." What is your opinion? Check with your dictionary to see if Uncle Henry was right about *copse*. Do you know from your reading what *breeching* is?

4. "She read on, steadied by the strongly marked rhythm, drawn forward swiftly from one clanging, sonorous rhyme to another." Rhythm is the musical effect given by the beat in poetry. Any line of verse can be divided into accented and unaccented syllables. The accented syllables have a heavier beat. This line

Thĕ Stág| ăt evé| hăd drúnk| hĭs fíll

is divided into four parts or *feet*, and each *foot* has two syllables, an unaccented one followed by an accented one. The arrangement of syllables, feet and accents, repeated from line to line, gives rhythmic pattern or *metre* to the poem. Why is the *rhyme* so noticeable in the poem that Betsy read?

5. You will find the whole poem entitled *The Lady of the Lake* in any book of poems by Sir Walter Scott. Try reading it, not puzzling over the words, but enjoying the story and the fine sound of the verse.

THE MAGIC OF BOOKS

Sir Arthur Conan Doyle [1859-1930] was a medical doctor of Scottish birth who is remembered for his stories of Sherlock Holmes, an amateur detective. Doyle loved books, and here we read of the part they played in his boyhood.

I do not think that life has any joy to offer so complete, so soul-filling as that which comes upon the imaginative lad, whose spare time is limited, but who is able to snuggle down into a corner with his book, knowing that the next hour is all his own. And how vivid and fresh it all is! Your very heart and soul are out on the prairies and the oceans with your hero. It is you who act and suffer and enjoy. You carry the long small-bore Kentucky rifle with which such amazing things are done, and you lie out upon the topsail yard, and get jerked by the flap of the sail into the Pacific, where you cling on to the leg of an albatross, and so keep afloat until the comic boatswain turns up with his crew of volunteers to handspike you into safety. What magic it is, this stirring of the boyish heart and mind! Long ere I came to my teens I had traversed every sea, and knew the Rockies like my own back garden. How often had I sprung upon the back of the charging buffalo and so escaped him. It was an everyday emergency to have to set the prairie on fire in front of me in order to escape from the fire behind, or to run a mile down a brook to throw the blood-hounds off my trail. I had creased horses, I had shot down rapids, I had strapped on my moccasins hind-foremost to conceal my tracks, I had lain under water with a reed in my mouth, and I had feigned madness to escape the torture. As to Indian braves whom I slew in single combat, I could have stocked a large graveyard, and, fortunately enough, though I was a good deal chipped about in these affairs, no real harm ever came of it, and I was always nursed back into health by a very fascinating young squaw. It was all more real than the reality. Since those days I have in very truth both shot bears and harpooned whales, but the performance was flat compared to the first time that I did it with Mr. Ballantyne or Captain Mayne Reid at my elbow.

(Conan Doyle not only loved reading books, but he wanted to write them as well. He has left us the following account of his first effort as author.)

I was six at the time, and have a very distinct recollection of the achievement. It was written, I remember, upon foolscap paper, in what might be called a fine bold hand—four words to the line—and was illustrated by marginal pen-and-ink sketches by the author. There was a man in it, and there was a tiger. I forget which was the hero, but it didn't matter much, for they became blended into one about the time the tiger met the man! I described at length, verbally and pictorially, the untimely end of that wayfarer. But when the tiger had absorbed him, I found myself slightly embarrassed as to how my story was to go on.   "It is very easy to get people into scrapes, and very hard to get them out again," I remarked, and I have often had cause to repeat that wise saying of my childhood.   On this occasion the situation was beyond me, and my book, like my man, was engulfed in my tiger.

—*Sir Arthur Conan Doyle*
From *Conan Doyle: His Life and Art*, by Hesketh Pearson.

STUDY AND ENJOYMENT

1. The adventure stories of R. M. Ballantyne and Thomas Mayne Reid were great favourites when Doyle was a boy.   Ballantyne came to Canada from Scotland as a lad of sixteen, and spent six years as a clerk with the Hudson Bay Company.   Three of his better known books are *The Young Fur Traders*, *The Coral Island*, and *The Dog Crusoe*.   Reid ran away to sea as a youth, and gathered stirring tales to tell in *The Rifle Rangers*, *The Boy Hunters*, *The Scalp Hunters*, and *The Boy Slaves*.

2. Which adventure mentioned by Conan Doyle interests you most?   Explain how it was possible.

3. *Albatross*, a very large bird with webbed feet, found in the region of the Pacific and southern oceans; *boatswain*, pronounced bō′sn, ship's officer in charge of sails; *handspike*, a wooden bar tipped with iron, used as a lever on shipboard to lift heavy weights; *traversed*, travelled across; *creased*, wounded by a shot in the crest or ridge of the neck, stunning the animal but not killing it; *feigned*, pretended.

4. Doyle once wrote:

   I have wrought my simple plan
   If I give one hour of joy
   To the boy who's half a man
   Or the man who's half a boy.

   What do you think he meant by those lines?

A LIBRARY OF ONE'S OWN

I bought my first book at the age of eight with my own unique capital.   Of course, prior to that time and to that memorable May morning I had been *given* several books which stood neatly arranged on the low shelf allotted to me in the family library. There were *Little Women* in plain brown, *Hans Christian Andersen* with the twelve swans winging their way across its red cover, *Gulliver's Travels* in a delectable shade of blue, *Sara Crewe* in green, *A Child's History of England* in dull navy, and sundry others much thumbed and worn from delicious hours of reading. But to be *given* a book, even one much loved and desired, and to buy for oneself with one's own savings are two vastly different things. The first makes one a mere owner of books, the second elevates one to that far more important position—a book collector.

My capital in those days was not money. An allowance of twenty-five cents a month could not, even with the most careful hoarding, promise many books. Church and Sunday School, tablets and pencils, constituted too many inroads upon my slender purse. There had to be other means of acquisition to me at eight.

The village grocery store afforded a way out. In February of the year 1895 its proprietor advertised a new kind of washing soap, strong to the nose and yellow in hue. As an added inducement to its purchase, he offered to give a book to any one buying twelve cakes and presenting him with the wrappers as indisputable proof. In those days mothers were not so likely to buy staples in quantities as they are today. Instead, purchases were made in cash and when needed. Hence from the very inception of my dream, an obstacle was placed in my path.

I remember with what eagerness I watched that laundry soap diminish slowly, week by week, with what jealous care I hoarded the wrappers one by one. An unprecedented desire for personal cleanliness drove me to utilize the soap for my baths, although its acrid odour and its tendency to roughen my skin were anything but pleasant. Daily, too, I watched the small shelf of books in the store, fearing lest they should disappear before less wary and more wealthy buyers or that the proprietor would discontinue his advertising tactics. But at last after many anxious weeks, I had amassed the required twelve wrappers, and immediately I assumed the responsibilities and joys of a collector of books.

It was on a May Saturday that I stood before the books in the grocery store, surrounded by bags and barrels, canisters and cans, and eyed suspiciously by the grocer's big black cat. The books were some thirty in number, all printed badly on rusty paper, all bound in the cheapest of bindings. But those facts at that age meant nothing to me. I was intent on finding among the thirty the friend I had been watching for weeks, the possible disappearance of whom had day by day caused me such anxiety. This was *The Swiss Family Robinson*. Since it was in those days accounted a book primarily for boys, my brother instead of me had received a copy the preceding Christmas and had been none too generous with his good fortune. I adored that book.

As I made my purchase by passing the soap wrappers to the grocer (who counted them suspiciously) and received the book of my choice, I became conscious of a new dignity. I was a different person as I walked up the village street with Fritz and Ernest, Ned and Franz. A book owner had by virtue of a consuming desire and twelve laundry soap wrappers become a book collector!

—*Mary Ellen Chase*

STUDY AND ENJOYMENT

1. Why did Mary Ellen Chase want the book so much? What parts of the story tell the reader how eagerly she longed for it?

2. How does the author help us to see each of these pictures clearly: (a) the little girl's library; (b) the grocery store?

3. This story is told with a chuckle. Now that the author is grown-up, she looks back upon her determined little eight-year-old self with an understanding smile. What parts of the story seem amusing to you?

4. *The Swiss Family Robinson*, by Johann Rudolf Wyss, is the story of a family wrecked on a lonely island. Fritz, Ernest, Ned and Franz were boys in the family. You will enjoy the book if you have not already read it.

THE DAY IS DONE

Henry Wadsworth Longfellow (1807-1882), one of the best known poets of the United States, for many years was a Professor in Harvard University. He gave up teaching to write poetry. It is really himself that he describes in the following poem. Some of his "simple and heartfelt" poems all the world knows—"Evangeline," "Hiawatha," "Santa Filomena," "The Arrow and the Song" and many more.

The day is done, and the darkness
    Falls from the wings of Night,
As a feather is wafted downward
    From an eagle in his flight.

I see the lights of the village
    Gleam through the rain and the mist,
And a feeling of sadness comes o'er me,
    That my soul cannot resist:

A feeling of sadness and longing,
    That is not akin to pain,
And resembles sorrow only
    As the mist resembles the rain.

Come, read to me some poem,
    Some simple and heartfelt lay,
That shall soothe this restless feeling,
    And banish the thoughts of day.

Not from the grand old masters,
    Not from the bards sublime,
Whose distant footsteps echo
    Through the corridors of Time.

For, like strains of martial music,
   Their mighty thoughts suggest
Life's endless toil and endeavour,
   And tonight I long for rest.

Read from some humbler poet,
   Whose songs gushed from his heart,
As showers from the clouds of summer,
   Or tears from the eyelids start;

Who, through long days of labour,
   And nights devoid of ease,
Still heard in his soul the music
   Of wonderful melodies.

Such songs have power to quiet
   The restless pulse of care,
And come like the benediction
   That follows after prayer.

Then read from the treasured volume
   The poem of thy choice,
And lend to the rhyme of the poet
   The beauty of thy voice.

And the night shall be filled with music,
   And the cares that infest the day
Shall fold their tents, like the Arabs,
   And as silently steal away.

—Henry Wadsworth Longfellow

STUDY AND ENJOYMENT

1. By what means did peace come to the poet? Why did he not want to hear "from the grand old masters"?

2. Word music is heard when words rhyme—that is, when they end with the same sound. Music is also heard when words begin with or contain the same sound, such as the *d* in the line:

> The day is done, and the darkness . . .

Such music is called *alliteration*. Notice the *f*'s in the first stanza. Read aloud the stanza that seems most musical to you.

3. This poem and "Country of Books" both tell of the power of books to drive away care and to lighten the spirit. How do they differ? Which poet "heard in his soul the music of wonderful melodies"? Which poem is the more worth memorizing? Why?

READ A BOOK

Master Skylark. By John Bennett. Appleton-Century-Crofts. Young Nicholas meets Shakespeare and sings for Queen Elizabeth.

Understood Betsy. By Dorothy Canfield. Holt. The "problem child" develops into a happy, self-reliant girl.

Two Hundred Best Poems for Boys and Girls. Edited by Marjorie Barrows. Whitman.

A Place for Herself. By Adele de Leeuw. Macmillan. A young girl organizes a travelling library and broadens her knowledge of people and books.

Breathless Episodes from Fiction. Edited by P. E. Herrick. Ryerson. The best chapters selected from our great books.

Trails to Adventure

THE SHIPS OF YULE

Bliss Carman was born in New Brunswick and lived there during his boyhood and youth. As a little lad he often watched the sailing ships come into the harbour and sail away again. He used to fancy that he had a fleet of ships of his own. Here he tells us of their imaginary journeys.

When I was just a little boy,
Before I went to school,
I had a fleet of forty sail
I called the Ships of Yule;

Of every rig, from rakish brig
And gallant barkentine,
To little Fundy fishing boats
With gunwales painted green.

They used to go on trading trips
Around the world for me,
For though I had to stay on shore
My heart was on the sea.

They stopped at every port of call
From Babylon to Rome,
To load with all the lovely things
We never had at home;

With elephants and ivory
Bought from the King of Tyre,
And shells and silk and sandal-wood
That sailor men admire;

With figs and dates from Samarcand,
And squatty ginger-jars,
And scented silver-amulets
From Indian bazaars;

With sugar-cane from Port of Spain,
And monkeys from Ceylon,
And paper lanterns from Pekin
With painted dragons on;

With cocoanuts from Zanzibar,
And pines from Singapore;
And when they had unloaded these
They could go back for more.

And even after I was big
And had to go to school,
My mind was often far away
Aboard the Ships of Yule.

—*Bliss Carman*

STUDY AND ENJOYMENT

1. *Brig* and *barkentine* are types of sailing vessels. You might look them up in a dictionary or in *The Picture Book of Ships* (Macmillan).

2. *Gunwale*, pronounced *gun'el* to rhyme with *funnel*, is the upper edge of a ship's side.

3. Do you know where all the places are at which the little boy's ships called? If not, perhaps you would look them up for a report to your class. Notice that all of the places have pleasant sounding names, and that many are associated with stories of long ago.

4. Which cargo do you prefer? Why? Can you imagine why Carman called this poem "The Ships of Yule"? You know, of course, that Yule is an old word for Christmas.

THE BEAR HUNT

A bear, the first to show itself in the Glengarry settlement for several years, has made a night visit to the Murray home, sampling honey left in the kitchen, and leaving deep scratches on the table top. Hughie Murray and his friend, Don Cameron, decide to go bear hunting, and slip secretly away to the swamp and beech bush, knowing full well that their parents, if consulted, would put a stop to the plan. After some hours of vain search, Camerons' black dogs lose the trail, and the boys strike for home. As their paths separate they agree that the sound of a shot will be a signal for the one to go to the other.

I

In a few minutes Hughie found himself alone in the thick underbrush of the swamp. The shadows were lying heavy, and the sunlight that still caught the tops of the tall trees was quite lost in the gloom of the low underbrush. Deep moss under foot, with fallen trees and thick-growing balsam and cedars, made the walking difficult, and every step Hughie wished himself out in the clearing. He began to feel, too, the oppression of the falling darkness. He tried whistling to keep up his courage, but the sound seemed to fill the whole woods about him, and he soon gave it up.

After a few minutes he stood still and called for Fido, but the dog had gone on some hunt of his own, and with a sense of deeper loneliness, he set himself again to his struggle with the moss and brush and fallen trees. At length he reached firmer ground, and began with more cheerful heart to climb up to the open.

Suddenly he heard a rustle, and saw the brush in front of him move.

"Oh, there you are, you brute," he cried, "come in here. Come in, Fido. Here, sir!"

He pushed the bushes aside, and his heart jumped and filled his mouth. A huge, black shape stood right across his path not ten paces away. A moment they gazed at each other, and then, with a low growl, the bear began to sway awkwardly toward him. Hughie threw up his gun and fired.   The bear paused, snapping viciously and tearing at his wounded shoulder, and then rushed on Hughie without waiting to rise on his hind legs.

Like a flash Hughie dodged behind the brush, and then fled like the wind toward the open. Looking over his shoulder, he saw the bear shambling after him at a great pace, and gaining at every jump, and his heart froze with terror. The balsams and spruces were all too low for safety. A little way before him he saw a small birch. If he could only make that he might escape. Summoning all his strength he rushed for the tree, the bear closing fast upon him. Could he spring up out of reach of the bear's awful claws?

Two yards from the tree he heard an angry snap and snarl at his heels. With a cry, he dropped his gun, and springing for the lowest bough, drew up his legs quickly after him with the horrible feeling of having them ripped asunder. To his amazement he found that the bear was not scrambling up the tree after him, but was still some paces off, with Fido skirmishing at long range. It was Fido's timely nip that had brought him to a sudden halt, and allowed Hughie to make his climb in safety.

"Good dog, Fido. Sic him! Sic him, old fellow!" cried out Hughie, but Fido was new to this kind of warfare, and at every jump of the raging brute he fled into the brush with his tail between his legs, returning, however, to the attack as the bear retired.

After driving Fido off, the bear rushed at the tree, and in a fury began tearing up its roots. Then, as if realizing the futility of this, he flung himself upon its trunk and began shaking it with great violence from side to side.

Hughie soon saw that the tree would not long stand such an attack. He slipped down to the lowest bough so that his weight might be taken from the swaying top, and encouraging Fido, awaited results.

He found himself singularly cool. Having escaped immediate danger, the hunter's instinct awoke within him, and he longed to get that bear. If he only had his gun, he would soon settle him, but the bear, unfortunately, had possession of that. He began hurriedly to cut off as stout a branch as he could to make himself a club. He was not a moment too soon, for the bear, realizing that he could neither tear up the tree by the roots nor shake his enemy out of it, decided, apparently, to go up for him.

He first set himself to get rid of Fido, which he partially succeeded in doing by chasing him a long distance off. Then, with a great rush, he flew at the tree, and with amazing rapidity began to climb.

Hughie, surprised by this swift attack, hastened to climb to the higher branches, but in a moment he saw that this would be fatal. Remembering that the bear is like the dog in his sensitive parts, he descended to meet his advancing foe, and reaching down, hit him a sharp blow on the snout. With a roar of rage and surprise the bear let go his hold, slipped to the ground, and began to tear up the earth, sneezing violently.

"Oh, if I only had that gun," groaned Hughie, "I'd get him. And if he gets away after Fido again, I believe I'll try it."

II

The bear now set himself to plan some new form of attack. He had been wounded, but only enough to enrage him, and his fury served to fix more firmly in his head the single purpose of getting into his grip this enemy of his in the tree, whom he appeared to have so nearly at his mercy.

Whatever his new plan might be, a necessary preliminary was getting rid of Fido, and this he proceeded to do. Round about the trees he pursued him, getting farther and farther away from the birch, till Hughie, watching his chance, slipped down the tree and ran for his gun. But no sooner had he stooped for it than the bear saw the move, and with an angry roar rushed for him.

Once more Hughie sprang for his branch, but the gun

caught in the boughs and he slipped to the ground, the
bear within striking distance.   With a cry he sprang again,
reached his bough and drew himself up, holding his precious
gun safe, wondering how he had escaped.   Again it was
Fido that had saved him, for as the bear had gathered
himself to spring, Fido, seeing his chance, rushed boldly in,
and flinging himself upon the hind leg of the enraged brute,
held fast.   It was the boy's salvation, but alas! it was
Fido's destruction, for wheeling suddenly, the bear struck
a swift downward blow with his powerful front paw.   With
a howl, poor Fido dragged himself away out of reach and
lay down, moaning pitifully.

The bear, realizing that he had got rid of one foe, now
proceeded more cautiously to deal with the other, and
began warily climbing the tree, keeping his wicked little
eyes fixed upon Hughie.

Meantime, Hughie was loading his gun with all speed.
He emptied his powder-horn into the muzzle, and with the
bear coming slowly nearer, began to search for his bullets.
Through one pocket after another his trembling fingers
flew, while with the butt of his gun he menaced his
approaching enemy.

"Where are those bullets?" he groaned.   "Ah, here they
are!" diving into his trousers pocket.   "Fool of a place to
keep them, too!"

He took a handful of slugs and bullets, poured them
into his gun, rammed down a wadding of leaves upon all,
retreating as he did so to the higher limbs, the bear following him steadily.   But just as he had his cap securely fixed
upon the nipple, the bear suddenly revealed his plan.
Holding by his front paws, he threw his hind legs off from
the trunk.   It was his usual method of felling trees.   The
tree swayed and bent till the top almost touched the
ground.   But Hughie, with his legs wreathed round the
trunk, brought his gun to his shoulder, and with its muzzle
almost touching the breast of the hanging brute, pulled
the trigger.

There was a terrific report, the bear dropped in a heap from the tree, and Hughie was hurled violently to the ground some distance away, partially stunned. He raised himself to see the bear struggling up to a sitting position, and gnashing his teeth, and flinging blood and foam from his mouth, begin to drag himself toward him. He was conscious of a languid indifference, and found himself wondering how long the bear would take to cover the distance.

But while he was thus cogitating there was a sharp, quick bark, and a great black form hurled itself at the bear's throat and bore the fierce brute to the ground.

Drawing a long sigh, Hughie sank back to the ground, with the sound of a far-away shot in his ears, and darkness veiling his eyes.

He was awakened by Don's voice anxiously calling him.

"Are you hurt much, Hughie? Did he squeeze you?"

Hughie sat up, blinking stupidly.

"What?" he asked. "Who?"

"Why the bear, of course."

"The bear? No. Man! It's too bad you weren't here, Don," he went on, rousing himself. "He can't be gone far."

"Not very," said Don, laughing loud. "Yonder he lies."

Hughie turned his head and gazed wondering, at the great black mass over which Don's black dogs were standing guard, and sniffing with supreme satisfaction.

Then all came back to him.

"Where's Fido?" he asked, rising. "Yes, it was Fido saved me, for sure. He tackled the bear every time he rushed at me, and hung onto him just as I climbed the tree the second time."

As he spoke he walked over to the place where he had last seen the dog. A little farther on, behind a spruce-tree, they found poor Fido, horribly mangled and dead.

Hughie stooped over him. "Poor old boy, poor old Fido," he said, in a low voice, stroking his head.

Don turned away and walked whistling toward the bear. As he sat beside the black carcass his two dogs came to him. He threw his arms round them, and he understood how Hughie was feeling behind the spruce-tree beside the faithful dog that had given him his life.

—Ralph Connor
From *Glengarry School Days*

THREE GALLOPING POEMS

Every one loves a spirited poem about a brave rider, a swift steed, and a racing gallop.　Fortunately there are many splendid poems of this sort.

You are familiar with the side-splitting horseback adventure of John Gilpin.　Then there is Scott's "Lochinvar," who came galloping out of the West, broadsword for war, and fair speech for love; and Masefield's "Cavalier," full of the clink of horses' feet, roll of drums, and "long plumes swaying."

Here are three fine galloping poems you will surely relish. "Trumpeter!　Sound to saddle and spur!"

How They Brought the Good News from Ghent to Aix

I sprang to the stirrup, and Joris, and he;
I galloped, Dirck galloped, we galloped all three;
"Good speed!" cried the watch, as the gate-bolts undrew;
"Speed!" echoed the wall to us galloping through;
Behind shut the postern, the lights sank to rest,
And into the midnight we galloped abreast.

Not a word to each other; we kept the great pace
Neck by neck, stride by stride, never changing our place;
I turned in my saddle and made its girths tight,
Then shortened each stirrup, and set the pique right,
Rebuckled the cheek-strap, chained slacker the bit,
Nor galloped less steadily Roland a whit.

'Twas moonset at starting; but while we drew near
Lokeren, the cocks crew, and twilight dawned clear;
At Boom, a great yellow star came out to see;
At Düffeld, 'twas morning as plain as could be;
And from Mecheln church-steeple we heard the half-chime,
So, Joris broke silence with, "Yet there is time!"

At Aershot, up leaped of a sudden the sun,
And against him the cattle stood black every one,
To stare thro' the mist at us galloping past,
And I saw my stout galloper Roland at last,
With resolute shoulders, each butting away
The haze, as some bluff river headland its spray:

And his low head and crest, just one sharp ear bent back
For my voice, and the other pricked out on his track;
And one eye's black intelligence—ever that glance
O'er its white edge at me, his own master, askance!
And the thick heavy spume-flakes which aye and anon
His fierce lips shook upwards in galloping on.

By Hasselt, Dirck groaned; and cried Joris, "Stay spur!
Your Roos galloped bravely, the fault's not in her,
We'll remember at Aix"—for one heard the quick wheeze
Of her chest, saw the stretched neck, and staggering knees,
And sunk tail, and horrible heave of the flank,
As down on her haunches she shuddered and sank.

So we were left galloping, Joris and I,
Past Looz and past Tongres, no cloud in the sky;
The broad sun above laughed a pitiless laugh,
'Neath our feet broke the brittle bright stubble like chaff;
Till over by Dalhem a dome-spire sprang white,
And "Gallop," gasped Joris, "for Aix is in sight!"

"How they'll greet us!"—and all in a moment his roan
Rolled neck and croup over, lay dead as a stone;
And there was my Roland to bear the whole weight
Of the news, which alone could save Aix from her fate,
With his nostrils like pits full of blood to the brim,
And with circles of red for his eye-sockets' rim.

Then I cast loose my buff-coat, each holster let fall,
Shook off both my jack-boots, let go belt and all,
Stood up in the stirrup, leaned, patted his ear,
Called my Roland his pet-name, my horse without peer;
Clapped my hands, laughed and sang, any noise, bad or
    good,
Till at length into Aix Roland galloped and stood!

And all I remember is,—friends flocking round,
As I sat with his head 'twixt my knees on the ground;
And no voice but was praising this Roland of mine,
As I poured down his throat our last measure of wine,
Which (the burgesses voted by common consent)
Was no more than his due who brought good news from
    Ghent.

—Robert Browning

STUDY AND ENJOYMENT

1. Who is the hero of this story? How does Browning make you feel this?
2. What do you think the message might have been?
3. Browning loved horses and a brisk gallop. One day, on board ship off
   the coast of Africa, he got thinking about riding, and wrote this poem
   on the flyleaf of a book he had been reading. The story in the poem has
   no historical foundation, but the places mentioned are all real. Ghent
   is in Belgium.
4. When on a train we realize how quickly we are travelling when we see the
   trees and telephone poles go rushing by. On this gallop, town after
   town flashes past, giving us a similar impression of speed. List the
   places to see how many there are. Word and phrases—such as *sprang,
   stride by stride* also add to the sense of speed. What others can you
   discover? Finally, and most important of all, the rhythm gives urgent
   pace to the lines. Note the pounding hoof beats as you read!

GILLESPIE

Riding at dawn, riding alone,
 Gillespie left the town behind;
Before he turned by the Westward road
 A horseman crossed him, staggering blind.

"The Devil's abroad in false Vellore,
 The Devil that stabs by night," he said,
"Women and children, rank and file,
 Dying and dead, dying and dead."

Without a word, without a groan,
 Sudden and swift Gillespie turned,
The blood roared in his ears like fire,
 Like fire the road beneath him burned.

He thundered back to Arcot gate,
 He thundered up through Arcot town,
Before he thought a second thought
 In the barrack yard he lighted down.

"Trumpeter, sound for the Light Dragoons,
 Sound to saddle and spur," he said;
"He that is ready may ride with me,
 And he that can may ride ahead."

Fierce and fain, fierce and fain,
 Behind him went the troopers grim;
They rode as ride the Light Dragoons,
 But never a man could ride with him.

Their rowels ripped their horses' sides,
 Their hearts were red with a deeper goad,
But ever alone before them all
 Gillespie rode, Gillespie rode.

FIERCE AND FAIN, FIERCE AND FAIN,
BEHIND HIM WENT THE TROOPERS GRIM

Alone he came to false Vellore,
  The walls were lined, the gates were barred;
Alone he walked where the bullets bit,
  And called above to the Sergeant's Guard.

"Sergeant, Sergeant, over the gate,
  Where are your officers all?" he said;
Heavily came the Sergeant's voice,
  "There are two living, and forty dead."

"A rope, a rope," Gillespie cried:
   They bound their belts to serve his need;
There was not a rebel behind the wall
   But laid his barrel and drew his bead.

There was not a rebel among them all
   But pulled his trigger and cursed his aim,
For lightly swung and rightly swung
   Over the gate Gillespie came.

He dressed the line, he led the charge,
   They swept the wall like a stream in spate,
And roaring over the roar they heard
   The galloper guns that burst the gate.

Fierce and fain, fierce and fain,
   The troopers rode the reeking flight:
The very stones remember still
   The end of them that stab by night.

They've kept the tale a hundred years,
   They'll keep the tale a hundred more:
Riding at dawn, riding alone,
   Gillespie came to false Vellore.

                              —*Sir Henry Newbolt*

STUDY AND ENJOYMENT
(Vellore and Arcot are Indian cities.)

1. Gillespie, riding alone, is overtaken by a horseman with bad news; dashing back to Arcot, he calls out the Dragoons; he outrides the troopers to Vellore and speaks with the Sergeant of the Guard; swung on a rope of belts over the gate, he clears the way for his followers; the garrison is taken and those that fled are ridden down; the story will live. What stanzas describe these?

2. In stanza 1 the word *riding* is repeated twice. Point out other places where repetition aids the movement of the poem. *Sudden and swift* is an example of alliteration adding vigour to a line. Can you find other examples.

3. A group might read this poem in unison, with solo voices taking the parts of the horseman, Gillespie, and the Sergeant.

BANNERMAN OF THE DANDENONG

I rode through the Bush in the burning noon
    Over the hills to my bride,—
The track was rough and the way was long,
And Bannerman of the Dandenong,
    He rode along by my side.

A day's march off my Beautiful dwelt,
    By the Murray streams in the West;—
Lightly lilting a gay love-song
Rode Bannerman of the Dandenong,
    With a blood-red rose on his breast.

"Red, red rose of the Western streams"
    Was the song he sang that day—
Truest comrade in hour of need;
Bay Mathinna his peerless steed—
    I had my own good grey.

There fell a spark on the upland grass—
    The dry Bush leapt into flame;—
And I felt my heart go cold as death,
And Bannerman smiled and caught his breath,—
    But I heard him name Her name.

Down the hill-side the fire-floods rushed,
    On the roaring eastern wind;—
Neck and neck was the reckless race,—
Ever the bay mare kept her pace,
    But the grey horse dropped behind.

He turned in the saddle—"Let's change, I say!"
    And his bridle rein he drew.

He sprang to the ground,—"Look sharp!" he said,
With a backward toss of his curly head—
  "I ride lighter than you!"

Down and up—it was quickly done—
  No words to waste that day!—
Swift as a swallow she sped along,
The good bay mare from Dandenong,—
  And Bannerman rode the grey.

The hot air scorched like a furnace blast
  From the very mouth of Hell:—
The blue gums caught and blazed on high
Like flaming pillars into the sky; . . .
  The grey horse staggered and fell.

"Ride, ride, lad,—ride for her sake!" he cried;—
  Into the gulf of flame
Were swept, in less than a breathing space,
The laughing eyes, and the comely face,
  And the lips that named *Her* name.

She bore me bravely, the good bay mare;—
  Stunned, and dizzy and blind,
I heard the sound of a mingling roar—
'Twas the river's rush that I heard before,
  And the flames that rolled behind.

Safe—safe, at Nammoora gate,
  I fell, and lay like a stone.
O love! thine arms were about me then,
Thy warm tears called me to life again,—
  But—O God! that I came alone!—

I and my Beautiful dwelt in peace,
 By the Murray streams in the West,—
But oft through the mist of my dreams along
Rides Bannerman of the Dandenong,
 With the blood-red rose on his breast.

—*Alice Werner*

STUDY AND ENJOYMENT

1. "Greater love hath no man than this, that a man should lay down his life for his friend." Who laid down his life in this poem? For whom, besides his friend, did he die? Which of the two men did the lady love? What picture do you get of Bannerman? Tell the story in your own words.
2. That Australia is the scene of this story may be gathered from these clues: Bush, Murray Stream, Dandenong, Nammoora, blue gums.
3. Red stands for heroism and sacrifice; the rose suggests love.
4. If you were an artist, what incident would you take for purpose of illustration in this poem? Why?

GULLIVER AMONG THE GIANTS

Gulliver's Travels, from which this story is taken, is a book that boys and girls have read for over two hundred years. It tells of the journeys of an Englishman who finds himself in countries built and peopled by the author's imagination. The first country Gulliver visited belonged to the Lilliputians (pronounced lĭl-ĭ-pū'shăns), a race of tiny people to whom he seemed a giant. On his next voyage, having been shipwrecked off Brobdingnag (brŏb'-dĭng-năg), a land of giants, he is found by a farmer who gives him as a plaything to his little daughter, Glumdalclitch, nine years old and forty feet tall.

I should have lived happy enough in that country, if my littleness had not exposed me to several ridiculous and troublesome accidents; some of which I shall venture to relate. Glumdalclitch often carried me into the gardens of the court in my smaller box, and would sometimes take me out of it, and hold me in her hand, or set me down to walk. I remember, before the dwarf left the queen, he followed us one day into those gardens; and my nurse having set me down, he and I being close together, near some dwarf apple trees, I must needs show my wit, by a silly allusion between him and the trees, which happens to hold in their language as it does in ours; whereupon the malicious rogue, watching his opportunity, when I was walking under one of them, shook it directly over my head, by which a dozen apples, each of them near as large as a Bristol barrel, came tumbling about my ears. One of them hit me on the back as I chanced to stoop, and knocked me down flat on my face; but I received no other hurt, and the dwarf was pardoned at my desire, because I had given the provocation. . . .

This accident absolutely determined Glumdalclitch never to trust me abroad for the future out of her sight. I had been long afraid of this resolution, and therefore concealed from her some little unlucky adventures that happened in those times when I was left by myself.

I cannot tell whether I was more pleased or mortified to observe, in those solitary walks, that the smaller birds did not appear to be at all afraid of me, but would hop about within a yard distance, looking for worms and other food with as much indifference and security as if no creature at all were near them. I remember a thrush had the confidence to snatch out of my hand with his bill a piece of cake that Glumdalclitch had just given me for my breakfast. When I attempted to catch any of these birds they would boldly turn against me, endeavouring to peck my fingers, which I durst not venture within their reach; and then they would turn back unconcerned, to hunt for worms or snails, as they did before. But one day I took a thick cudgel, and threw it with all my strength so luckily at a linnet that I knocked him down, and seizing him by the neck with both my hands, ran with him in triumph to my nurse. However, the bird, who had only been stunned, recovering himself, gave me so many boxes with his wings on both sides of my head and body, though I held him at arm's length, and was out of the reach of his claws, that I was twenty times thinking to let him go. But I was soon relieved by one of our servants, who wrung off the bird's neck, and I had him next day for dinner, by the queen's command.   This linnet, as near as I can remember, seemed to be somewhat larger than an English swan. . . .

The queen, who often used to hear me talk of my sea voyages, and took all occasions to divert me when I was melancholy, asked me whether I understood how to handle a sail or an oar, and whether a little exercise of rowing might not be convenient for my health.   I answered that I understood both very well   But I could not see how this could be done in their country, where the smallest wherry was equal to a first-rate man-of-war among us, and such a boat as I could manage would never live in any of their rivers.   Her majesty said if I would contrive a boat, her own joiner should make it, and she would provide a place for me to sail in.   The fellow was an ingenious workman, and by my instructions in ten days finished a pleasure-boat, with all its tackling, able conveniently to hold eight Europeans. When it was finished the queen was so delighted that she ran with it in her lap to the king, who ordered it to be put in a cistern full of water, with me in it, by way of trial, where I could not manage my two sculls, or little oars, for want of room.   But the queen had before contrived another project.   She ordered the joiner to make a wooden trough of three hundred feet long, fifty broad, and eight deep; which, being well pitched to prevent leaking, was placed on the floor along the wall in an outer room of the palace. It had a tap near the bottom to let out the water when it began to grow stale; and two servants could easily fill it in half an hour.   Here I often used to row for my own diversion, as well as that of the queen and her ladies, who thought themselves well entertained with my skill and agility.   Sometimes I would put up my sail, and then my business was only to steer, while the ladies gave me a gale with their fans; and when they were weary, some of their pages would blow my sail forward with their breath, while I showed my art by steering starboard or larboard as I pleased. When I had done, Glumdalclitch always carried back my boat into her closet, and hung it on a nail to dry.

In this exercise I once met with an accident, which had like to have cost me my life; for one of the pages having put my boat into the trough, the governess who attended Glumdalclitch very officiously lifted me up, to place me in the boat. But I happened to slip through her fingers, and should have infallibly fallen down forty feet, upon the floor, if, by the luckiest chance in the world, I had not been stopped by a corking-pin that stuck in the good gentlewoman's stomacher; the head of the pin passed between my shirt and the waistband of my breeches, and thus I was held by the middle in the air, till Glumdalclitch ran to my relief.

But the greatest danger I ever underwent in that kingdom was from a monkey, who belonged to one of the clerks of the kitchen. Glumdalclitch had locked me up in her closet, while she went somewhere upon business, or a visit. The weather being warm, the closet window was left open, as well as the windows and the door of my bigger box, in which I usually lived, because of its largeness and conveniency. As I sat quietly meditating at my table I heard something bounce in at the closet window, and skip about from one side to the other: whereat, although I was alarmed, yet I ventured to look out, but not stirring from my seat; and then I saw this frolicsome animal frisking and leaping up and down, till at last he came to my box, which he seemed to view with pleasure and curiosity, peeping in at the door and every window. I retreated to the farther corner of my room or box; but the monkey, looking in at every side, put me in such a fright that I wanted presence of mind to conceal myself under the bed, as I might easily have done. After some time spent in peeping, grinning, and chattering, he at last espied me; and reaching one of his paws in at the door, as a cat does when she plays with a mouse, he at length caught hold of my coat and dragged me

out. He took me up in his right forefoot, and held me as a
nurse does a child she is going to suckle, just as I have seen
the same sort of creature do with a kitten in Europe; and
when I offered to struggle, he squeezed me so hard that I
thought it more prudent to submit. I have good reason to
believe that he took me for a young one of his own species,
by his often stroking my face very gently with his other
paw. In these diversions he was interrupted by a noise at
the closet door, as if somebody were opening it; whereupon
he suddenly leaped up to the window at which he had come
in, and thence upon the leads and gutters, walking upon
three legs, and holding me in the fourth, till he clambered up
to a roof that was next to ours. I heard Glumdalclitch
give a shriek at the moment he was carrying me out. The
poor girl was almost distracted: that quarter of the palace
was all in an uproar; the servants ran for ladders; the
monkey was seen by hundreds in the court sitting upon the
ridge of a building, holding me like a baby in one of his
fore-paws, and feeding me with the other by cramming into
my mouth some victuals he had squeezed out of the bag on
one side of his chaps, and patting me when I would not eat;
whereat the rabble below could not forbear laughing; neither
do I think they justly ought to be blamed, for without
question the sight was ridiculous enough to everybody but
myself. Some of the people threw up stones, hoping to
drive the monkey down; but this was strictly forbidden, or
else, very probably, my brains had been dashed out.

The ladders were now applied, and mounted by several
men, which the monkey observing, and finding himself
almost encompassed, not being able to make speed enough
with his three legs, let me drop on a ridge tile, and made
his escape. Here I sat for some time, five hundred yards
from the ground, expecting every moment to be blown
down by the wind, or to fall by my own giddiness, and come
tumbling over and over from the ridge to the eaves; but an

honest lad, one of my nurse's footmen, climbed up, and putting me into his breeches pocket, brought me down safe.

—Jonathan Swift

From *Gulliver's Travels*

STUDY AND ENJOYMENT

1. In what way was Gulliver treated as a plaything? How did Gulliver annoy the dwarf? How did the dwarf get even with him?
2. In each paragraph find at least one example that shows that the country is really a land of giants. What features of the wooden trough resemble a modern swimming pool?
3. A *stomacher* (pronounced stomatsher) is the lower front part of the bodice or waist of a lady's dress. It is an old-fashioned word and describes an old-fashioned dress. A *corking-pin* was a very large pin. A *wherry* is a light row-boat.
4. What part of the story do you find the most amusing? the most exaggerated?

THE BEAR THAT THOUGHT HE WAS A DOG

Hoof and Claw, from which this story is taken, contains other good stories about animals. The story here has been condensed so that it would not be too long for your Reader. The parts left out are interesting, too, as you may discover if you get the book from the library.

I. A MAN WITH A GUN

The gaunt, black mother lifted her head from nuzzling happily at the velvet fur of her little one. The cub was but twenty-four hours old, and engrossed every emotion of her savage heart; but her ear had caught the sound of heavy footsteps coming up the mountain. They were confident, fearless footsteps, taking no care whatever to disguise themselves, so she knew at once that they were the steps of the only creature that presumed to go so noisily through the great silences. Her heart pounded with anxious suspicion. She gave the cub a reassuring lick, deftly set it aside with her great paws, and thrust her head forth cautiously from the door of the den.

She saw a man—a woodsman in brownish-grey home-

WOOF GREW UP THINKING HIMSELF TO BE A DOG

spuns and heavy leg-boots, and with a gun over his shoulder—slouching up along the faintly marked trail which led close past her doorway. Her own great tracks on the trail had been hidden that morning by a soft and thawing fall of belated spring snow—"the robin snow," as it is called in New Brunswick—and the man, absorbed in picking his way by this unfamiliar route over the mountain, had no suspicion that he was in danger of trespassing. But the bear, with that tiny black form at the bottom of the den filling her whole horizon, could not conceive that the man's approach had any other purpose than to rob her of her treasure. She ran back to the little one, nosed it gently into a corner, and anxiously pawed some dry leaves half over it. Then, her eyes aflame with rage and fear, she betook herself once more to the entrance, and crouched there motionless to await the coming of the enemy.

The man swung up the hill noisily, grunting now and again as his foothold slipped on the slushy, moss-covered stones. He fetched a huge breath of satisfaction as he gained a little strip of level ledge, perhaps a dozen feet in length, with a scrubby spruce bush growing at the other end of it. Behind the bush he made out what looked as if it might be the entrance to a little cave. Interested at once, he strode forward to examine it. At the first stride a towering black form, jaws agape and claws outstretched, crashed past the fir bush and hurled itself upon him.

A man brought up in the backwoods learns to think quickly, or, rather, to think and act in the same instant. Even as the great beast sprang, the man's gun leaped to its place and he fired. His charge was nothing more than heavy duck-shot, intended for some low-flying flock of migrant geese or brant. But at this close range, some seven or eight feet only, it tore through its target like a heavy mushroom bullet, and with a stopping force that halted the animal's charge in mid-air like the blow of a steam hammer. She fell in her tracks, a heap of huddled fur and grinning teeth.

"That was a close call!" remarked the man.

Entering the half darkness of the cave, he quickly discovered the cub in its hiding-place. Young as it was, when he picked it up, it whimpered with terror and struck out with its baby paws, recognizing the smell of an enemy. The man grinned at this display of spirit.

"Ye're chock-full o' ginger!" said he. And then, being of an understanding heart and an experimental turn of mind, he laid the cub down and returned to the body of the mother. With his knife he cut off several big handfuls of the shaggy fur and stuffed it into his pockets. Then he rubbed his hands, his sleeves, and the breast of his coat on the warm body.

"There, now," said he, returning to the cave and once more picking up the little one, "I've made ye an orphant, to be sure, but I'm goin' to soothe yer feelin's all I kin. Ye must make believe as how I'm yer mammy till I kin find ye a better one."

Pillowed in the crook of his captor's arm, and with his nose snuggled into a bunch of his mother's fur, the cub ceased to wonder at a problem too hard for him, and dozed off into an uneasy sleep.   And the man, pleased with his new plaything, went gently that he might not disturb the slumber.

II. A New Mother

Now it chanced that at Jabe Smith's farm, on the other side of the mountain, there had just been a humble tragedy. Jabe Smith's dog, a long-haired brown retriever, had been bereaved of her new-born puppies.   Six of them she had borne, but five had been straightway taken from her and drowned.   For two days, in her box in the corner of the dusky stable, the brown mother had wistfully poured out her tenderness upon the one remaining puppy; and then, when she had run into the house for a moment to snatch a bite of breakfast, one of Smith's big red oxen had strolled into the stable and blundered a great splay hoof into the box.   That had happened in the morning; and all day the mother had moped, whimpering and whining, about the stable, casting long distraught glances at the box in the corner, which she was unwilling either to approach or to quite forsake.

When her master returned, and came and looked in hesitatingly at the stable door, the brown mother saw the small furry shape in the crook of his arm.   Her heart yearned to it at once.   She fawned upon the man coaxingly, lifted herself with her forepaws upon his coat, and reached up till she could lick the sleeping cub.   Somewhat puzzled, Jabe Smith went and looked into the box.   Then he understood.

"If you want the cub, Jinny, he's yours all right.   And it saves me a heap o' bother."

Driven by hunger, and reassured by the handful of fur

which the woodsman left with him, the cub promptly accepted his adoption. Jinny was a good mother. She loved the cub with a certain extravagance, and gave herself up to it utterly, and the cub repaid her devotion by imitating her in all ways possible. The bear, being by nature a very silent animal, Jinny's noisy barking seemed always to stir his curiosity and admiration; but his attempts to imitate it resulted in nothing more than an occasional grunting *woof*. This throaty syllable came to be accepted as his name, and he speedily learned to respond to it.

In the course of no long time, Jabe Smith realized that Woof was growing up thinking himself to be a dog, a belief which seemed to be accepted by others in the household. The cats scratched him when he was little, and with equal confidence they scratched him when he was big. Mrs. Smith, as long as she was in good humour, allowed him the freedom of the house, coddled him with kitchen tid-bits, and laughed when his bulk got in the way of her mopping or sweeping. But when storm was in the air, she regarded him no more than a black poodle. At the heels of the more nimble Jinny, he would be chased from the kitchen door, with Mrs. Jabe's angry broom thwacking at the spot where Nature had forgotten to give him a tail.

And so, with nothing to mar his content but the occasional fury of Mrs. Jabe's broom, Woof led the sheltered life, and was glad to be a dog.

III. Woof Makes a New Friend

(*In his third year, however, Woof felt the call of the wild. Taking to the woods, he forgot the farm for a time. But, when the frosts came, and the ground was crisp with the new-fallen leaves, he headed straight back for home. Alas! fire had destroyed the farm-house, and the Smiths had left for parts unknown. Greatly puzzled, Woof set off again on his wanderings.*)

About three weeks later, forlorn of heart and desperate

with hunger, Woof found himself in a part of the forest where he had never been before. But some one else had been there; before him was a broad trail, just such as Jabe Smith and his wood sled used to make. Here were the prints of horses' hooves. Woof's heart bounded hopefully. He hurried along down the trail. Then a faint delectable savour, drawn across the sharp, still air, met his nostrils. Pork and beans—oh, assuredly! He paused for a second to sniff the fragrance again, and then lurched onwards at a rolling gallop. He rounded a turn of the trail, and there before him stood a logging camp.

To Woof a human habitation stood for friendliness and food and shelter. He approached, therefore, without hesitation.

There was no sign of life about the place, except for the smoke rising liberally from the stove-pipe chimney. The door was shut, but Woof knew that doors frequently opened if one scratched at them and whined persuasively. He tried it, then stopped to listen for an answer. The answer came—a heavy, comfortable snore from within the cabin. It was mid-morning, and the camp cook, having got his work done up, was sleeping in his bunk the while the dinner was boiling.

Woof scratched and whined again. Then, growing impatient, he reared himself on his haunches in order to scratch with both paws at once. His luck favoured him, for he happened to scratch on the latch. It lifted, the door swung open suddenly, and he half fell across the threshold. He had not intended so abrupt an entrance, and he paused, peering with diffidence and hope into the homely gloom.

The snoring had stopped suddenly. At the rear of the cabin Woof made out a large, round, startled face, fringed with scanty red whiskers and a mop of red hair, staring at him from over the edge of an upper bunk. Woof had hoped to find Jabe Smith there. But this was a stranger, so he suppressed his impulse to rush in and wallow delightedly over the bunk. Instead of that, he came only half-way over the threshold.

To a cool observer of even the most limited intelligence it would have been clear that he intended to be friendly. But the cook of Conroy's Camp was taken by surprise, and he was not a cool observer—in fact, he was frightened. A gun was leaning against the wall below the bunk. A large, hairy hand stole forth, reached down and clutched the gun.

Woof wagged his haunches more coaxingly than ever, and took another hopeful step forward. Up went the gun. There was a blue-white spurt, and the report clashed deafeningly within the narrow quarters.

The cook was a poor shot at any time, and at this moment he was at a special disadvantage. The bullet went close over the top of Woof's head and sang waspishly across the clearing. Woof turned and looked over his shoulder to see what the man had fired at. If anything was hit, he wanted to go and get it and fetch it for the man, as Jabe and Jinny had taught him to do. But he could see no result of the shot. He whined again, and ventured all the way into the cabin.

The cook felt desperately for another cartridge. There was none to be found. He remembered that they were all in the chest by the door. He crouched back in the bunk, making himself as small as possible, and hoping that a certain hunk of bacon on the bench by the stove might divert the terrible stranger's attention and give him a chance to make a bolt for the door.

But Woof had not forgotten either the good example of Jinny or the discipline of Mrs. Jabe's broom. Far be it from him to help himself without leave. But he was very hungry. Something must be done to win the favour of the strangely unresponsive round-faced man in the bunk. Looking about him anxiously, he espied a pair of greasy cowhide "larrigans" lying on the floor near the door. Picking one up in his mouth, after the manner of his retriever foster-mother, he carried it over and laid it down, as a humble offering, beside the bunk.

Now the cook, though he had been undeniably frightened, was by no means a fool. This touching gift of one of his own larrigans opened his eyes and his heart. Such a bear, he was assured, could harbour no evil intentions. He sat up in his bunk.

"Hullo!" said he. "What ye doin' here, sonny? What d'ye want o' me, anyhow?"

The huge black beast wagged his hind quarters frantically, and wallowed on the floor in his fawning delight at the sound of a human voice.

"Seems to think he's a kind of a dawg," muttered the cook thoughtfully. And then the light of certain remembered rumours broke upon his memory.

"I'll be jiggered," said he, "ef 'tain't that there tame b'ar Jabe Smith, over to East Fork, used to have afore he was burnt out!"

Climbing confidently from the bunk, he proceeded to pour a generous portion of molasses over the contents of the scrap pail, because he knew that bears had a sweet tooth. When the choppers and drivers came trooping in for dinner, they were somewhat taken aback to find a huge bear sleeping beside the stove. As the dangerous-looking slumberer seemed to be in the way—none of the men caring to sit too close to him—to their amazement the cook smacked the mighty hindquarters with the flat of his hand, and bundled him unceremoniously into a corner. "'Pears to think he's some kind of a dawg," explained the cook, "so I let him come along in for company. He'll fetch yer larrigans an' socks an' things fer ye. An' it makes the camp a sight homier, havin' somethin' like a cat or a dawg about."

"Right you are!" agreed the boss. "But what was that noise we heard, along about an hour back? Did you shoot anything?"

"Oh, that was jest a little misunderstandin', before him an' me got acquainted," explained the cook, with a trace of embarrassment. "We made it up all right."

—*Sir Charles G. D. Roberts*
Adapted from *Hoof and Claw*

STUDY AND ENJOYMENT

Sir Charles G. D. Roberts, a cousin of Bliss Carman, was born near Fredericton, New Brunswick, January 10, 1860. He lives in the hearts of Canadians for his poems, adventure tales, romances, and stories of animals. You may get better acquainted with him by reading *The Evening Hour at Kingscroft* in this Reader.

1. How did the bear get its name? Why did it think it was a dog? What did the bear do, at the end of the story, that banished the cook's fear?

2. Select five expressions that show clearly the love of the mother bear for the cub. What do you learn about Jabe Smith from the way he treated the cub and his own dog? Mrs. Smith was not always in good humour. What is meant by "when storm was in the air"?

3. As Woof drew near the bunk house "a delectable savour met his nostrils." Express this in words you would use. What was this delightful fragrance? What is the most pleasant fragrance of food that you know?

THE ESCAPE FROM THE PRESS GANG

Bob Loveday has been a seaman, but now works in his father's mill. England is at war with Napoleon, and a "press gang" is combing the country for those whom they can press into the navy. The marines plan to attack the mill after dark, and Anne hastens to warn Bob, whom they hope to seize.

I

Anne, scarcely knowing what she did, descended the ladder and ran to the back door, hastily unbolting it to save Bob's time, and gently opening it in readiness for him. She had no sooner done this than she felt hands laid upon her shoulder from without, and a voice exclaiming, "That's how we do it—quite an obliging young man!"

Though the hands held her rather roughly, Anne did not mind for herself, and turning, she cried desperately, in tones intended to reach Bob's ears, "They are at the back door; try the front!"

But inexperienced Miss Garland little knew the shrewd habits of the gentlemen she had to deal with, who, well used to this sort of pastime, had already posted themselves at every outlet from the premises.

"Bring the lantern," shouted the fellow who held her. "Why, 'tis a girl! I half thought so. Here is a way in," he continued to his comrades, hastening to the foot of the ladder which led to Bob's room.

"What d'ye want?" said Bob, quietly opening the door and showing himself still radiant in the full dress that he had worn with such effect at Weymouth at the Theatre Royal, which he had been about to change for his mill suit when Anne gave the alarm.

"This gentleman can't be the right one," observed a marine, rather impressed by Bob's appearance.

"Yes, yes; that's the man," said the sergeant. "Now take it quietly, my young cock-o'-wax. You look as if you meant to, and 'tis wise of ye."

"Where are you going to take me?" said Bob.

"Only aboard the *Black Diamond*. If you choose to take the bounty[1] and come voluntarily, you'll be allowed to go ashore whenever your ship's in port. If you don't, and we've got to pinion ye, you will not have your liberty at all. As you must come, willy nilly, you'll do the first if you've any brains whatever."

Bob's temper began to rise. "Don't talk so large about your pinioning, my man. When I've settled—"

"Now or never, young blowhard," interrupted his informant.

"Come, what jabber is this going on?" said the lieutenant, stepping forward. "Bring your man."

One of the marines set foot on the ladder, but at the same moment a shoe from Bob's hand hit the lantern with

[1] The reward offered to those who came willingly.

THE FUGITIVE MADE HASTE TO CLIMB OUT ON A LOW HANGING BRANCH

well-aimed directness, knocking it clean out of the grasp of the man who held it. In spite of the darkness they began to scramble up the ladder. Bob thereupon shut the door, which, being of but slight construction, was, as he knew, only a momentary defence. But it gained him time enough to open the window, gather up his legs upon the sill, and spring across into the apple tree growing without. He alighted without much hurt beyond a few scratches from the boughs, a shower of falling apples testifying to the force of his leap.

"Here he is!" shouted several below, who had seen Bob's figure flying like a raven's across the sky.

There was stillness for a moment in the tree. Then the fugitive made haste to climb out upon a low-hanging branch toward the garden, at which the men beneath all rushed in that direction to catch him as he dropped, saying: "You

may as well come down, old boy. 'Twas a spry jump and
we give you credit for it."

The latter movement of Loveday had been a mere feint.
Partly hidden by leaves, he glided back to the other part
of the tree, from whence it was easy to jump upon a thatch-
covered outhouse. This intention they did not appear to
suspect, which gave him the opportunity of sliding down
the slope and entering the back door of the mill.

"He's here, he's here!" the men exclaimed, running back
from the tree.

By this time they had obtained another light, and
pursued him closely along the back quarters of the mill.
Bob had entered the lower room, seized hold of the chain by
which the flour sacks were hoisted from story to story by
connection with the mill wheel, and pulled the rope that
hung alongside for the purpose of throwing it into gear.

The foremost pursuers arrived just in time to see
Captain Bob's legs and shoe buckles vanishing through the
trap-door overhead, his person having been whirled up by
the machinery like any bag of flour, and the trap falling
to behind him.

"He's gone up by the hoist!" said the sergeant, running
up the ladder in the corner to the next floor, and elevating
the light just in time to see Bob's suspended figure ascend-
ing in the same way through the same sort of trap into
the second floor. The second trap also fell together behind
him, and he was lost to view as before.

It was more difficult to follow now; there was only a
flimsy little ladder, and the men ascended cautiously.
When they stepped out upon the loft it was empty.

"He must have let go here," said one of the marines,
who knew more about mills than the others. "If he had
held fast a moment longer, he would have been dashed
against that beam."

They looked up. The hook by which Bob had held on
had ascended to the roof, and was winding around the

cylinder. Nothing was visible elsewhere but boarded divisions like the stalls of a stable, on each side of the stage they stood upon, these compartments being more or less heaped up with wheat and barley in the grain.

"Perhaps he's buried himself in the corn."

The whole crew jumped into the corn bins and stirred about their yellow contents; but neither arm, leg, nor coat-tail was uncovered. They removed sacks, peeped among the rafters of the roof, but to no purpose. The lieutenant began to fume at the loss of time.

"What fools to let the man go! Why, look here! What's this?" He had opened the door by which sacks were taken in from wagons without, and dangling from the cathead[1] projecting above it was the rope used in lifting them. "There's the way he went down," the officer continued. "The man's gone."

Amidst mumblings and growls the gang descended the pair of ladders and came into the open air; but Captain Bob was nowhere to be seen. They turned from the door, and leaving four of the marines to keep watch, the remainder of the party marched into the lane as far as where another road branched off. While they were pausing to decide which course to take, one of the soldiers held up the light. A black object was discernible upon the ground before them, and they found it to be a hat—the hat of Bob Loveday.

"We are on the track," cried the sergeant, deciding for this direction.

They tore on rapidly, and footsteps in the road ahead of them became audible, increasing in clearness, which told that they gained upon the fugitive, who in another five minutes stopped and turned. The rays of the candle fell upon Anne.

"What do you want?" she said, showing her frightened face.

[1]An arm of timber or iron.

They made no reply, but wheeled round and left her. She sank down on the bank to rest, having done all she could. It was she who had taken down Bob's hat from a nail and dropped it at the turning, with the view of misleading them till he should have got clear off.

But Anne Garland was too anxious to remain long away from the centre of operations. When she got back, she found that the press gang were standing in the court discussing their next move.

"Waste no more time here," the lieutenant said. "Two more villages to visit tonight, and the nearest three miles off. There's nobody else in this place, and we can't come back again."

When they were moving away, one of the marines, who had kept his eye on Anne and noticed her distress, contrived to say in a whisper, as he passed her: "We are coming back again as soon as it begins to get light; that's only said to deceive ye. Keep the young man out of the way."

They went as they had come; and the little household then met together, Mrs. Loveday having by this time dressed herself and come down. Anne told what the friendly marine had said to her; and fearing lest Bob was in the house, and would be discovered there when daylight came, they searched and called for him everywhere.

"Well," said Loveday, "you two go and lie down now, and I'll bide up; and as soon as he comes in, which he'll do most likely in the course of the night, I'll let him know that they are coming again."

II

Anne and Mrs. Loveday went to their bedrooms, and the miller entered the mill as if he were simply staying up to grind. But he continually left the flour shute to go outside and walk round. Each time he could see no living being near the spot.

At length the curtains of Anne's bed began to reveal their pattern, and day dawned. But while the light was no more than a suffusion[1] of pallor, she arose, put on her hat, and determined to explore the surrounding premises before the men arrived. Emerging into the raw loneliness of the daybreak, she went upon the bridge and looked up and down the road. It was as she had left it, empty, and the solitude was rendered yet more insistent by the silence of the mill wheel, which was now stopped, the miller having given up expecting Bob and retired to bed about three o'clock. The footprints of the marines still remained in the dust on the bridge, all the heelmarks toward the house, showing that the party had not as yet returned.

While she lingered she heard a slight noise in the other direction, and, turning, saw a woman approaching. The woman came up quickly, and, to her amazement, Anne recognized Matilda, an old friend of Bob's. She had plainly walked all the way from Weymouth, for her shoes were covered with dust.

"Have the press gang been here?" she gasped. "If not, they are coming! They got him! I am too late!"

"No; they are coming back again. Why did you—"

"I came to try to save him. Can we save him? Where is he?"

Anne looked the woman in the face, and it was impossible to doubt that she was in earnest.

"I don't know," she answered. "I am trying to find him before they come."

"Will you not let me help you?" cried Matilda. It was she who, after a quarrel with Bob, had given the press gang information as to his whereabouts. Now, repentant, she had risen before day and hastened to know the worst, and if possible, hinder consequences which she had been the first to set in train.[2]

After going hither and thither in the adjoining field

[1]Overspreading.   [2]Cause to begin.

Anne entered the garden. The walks were bathed in grey dew, and as she passed observantly along them, it appeared as if they had been brushed by some foot at a much earlier hour. At the end of the garden, bushes of broom, laurel, and yew formed a constantly encroaching shrubbery that had come there almost by chance and was never trimmed.

Behind these bushes was a garden seat, and upon it lay Bob, sound asleep.

The ends of his hair were clotted with damp, and there was a foggy film upon the mirror-like buttons of his coat and upon the buckles of his shoes. His bunch of new gold seals were dimmed by the same insidious dampness; his shirt frill and muslin neckcloth were limp as seaweed. It was plain that he had been there a long time. Anne shook him, but he did not awake, his breathing being low and stertorous.[1]

"Shake him again," said Matilda.

Anne shook him again, but he slept on. Then she noticed that his forehead bore the mark of a heavy wound.

"I fancy I hear something!" said her companion, starting forward, and endeavouring to wake Bob herself. "He is stunned or drugged!" she said; "there's no rousing him."

Anne raised her head and listened. From the direction of the eastern road came the sound of a steady tramp. "They are coming back!" she said, clasping her hands. "They will take him, ill as he is! He won't open his eyes— no, it is no use! Oh, what shall we do?"

Matilda did not reply, but running to the end of the seat on which Bob lay, tried its weight in her arms.

"It is not too heavy," she said. "You take that end, and I'll take this. We'll carry him away to some place of hiding."

Anne instantly seized the other end, and they proceeded with their burden at a slow pace to the lower garden gate, which they reached as the tread of the press gang

[1]Hoarse, as in snoring.

resounded over the bridge that gave access to the mill court, now hidden from view by the hedge and the trees of the garden.

"We will go inside this field," said Anne, faintly.

"No," said the other, "they will see our foot tracks in the dew. We must go into the road."

"It is the very road they will come down when they leave the mill."

"It cannot be helped; it is neck or nothing with us now."

So they emerged upon the road, and staggered along without speaking, occasionally resting for a moment to ease their arms, then shaking him to arouse him, and finding it useless, seizing the seat again. When they had gone about two hundred yards, Matilda betrayed signs of exhaustion, and she asked, "Is there no shelter near?"

"When we get to that little field of corn," said Anne.

"It is so very far. Surely there is some place near?"

She pointed to a few scrubby brushes overhanging a little stream which passed under the road near this point.

"They are not thick enough," said Anne.

"Let us take him under the bridge," said Matilda. "I can go no farther."

Entering the opening by which cattle descended to drink, they waded into the weedy water, which here rose a few inches above their ankles. To ascend the stream, stoop under the arch, and reach the centre of the roadway, was the work of a few minutes.

"If they look under the arch we are lost," murmured Anne.

"There is no parapet[1] to the bridge, and they may pass over without heeding."

They waited, their heads almost in contact with the reeking[2] arch and their feet encircled by the stream, which was at its summer lowness now. A quarter of an hour dragged by, and then indications reached their ears that

[1]A railing or wall. [2]Giving off bad air.

the re-examination of the mill had begun and ended. The well-known tramp drew nearer.

The gang passed the arch, and the noise regularly diminished as if no man among them had thought of looking aside for a moment.

Matilda broke the silence. "I wonder if they have left a watch behind?" she said doubtfully.

"I will go and see," said Anne. "Wait till I return."

"No; I can do no more. When you come back I shall be gone."

Anne went out from the water and hastened toward the mill. She entered by the garden, and seeing no one— advanced and peeped in at the window. Her mother and Mr. Loveday were sitting within as usual.

"Are they all gone?" said Anne, softly.

"Yes. They did not trouble us much, beyond going into every room and searching about the garden, where they saw steps. They have been lucky tonight; they have caught fifteen or twenty men at places farther on, so the loss of Bob was no hurt to their feelings. I wonder where in the world the poor fellow is!"

"I will show you," said Anne. Explaining in a few words what had happened, she was promptly followed by Loveday along the road. Matilda was gone, and Bob lay on the seat as she had left him.

Bob was brought out and water thrown upon his face; but though he moved he did not rouse himself until some time after he had been borne into the house. Here he opened his eyes and saw them standing round, and gathered a little consciousness.

"You are all right, my boy!" said his father. "What happened to ye? Where did you get that terrible blow?"

"Ah—I can mind now," murmured Bob, with a stupefied gaze around. "I fell in slipping down the topsail halyard[1]—the rope, that is, was too short—and I fell upon

---

[1] A rope for hoisting a ship's topsail.

my head. And then I went away. When I came back I
thought I wouldn't disturb ye; so I lay down out there to
sleep out the watch; but the pain in my head was so
great that I couldn't get to sleep. So I picked some of the
poppy heads in the border, which I once heard was a good
thing for sending folks to sleep when they are in pain. So
I munched up all I could find and dropped off quite nicely."

"Why, you might never have woke again!" said Mrs.
Loveday, holding up her hands. "How is your head now?"

"I hardly know," replied the young man, putting his
hand to his forehead and beginning to doze again. "Where
be those fellows that boarded us? With this—smooth
water and—fine breeze we ought to get away from 'em.
Haul in—the larboard braces, and—bring her to the wind."

"You are at home, dear Bob," said Anne, bending
over him, "and the men are gone."

"Come along upstairs; thou art hardly awake now,"
said his father; and Bob was assisted to bed.

—*Thomas Hardy*
From *The Trumpet Major*

STUDY AND ENJOYMENT

1. How does Bob outwit the marines? Which was his cleverest trick? What
   part in the escape had Anne? had Matilda? What did you find out about
   Matilda?

2. How is Bob's strange drowsiness explained? His half-conscious remarks
   to his father show that he has been at sea. "Slipping down the topsail halyard" is one nautical expression. Select four more.

3. Sailors were so badly treated in the British Navy during the Napoleonic
   wars that, in 1797, there was a mutiny of the North Sea Fleet. Conditions were so vile that the only way to get men for the navy was by
   means of the press gang. The press gang, generally of marines, had the
   power to compel eligible men by force to enlist in the navy. It was a
   form of legal kidnapping.

4. Thomas Hardy (1840-1931) was born in Dorsetshire, England. He
   published novels and books of verse. You will find one of his poems,
   "Weathers," in this Reader. The complete story of Bob Loveday is
   told in *The Trumpet Major*.

ROBINSON CRUSOE'S STORY

The night was thick and hazy
When the "Piccadilly Daisy"
Carried down the crew and captain in the sea;
And I think the water drowned 'em;
For they never, never found 'em,
And I know they didn't come ashore with me.

Oh! 'twas very sad and lonely
When I found myself the only
Population on this cultivated shore;
But I've made a little tavern
In a rocky little cavern,
And I sit and watch for people at the door.

I spent no time in looking
For a girl to do my cooking,
As I'm quite a clever hand at making stews;
But I had that fellow Friday,
Just to keep the tavern tidy,
And to put a Sunday polish on my shoes.

I sometimes seek diversion
In a family excursion
With the few domestic animals you see;
And we take along a carrot
And refreshment for the parrot,
And a little can of jungleberry tea.

If the roads are wet and muddy
We remain at home and study,—
For the Goat is very clever at a sum.—
And the Dog, instead of fighting,
Studies ornamental writing,
While the Cat is taking lessons on the drum.

We retire at eleven,
And we rise again at seven;
And I wish to call attention, as I close,
To the fact that all the scholars
Are correct about their collars,
And particular in turning out their toes.

—Charles E. Carryl

STUDY AND ENJOYMENT

1. Some poets write nonsense poems that are intended only to make us laugh. Charles E. Carryl is one of these poets. If you have read *Robinson Crusoe* you will remember that Crusoe was shipwrecked and lived alone on an island for twenty-four years. He did have a dog which swam to shore after him, and a goat and a parrot which he caught on his island. Many years later, Friday escaped from the cannibals and became Crusoe's servant and companion. But this poem has no other connection with the story. Just read it out loud, and find whether you think it is amusing. Either you like nonsense or you don't. You can't be *taught* to like a nonsense poem.

2. And now, if you like nonsense, you will recall Edward Lear, with his five-line jingles or limericks and his "The Owl and the Pussy-Cat." Then we have Lewis Carroll, who wrote *Alice in Wonderland* and *Through the Looking Glass.* His "Jabberwocky," "The Walrus and the Carpenter," and "You Are Old, Father William," are among the great nonsense poems of our language. You will find these poems in most anthologies of children's verse.

THE STOPGAP

The troop of Sea Scouts, to which Tom Dawson belonged, had saved up enough money to pay their passage to the West Indies on board the *S.S. Antibar.* Tom, who had won his wireless proficiency badge, took great interest in the wireless cabin, where the friendly Chief Radio Officer taught him about the ship's instruments. Then misfortune struck the *Antibar.*

The trouble began at eight bells midnight when Senior Radio Officer Radford was found by his relief writhing in the wireless cabin.

An hour later the unfortunate man was being operated on for appendicitis by the ship's doctor.

That put the whole of the work of the radio department

upon the shoulders of the two juniors, or would have done had not Captain Stopford agreed to Carbery's suggestion that Sea Scout Dawson should be temporarily signed on as watcher. That is to say, he was to stand by and listen-in, reporting to either of the two operators whenever a signal intended for the ship came in and more especially for the ominous S.O.S. that might be picked up from another vessel in dire distress.

Soon after daybreak another misfortune overtook the ship. One of the firemen overcome by the intense heat suddenly went "off his head." His idea of relief was to take a cold bath in mid-Atlantic and accordingly he jumped overboard.

Promptly the starboard motor lifeboat was lowered. This boat was fitted with wireless and it was the duty of Evans, the junior operator, to go along in her, the third officer being in charge.

They recovered the fireman all right, two miles astern, notwithstanding the fact that he swam strongly away from the rescuing boat.

The passengers lining the ship's side cheered lustily as the lifeboat returned from her successful errand; but their cheers froze on their lips when they saw the blood-stained bandaged form of Radio Officer Evans lying in the stern sheets.

The maniacal fireman had signalized his rescue by making a sudden onslaught on the person nearest to him, who happened to be the junior wireless operator. Evans was alive—just.

So of the three wirelessmen only James Carbery remained fit for duty. The Board of Trade requires that a vessel of the size of the *Antibar* should carry three operators. The Postmaster-General also ordains that every operator must hold a "ticket" or official document testifying to his efficiency

In the present circumstances red tape regulations had to go by the board. Jimmy Carbery volunteered to stand double watches while Sea Scout Dawson "took on" for the remaining eight hours per day.

For the next three days the illegal compact was carried out as arranged, Jimmy Carbery living and having his meals in the wireless room while his youthful assistant "carried on" from noon to eight p.m.—an arrangement that gave him plenty of rest.

Quite pardonably Tom felt proud of himself. He was the envy of the remaining members of the patrol and a sort of hero in the eyes of the other passengers. Even the grim and aloof Old Man condescended to give him a smile and a few words of encouragement.

"Another thirty hours and we've finished the stunt, Dawson," remarked Radio Officer Carbery, when just before eight bells in the second dog watch he prepared to relieve his young assistant. "Well, cheerio! Sleep well; there'll be precious little for you to worry about tonight!"

Jimmy Carbery, although he was an efficient radio officer, was no prophet.

Shortly after midnight the main steam pipe of the port engine burst, filling the engine-room with clouds of scalding vapour.

Unfortunately the explosion also fractured the main oil fuel supply, and either an overturned oil-lamp or else a "short" in one of the electric leads did the rest. A gust of oil ignited, and then ensued a battle between fire and the fire-quenching properties of steam. The fire, originated low down in the engine-room, gained the mastery and soon both the engine and boiler rooms were a raging inferno.

The few survivors from this part of the ship had to abandon their posts. The starboard engine continued to function, and by aid of this help Captain Stopford was able to keep the ship stern on to the wind; thus giving the breeze less chance to fan the flames.

It was a forlorn task. Soon the starboard propeller ceased to revolve and the ship, losing way, drifted broadside-on in the trough of the sea.

Rapidly the flames spread, tongues of fire greedily licking the cabins amidships and throwing up clouds of red-tinged smoke well over the bridge.

It was out of the question to attempt to assure the passengers that there was really no danger. One and all realized that there was, but there was no panic. Calmly they donned their lifebelts and took up their stations aft, for the boat-deck and those immediately under it were by this time almost unbearable.

At the first alarm, Tom Dawson was up.

Dressing hurriedly, he made his way to the wireless cabin where Carbery was sending out a general distress signal—the ominous S.O.S.

Ships there were that were quick to acknowledge the call, but unfortunately they were too far away to be able to render assistance before the *Antibar* sank. Apparently the only chance left for the passengers and crew was to take to the boats. Many of the latter were already enveloped in flames, while in any case the heavy sea made the launching of the remaining boats a hazardous operation.

Jimmy Carbery, headphones on this time, turned and caught sight of the Sea Scout.

"Here, you hop it!" he exclaimed. "No place for you— fall in with your chums."

For once at least Tom Dawson flatly refused to carry out an order.

"I'll stand by here," he replied. "I'm a wireless operator even if I'm only a stopgap."

"That's the sort!" was Jimmy's somewhat astonishing rejoinder. "All the same, you'd better hook it."

But Tom did not. He stood by anxiously watching his companion's calm and deliberate efforts to tune in to a vessel within easy steaming distance.

At frequent intervals one of the deck officers, and some-times a messenger-boy, would come to the now open door of the wireless-room asking, for the Old Man's information, whether prompt help was likely to be forthcoming.

But no! Again and again calls were picked up, all from vessels whose distance or slow speed rendered them incapable of arriving in time.

The heat in the wireless cabin grew almost unbearable. Tom had to go out more than once to draw in deep breaths of air that was slightly less suffocating than that of the confined space.

Flames were now licking the deck and blistering the paint from the outside of the range of cabins.

Suddenly Carbery laid aside his earphones and beckoned to the Sea Scout.

"Hang on to these a tick," he spluttered. "I'm feeling a bit muzzy. . . . Be all right in half a tick. . . . There's the paper giving the ship's position. Try if you can pick up. . . . No, dash you! Let me alone and get on with the job."

Even as Tom picked up the earphones Carbery toppled upon the deck like a sack of flour.

It was a case of stern duty *versus* inclination.

Tom let his companion lie where he fell. All he could do without risking the loss of an all-important signal was to press the push of the electric bell on the off-chance that a messenger was still at his post.

Then—

Above the crackling and hissing of the flames came a succession of signals that so far were unintelligible.

Tom wrote them down and proceeded to decode the message.

"From s.s. *Getaway*. We are within eighteen miles of you. Steaming at fifteen knots."

He was in the act of sending out the acknowledgement to the succouring vessel when the transmitter suddenly went dumb, which was hardly to be wondered at, seeing that the bulkhead of the wireless cabin was smouldering.

"Anything through?" bawled a hoarse voice.

Tom turned, saw the Second Officer's bulky form framed in the doorway.

"Yes, sir! But set's out of action. And Mr. Carbery here—"

The air was so full of smoke that the Second Officer had failed to notice the radio operator's senseless form upon the deck.

He bent down, gripped James under the shoulders and heaved him clear of the cabin.

"Righto. I'll see to him," he exclaimed hurriedly. "Take the message to the Old Man yourself. No use your hanging on here any longer."

With that the Sea Scout, in the knowledge that he had stuck to his post to the end, snatched up the deciphered signal and raced to the bridge.

"Just through, sir!" he reported. "No further signals can be made or received. Set burnt out, sir."

Captain Stopford's hand trembled a little as he took the proffered signal. Then he gave a gasp of relief. Help was at hand.

"Good!" he exclaimed. "Radio out of order, eh? Tell the wireless operator to report to me on the bridge."

Sea Scout squared his shoulders and saluted.

"He's here now, sir!" he replied. "Mr. Carbery's insensible and I've just been carrying on."

Even in the hour of peril the Old Man's face relaxed into a grim smile. He placed a hand rather heavily on the shoulder of Tom the stop-gap.

"You'll do, my lad! You'll do!" he exclaimed.

And Sea Scout Dawson wished for no other reward.

—*Percy Westerman*

STUDY AND ENJOYMENT

1. How did Sea Scout Dawson get his first chance to put his knowledge of wireless into practice? (A "stopgap" is a temporary substitute.)
2. *Signalized* means to make remarkable or noteworthy. Now, try to write in your own words: "The maniacal fireman had signalized his rescue by making a sudden onslaught on the person nearest to him."

3. What is *red tape*? Why did it have to "go by the board" after Radio Officer Evans was badly hurt? What was the illegal compact? Who is the Old Man?

4. You often see the word *versus* in reports of games, for example, Brandon versus Winnipeg. Explain: "It was a case of stern duty versus inclination." How did Tom decode the message? What did Tom mean when he said, "He's here now, sir."?

5. The last four sentences of this story may remind you of Newbolt's poem, "Vitai Lampada":

> And it's not for the sake of a ribboned coat,
>   Or the selfish hope of a season's fame,
> But his Captain's hand on his shoulder smote
>   "Play up! play up! and play the game!"

"ONE MINUTE LONGER"

Nearly every one likes a story about a dog. Albert Payson Terhune, whose own dog was the hero of his master's books, *Lad: A Dog*, and *Lad of Sunnybank*, here tells a story of another fine collie.

I

Wolf was a collie, red-gold and white of coat, with a shape more like his long-ago wolf ancestors' than like a domesticated dog's. It was from this ancestral throwback that he was named Wolf.

He looked not at all like his great sire, Sunnybank Lad, nor like his dainty, thoroughbred mother, Lady. Nor was he like them in any other way, except that he inherited old Lad's staunchly gallant spirit and loyalty and uncanny brain. No, in traits as well as in looks he was more wolf than dog. He almost never barked, his snarl supplying all vocal needs.

The Mistress or the Master or the Boy—any of these three could romp with him, roll him over, tickle him, or subject him to all sorts of playful indignities. And Wolf entered gleefully into the fun of the romp. But let any human besides these three lay a hand on his slender body, and a snarling plunge for the offender's throat was Wolf's invariable reply to the caress.

It has been so since his puppyhood. He did not fly at accredited guests nor, indeed, pay any heed to their presence, as long as they kept their hands off him. But to all of these the Boy was forced to say at the very outset of the visit:

"Pat Lad and Bruce all you want to, but please leave Wolf alone. He doesn't care for people. We've taught him to stand for a pat on the head from guests—but don't touch his body."

Then to prove his own immunity, the Boy would proceed to tumble Wolf about, to the delight of them both.

In romping with humans whom they love, most dogs will bite, more or less gently—or pretend to bite—as a part of the game. Wolf never did this. In his wildest and roughest romps with the Boy or with the Boy's parents, Wolf did not so much as open his mighty jaws. Perhaps because he dared not trust himself to bite gently. Perhaps because he realized that a bite is not a joke, but an effort to kill.

There had been only one exception to Wolf's hatred for mauling at strangers' hands. A man came to The Place on a business call, bringing along a chubby two-year-old daughter. The Master warned the baby that she must not go near Wolf, although she might pet any of the other collies. Then he became so much interested in the business talk that he and his guest forgot all about the child.

Ten minutes later the Master chanced to shift his gaze to the far end of the room. And he broke off, with a gasp, in the very middle of a sentence.

The baby was seated astride Wolf's back, her tiny heels digging into the dog's sensitive ribs, and each of her chubby fists gripping one of his ears. Wolf was lying there, with an idiotically happy grin on his face and wagging his tail in ecstasy.

No one knew why he had submitted to the baby's tugging hand except because she *was* a baby, and because the gallant heart of the dog had gone out to her helplessness.

Wolf was the official watchdog of The Place; and his name carried dread to the loafers and tramps of the region. Also, he was the Boy's own special dog. He had been born on the Boy's tenth birthday, five years before this story of ours begins; and ever since then the two had been inseparable chums.

II

One sloppy afternoon in late winter, Wolf and the Boy were sprawled, side by side, on the fur rug in front of the library fire. The Mistress and the Master had gone to town for the day. The house was lonely, and the two chums were left to entertain each other.

The Boy was reading a magazine. The dog beside him was blinking in drowsy comfort at the fire. Presently, finishing the story he had been reading, the Boy looked across at the sleepy dog.

"Wolf," he said, "here's a story about a dog. I think he must have been something like you. Maybe he was your great-great-great-great-grandfather. He lived an awfully long time ago—in Pompeii. Ever hear of Pompeii?"

Now, the Boy was fifteen years old, and he had too much sense to imagine that Wolf could possibly understand the story he was about to tell him. But, long since, he had fallen into a way of talking to his dog, sometimes, as if to another human. It was fun for him to note the almost pathetic eagerness wherewith Wolf listened and tried to grasp the meaning of what he was saying. Again and again, at the sound of some familiar word or voice inflection, the collie would prick up his ears or wag his tail, as if in the joyous hope that he had at last found a clue to his owner's meaning.

"You see," went on the Boy, "this dog lived in Pompeii, as I told you. You've never been there, Wolf."

Wolf was looking up at the Boy in wistful excitement, seeking vainly to guess what was expected of him.

"And," continued the Boy, "the kid who owned him seems to have had a regular knack for getting into trouble all the time. And his dog was always on hand to get him out of it. It's a true story, the magazine says. The kid's father was so grateful to the dog that he bought him a solid silver collar. Solid silver! Get that, Wolfie?"

Wolf did not "get it." But he wagged his tail hopefully, his eyes alight with bewildered interest.

"And," said the Boy, "what do you suppose was engraved on the collar? Well, I'll tell you: *This dog has thrice saved his little master from death. Once by fire, once by flood, and once at the hands of robbers.* How's that for a record, Wolf? For *one* dog, too."

At the words *Wolf* and *dog*, the collie's tail smote the floor in glad comprehension. Then he edged closer to the Boy as the narrator's voice presently took on a sadder note.

"But at last," resumed the Boy, "there came a time when a dog couldn't save the kid. Mount Vesuvius erupted. All the sky was pitch-dark, as black as midnight, and Pompeii was buried under lava and ashes. The dog could easily have got away by himself—dogs can see in the dark, can't they, Wolf?—but he couldn't get the kid away. And he wouldn't go without him. You wouldn't have gone without me, either, would you, Wolf? Pretty nearly two thousand years later, some people dug through the lava that covered Pompeii. What do you suppose they found? Of course they found a whole lot of things. One of them was that dog—silver collar and inscription and all. He was lying at the feet of a child. The child he couldn't save. He was one grand dog—hey, Wolf?"

The continued strain of trying to understand began to get on the collie's high-strung nerves. He rose to his feet, quivering, and sought to lick the Boy's face, thrusting one upraised white forepaw at him in appeal for a handshake. The Boy slammed shut the magazine.

"It's slow in the house here, with nothing to do," he said to his chum, "I'm going up the lake with my gun to see if any wild ducks have landed in the marshes yet. It's almost time for them. Want to come along?"

The last sentence Wolf understood perfectly. On the instant he was dancing with excitement at the prospect of a walk. Being a collie, he was of no earthly help in a hunting trip; but, on such tramps, as everywhere else, he was the Boy's inseparable companion.

III

Out over the slushy snow the two started, the Boy with his light single-barreled shotgun slung over one shoulder, the dog trotting close at his heels. The March thaw was changing to a sharp freeze. The deep and soggy snow was crusted over, just thick enough to make walking a genuine difficulty for both dog and Boy.

The Place was a promontory that ran out into the lake, on the opposite bank from the mile-distant village. Behind, across the highroad, lay the winter-choked forest. At the lake's northerly end, two miles beyond The Place, where the reedy marshes were, a month hence, wild duck would congregate. Thither, with Wolf, the Boy plowed his way through the biting cold.

The going was heavy and heavier. A quarter mile below the marshes the Boy struck out across the upper corner of the lake. Here the ice was rotten at the top, where the thaw had nibbled at it, but underneath it was still a full eight inches thick, easily strong enough to bear the Boy's weight.

Along the gray ice field the two plodded. The skim of water, which the thaw had spread an inch thick over the ice, had frozen in the day's cold spell. It crackled like broken glass as the chums walked over it. The Boy had on big hunting boots. So, apart from the extra effort, the glass-like ice did not bother him. To Wolf it gave acute pain. The sharp particles were forever getting between the callous black pads of his feet, pricking and cutting him sharply.

Little smears of blood began to mark the dog's course; but it never occurred to Wolf to turn back or to betray by any sign that he was suffering. It was all a part of the day's work—a cheap price to pay for the joy of tramping with his adored young master.

Then, forty yards or so on the hither side of the marshes, Wolf beheld an amazing phenomenon. The Boy had been walking directly in front of him, gun over shoulder. With no warning at all, the youthful hunter fell, feet foremost, out of sight, through the ice.

The light shell of new-frozen water that covered the lake's thicker ice also masked an air hole nearly three feet wide. Into this, as he strode carelessly along, the Boy had stepped. Straight down he had gone, with all the force of his hundred and twenty pounds and with all the impetus of his forward stride.

Instinctively, he threw out his hands to restore his balance. The only effect of this was to send the gun flying ten feet away.

Down went the Boy through less than three feet of water (for the bottom of the lake at this point had started to slope upward towards the marshes) and through nearly two feet more of sticky marsh mud that underlay the lake-bed.

His outflung hands struck against the ice on the edges of the air hole, and clung there.

Spluttering and gurgling, the Boy brought his head above the surface and tried to raise himself, by his hands, high enough to wriggle out upon the surface of the ice. Ordinarily this would have been simple enough for so strong a lad. But the gluelike mud had imprisoned his feet and the lower part of his legs and held them powerless.

Try as he would, the Boy could not wrench himself free of the slough. The water, as he stood upright, was on a level with his mouth. The air hole was too wide for him, at such a depth, to get a good purchase on its edges and lift himself bodily to safety.

Gaining such a finger-hold as he could, he heaved with

all his might, throwing every muscle of his body into the struggle. One leg was pulled almost free of the mud, but the other was driven deeper into it. And, as the Boy's fingers slipped from the smoothly wet ice edge, the attempt to restore his balance drove the free leg back, knee-deep into the mire.

IV

Ten minutes of this hopeless fighting left the Boy panting and tired out. The icy water was numbing his nerves and chilling his blood into torpidity.[1] His hands were without sense of feeling, as far up as the wrists. Even if he could have shaken free his legs from the mud, now, he had not strength enough left to crawl out of the hole.

He ceased his uselessly frantic battle and stood dazed. Then he came sharply to himself. For, as he stood, the water crept upward from his lips to his nostrils. He knew why the water seemed to be rising. It was not rising. It was he who was sinking. As soon as he stopped moving, the mud began, very slowly, but very steadily, to suck him downward.

This was not a quicksand, but it was a deep mud bed. And only by constant motion could he avoid sinking farther and farther down into it. He had less than two inches to spare, at best, before the water would fill his nostrils; less than two inches of life, even if he could keep the water down to the level of his lips.

There was a moment of utter panic. Then the Boy's brain cleared. His only hope was to keep on fighting—to rest when he must, for a moment or so, and then to renew his numbed grip on the ice edge and try to pull his feet a few inches higher out of the mud. He must do this as long as his chilled body could be scourged into obeying his will.

He struggled again, but with virtually no result in raising himself. A second struggle, however, brought him chin-

[1]Numbness.

high above the water. He remembered confusedly that some of these earlier struggles had scarcely budged him, while others had gained him two or three inches. Vaguely, he wondered why. Then turning his head, he realized.

Wolf, as he turned, was just loosing his hold on the wide collar of the Boy's mackinaw. His cut forepaws were still braced against a flaw of ragged ice on the air hole's edge, and all his tawny body was tense.

The Boy noted that; and he realized that the repeated effort to draw his master to safety must have resulted, at least once, in pulling the dog down into the water with the floundering Boy.

"Once more, Wolfie! *Once more!*" chattered the Boy through teeth that clicked together like castanets.

The dog darted forward, caught his grip afresh on the edge of the Boy's collar, and tugged with all his fierce strength, growling and whining ferociously the while.

The Boy seconded the collie's tuggings by a supreme struggle that lifted him higher than before. He was able to get one arm and shoulder clear. His numb fingers closed about an up-thrust tree limb which had been washed downstream in the autumn freshets and had been frozen into the lake ice.

With this new purchase and aided by the dog, the boy tried to drag himself out of the hole. But the chill of the water had done its work. He had not the strength to move farther. The mud still sucked at his calves and ankles. The big hunting boots were full of water that seemed to weigh a ton.

He lay there gasping and chattering. Then through the gathering twilight, his eyes fell on the gun, lying ten feet away.

"Wolf!" he ordered, nodding towards the weapon. "Get it! *Get* it!"

Not in vain had the Boy talked to Wolf, for years, as if the dog were human. At the words and the nod, the collie trotted over to the gun, lifted it by the stock, and hauled it awkwardly along over the bumpy ice to his master, where he laid it down at the edge of the air hole.

The dog's eyes were cloudy with trouble, and he shivered and whined as with ague.[1] The water on his thick coat was freezing to a mass of ice. But it was from anxiety that he shivered and not from cold.

Still keeping his numb grasp on the tree branch, the boy balanced himself as best he could and thrust two fingers of his free hand into his mouth to warm them into sensation again.

When this was done, he reached out to where the gun lay and pulled its trigger. The shot boomed deafeningly through the twilight winter silences. The recoil sent the weapon sliding sharply back along the ice, spraining the Boy's trigger finger and cutting it to the bone.

"That's all I can do," said the Boy to himself. "If anyone hears it, well and good. I can't get at another cartridge. I couldn't put it into the breech if I had it. My hands are too numb."

V

For several endless minutes he clung there, listening. But this was a desolate part of the lake, far from any road; and the season was too early for other hunters to be abroad. The bitter cold, in any case, tended to make sane folk hug the fireside rather than to venture so far into the open. Nor was the single report of a gun uncommon enough to call for investigation in such weather.

All this the Boy told himself, as the minutes dragged by. Then he looked again at Wolf. The dog, head on one side, still stood protectingly above him. The dog was cold and in pain. But being only a dog, it did not occur to him to trot off home to the comfort of the library fire and leave his master to fend for himself.

Presently, with a little sigh, Wolf lay down on the ice, his nose across the Boy's arm. Even if he lacked strength

[1]Ague (ā′gū) a chill.

to save his beloved master, he could stay and share the
Boy's sufferings.

But the Boy himself thought otherwise. He was not
at all minded to freeze to death, nor was he willing to let
Wolf imitate the dog of Pompeii by dying helplessly at his
master's side. Controlling for an instant the chattering
of his teeth, he called, "Wolf!"

The dog was on his feet again at the word, alert, eager.

"Wolf!" repeated the Boy. "*Go!* Hear me? *Go!*"
He pointed homeward.

Wolf stared at him, hesitant. Again the Boy called in
vehement command, "*Go!*"

The collie lifted his head to the twilight sky with a wolf
howl hideous in its grief and appeal—a howl as wild and
discordant as that of any of his savage ancestors. Then,
stooping first to lick the numb hand that clung to the
branch, Wolf turned and fled.

Across the cruelly sharp film of ice he tore, at top speed,
head down, whirling through the deepening dusk like a
flash of tawny light.

Wolf understood what was wanted of him. Wolf
always understood. The pain in his feet was as nothing.
The stiffness of his numbed body was forgotten in the
urgency for speed.

The Boy looked drearily after the swift-vanishing figure
which the dusk was swallowing. He knew the dog would
try to bring help, as has many another and lesser dog in
times of need. Whether or not that help could arrive in
time, or at all, was a point on which the Boy would not let
himself dwell. Into his benumbed brain crept the memory
of an old Norse proverb he had read in school:

Heroism consists in hanging on, one minute longer.

Unconsciously he tightened his feeble hold on the tree
branch and braced himself.

From the marshes to The Place was a full two miles.
Despite the deep and sticky snow, Wolf covered the

distance in less than nine minutes. He paused in front of
the gate lodge, at the highway entrance to the drive. But
the superintendent and his wife had gone to Paterson,
shopping, that afternoon.

Down the drive to the house he dashed. The maids
had taken advantage of their employers' day in New
York to walk across the lake to the village, to a motion-
picture show.

Wise men claim that dogs have not the power to think
or to reason things out in a logical way. So perhaps it was
mere chance that next sent Wolf's flying feet across the lake
to the village. Perhaps it was chance and not the knowledge that where there is a village there are people.

Again and again, in the car, he had sat upon the front
seat alongside the Mistress when she drove to the station to
meet guests. There were always people at the station.
And to the station Wolf now raced.

The usual group of platform idlers had been dispersed
by the cold. A solitary baggageman was hauling a trunk
and some boxes out of the express coop to the platform, to
be put aboard the five o'clock train from New York.

As the baggageman passed under the clump of station
lights, he came to a sudden halt. For out of the darkness
dashed a dog. Full tilt, the animal rushed up to him and
seized him by the skirt of the overcoat.

The man cried out in scared surprise. He dropped the
box he was carrying and struck at the dog, to ward off the
seemingly murderous attack. He recognized Wolf, and he
knew the collie's repute.

But Wolf was not attacking. Holding tight to the coat
skirt, he backed away, trying to draw the man with him and
all the while whimpering aloud like a nervous puppy.

A kick from the heavy-shod boot broke the dog's hold
on the coat skirt, even as a second yell from the man brought
four or five other people running out from the station
waiting room.

One of these, the telegraph operator, took in the scene

at a single glance. With great presence of mind he bawled loudly, "Mad dog!"

This as Wolf, reeling from the kick, sought to gain another grip on the coat skirt. A second kick sent him rolling over and over on the tracks, while other voices took up the panic cry of "Mad dog!"

Now, a mad dog is supposed to be a dog afflicted by rabies. Once in ten thousand times, at the very most, a mad-dog hue and cry is justified. Certainly not oftener. A harmless and friendly dog loses his master on the street. He runs about, confused and frightened, looking for the owner he has lost. A boy throws a stone at him. Other boys chase him. His tongue hangs out, and his eyes glaze with terror. Then some fool bellows, "Mad dog!"

And the cruel chase is on—a chase that ends in the pitiful victim's death. Yes, in every crowd there is a voice ready to raise that asinine and murderously cruel shout.

So it was with the men who witnessed Wolf's frenzied effort to take aid to the imperilled Boy.

Voice after voice repeated the cry. Men groped along the platform edge for stones to throw. The village policeman ran puffingly upon the scene, drawing his revolver.

Finding it useless to make a further attempt to drag the baggageman to the rescue, Wolf leaped back, facing the ever larger group. Back went his head again in that hideous wolf howl. Then he galloped away a few yards, trotted back, howled once more, and again galloped lakeward.

All of which only confirmed the panicky crowd in the belief that they were threatened by a mad dog. A shower of stone hurtled about Wolf as he came back a third time to lure these dull humans into following him.

One pointed rock smote the collie's shoulder, glancingly, cutting it to the bone. A shot from the policeman's revolver fanned the fur of his ruff, as it whizzed past.

Knowing that he faced death, he nevertheless stood his ground, not troubling to dodge the fusillade of stones, but

BACK WENT HIS HEAD AGAIN IN THAT HIDEOUS WOLF HOWL

continuing to run lakeward and then trot back, whining with excitement.

A second pistol shot flew wide. A third grazed the dog's hip. From all directions people were running towards the station. A man darted into the house next door and emerged carrying a shotgun. This he steadied on the veranda rail not forty feet away from the leaping dog and made ready to fire.

It was then the train from New York came in. And, momentarily, the sport of "mad-dog" killing was abandoned, while the crowd scattered to each side of the track.

From a front car of the train the Mistress and the Master emerged into a bedlam of noise and confusion.

"Best hide in the station, Ma'am!" shouted the telegraph operator at the sight of the Mistress. "There is a mad dog loose out here. He's chasing folks around, and—"

"Mad dog!" repeated the Mistress in high contempt. "If you knew anything about dogs, you'd know mad ones never 'chase folks around,' any more than diphtheria patients do. Then—"

A flash of tawny light beneath the station lamp, a scurrying of frightened idlers, a final wasted shot from the policeman's pistol—as Wolf dived headlong through the frightened crowd toward the voice he heard and recognized.

Up to the Mistress and the Master galloped Wolf. He was bleeding, his eyes were bloodshot, his fur was rumpled. He seized the astounded Master's gloved hand lightly between his teeth and sought to pull him across the tracks and towards the lake.

The Master knew dogs. Especially he knew Wolf. And without a word he suffered himself to be led. The Mistress and one or two inquisitive men followed.

Presently, Wolf loosed his hold on the Master's hand and ran on ahead, darting back every few moments to make certain he was followed.

"*Heroism—consists—in—hanging—on—one—minute— longer,*" the Boy was whispering deliriously to himself for the hundredth time, as Wolf pattered up to him in triumph, across the ice, with the human rescuers a scant ten yards behind.

—*Albert Payson Terhune*
From *Buff, a Collie*

STUDY AND ENJOYMENT

1. At the beginning of this story we are told that Wolf has inherited old Lad's staunchly gallant spirit and loyalty and uncanny brain. What incidents best show his gallant spirit? his loyalty? his uncanny brain?

2. How did the old Norse proverb help the boy? Another story that illustrates the truth of the proverb is the one about the Dutch boy who held his hand in the hole in the dyke until help came. Can you think of other examples?

3. What words does Mr. Terhune want you to take the opposite meaning of when he writes of the telegraph operator? How does the author make you feel that nearly always the cry of "Mad dog!" is wrong?

AMY JOHNSON REACHES AUSTRALIA

Amy Johnson's name deserves a place in every list of famous pioneers of air travel.   Here is the story of her most memorable flight.

I

Two schoolgirls stood outside the Hull aerodrome.   The Surrey Flying Services were making one of their visits to the City.   Five-shilling joy-rides were to be had, and the schoolgirl sisters glanced at each other.

"Let's have five shillings' worth, shall we?" said the elder of the two.

Her name was Amy Johnson, and the five-shilling joy-ride was her first experience of travelling by air!

"I mean to have an aeroplane of my own," decided Amy, as she left the flying-ground.

It did not seem likely to be a wish which would be granted; these are not the days of magic flying carpets, but Amy Johnson as a modern girl was quite aware of that fact.   She certainly possessed plenty of imagination, but she had always been possessed, too, of plenty of perseverance and doggedness.   What Amy wanted, she generally got, but not by sitting down and wishing, nor yet by wheedling for favours; she got busy and got what she wanted by her own efforts.   But after schooldays she did not start right away on a flying career; she took her Degree at Sheffield University and went on to a secretarial job in London.

She had not forgotten, however, what she meant to do; and more, she gradually evolved even higher wishes.   She wanted to do something big in her life, but that something must be to do with the air.   And she was not out for big rewards, although flying across to America was in those days a feat which meant a money prize.   "I mean to get there," said Amy Johnson, pointing to Australia on a map.

Well, she got there; she was the first woman to fly solo to Australia as all the world knew on Empire Day, 1930;

but a gruelling training and a gruelling flight, that in many
ways was also a fight, went before that moment when a fair,
slim, blue-eyed girl stepped down from her Gypsy Moth
machine at Port Darwin.

II

How did a girl, employed by day in an office, ever
manage even the training part?   Any girl could not have
managed it perhaps, but a girl with grit and determination
and a dogged desire could do it, as Amy proved.   She
spent all her spare time in learning about Flying matters
and even constructed a model of a seaplane during hobby-
hours.   When her chance came to take up Flying as a career
she was ready.

She was also steady in working towards the goal towards
which she looked hopefully—Australia; she would be the
first girl to get there, alone, by air.   She had joined the
London Aeroplane Club in 1928, working at week-ends and
during the evenings between intervals of secretarial work;
she set off on her great adventure from Stag Lane Aerodrome on May 5, 1930.

And the years between those dates were spent in
working hard, and her keenness was noticed quickly enough
by the trainers who probably sum up pretty accurately the
characters of the different individuals who set out to "learn
to fly."   She passed her first test as a pilot, and gained the
"A" license in July, 1929, but, although that had satisfied
most girl-fliers, it was not enough for Amy.   Australia still
seemed her magnet and, having taken her decision to fly
there, Amy joined the mechanical section of the London
Club, and worked with, and as one of, the overalled
mechanics after her every-day secretarial work was done.
Doffing town garb for overalls, she learned all about the
ins and outs of the machines, one of which—not too far off
now, as she told herself—would carry her alone for thousands of miles across unknown continents.   But until her
start-off in the second-hand Gypsy Moth machine, which

she had obtained from Captain Hope and had painted green—Amy's favourite and luckiest colour—she had only flown two hundred miles in a straight flight, and had never even crossed the Channel by air!

She was dauntless! In the eyes of most of the world she was foolhardy. "But I'll back you, if no one else will," said her father, and he came down to Stag Lane to see her start. Not many people were around; those were not the days when a sight of Amy would bring crowds; she was the unknown girl who had her reputation to make. As she had tried on her parachute the day before, Amy had quite realized that the way to Australia meant danger, but the girl who had prepared herself in every way possible, prepared herself for even the dread emergencies that call for the use of a parachute. "I didn't think of things like that," said Jean Batten, four years later, as she crossed the Timor Sea and remembered Amy's parachute; but Amy had levelly considered ahead every possibility, and having made her preparations she started—undaunted. "I'm not out to make a record; I just want to fly to Australia and I shall be as quick as I can," said Amy, and kissed her father and was off, while one or two onlookers sent up a cheer. They thought her a plucky girl, but how many of them thought she would get there? Very few, perhaps; but Amy, herself, had made up her mind.

By six o'clock she was at Vienna, and just that was something for a girl-flyer who had never even crossed the Channel before; next day when she reached Constantinople, 1,600 miles of her flight lay behind her, satisfactorily accomplished. She was at Aleppo on the third day with over two thousand miles behind her covered in three days; but matters were not to be quite such plain-sailing in the air after that, although by that time the name of Amy Johnson was beginning to be spoken of with some amazement.

III

It was during her flight towards Baghdad that Amy came down in the desert in a blinding sand-storm.

Sand-storms are terrible; there was another terror, though, for a girl, alone and at the mercy of anyone who might chance upon her and her plane which lay forced down into the desert. Uncivilized Arabs were that danger, but Amy, who had foreseen every kind of danger, and made her preparations accordingly, was equipped not only with her parachute but with a revolver in case of need. She waited for two hours in that blinding sand-storm whose force might have wrought havoc, as she knew, to the wings of her Moth—alone she thrust all her available baggage against the Moth's wheels for fear it should nose over; she foresaw everything that might happen, and was prepared.

Perhaps the sand-storm kept the Arabs away, for there was no need of the revolver; Amy hadn't enjoyed the experience of which she told when she reached Baghdad next day, but she had reached Baghdad and she was one stage further to her goal, and that was what mattered most. Even had she known that worse experiences were ahead, nothing would have daunted Amy. Baghdad had been reached on May 8, and on her fifth day she landed at Bandar Abbas on the Persian Gulf.

The world was talking about Amy by that time, although probably she never considered that possibility; she had been expected to make a landing at Basra, at the Persian Gulf's mouth, and lookers-out at Basra were anxious. But a wind-storm and bad visibility had not brought an end, as was feared, to the game attempt, and by May 10 Amy had reached Karachi, the gateway of India.

She had then been in the air for six days. Her next stop should have been Calcutta, but in crossing India she was forced down at Jhansi through lack of petrol. When she finally reached Calcutta on May 12, Amy realized that half of the great task which she had set herself was accomplished, and she probably felt the strain of those adventurous days.

And worse was ahead of her, as possibly after her study of conditions she was well aware; a dangerous track must be followed before her goal was reached. But the girl who had said "I mean to get to Australia," still meant to get there, although after leaving Calcutta she struck terrible rain and winds. Perhaps the superstitious would have considered it an ill omen when, near Rangoon, the undercarriage of her plane was damaged while she was landing, but next day, after the breakage was repaired, she started away towards Bangkok, nearly four hundred miles distant. It was a dangerous course, across mountain and jungle country, and weather was against Amy from the start: she was flying blind part of the time, and on account of the heavy rains and clouds missed the mountain pass through which she had intended to cut off miles of her journey. When she reached the aerodrome of Don Muang she had been flying for twelve days and perhaps the last hop had been more exhausting than any other.

IV

But in spite of that she was off early next day *en route* to Singapore, which she reached on her fourteenth day.

But she had a long and a dangerous and a difficult flight ahead of her, still; perhaps the worst stretch of all; the Java Sea had to be crossed to reach the Sumatran coast, and the storms were terrific as she went. Instead of landing as she had hoped, at Semarang, she was forced to come down in the midst of a sugar plantation thirty miles from Tegal, and, a forced landing was not her only mishap, for the fabric of her plane's wings was pierced with the canes of the plantation.

A night was spent perforce near by while repairs were carried out, and she was off, to reach Semarang safely this time on her sixteenth day, and to fly onwards to Sourabaya, where she landed amidst a crowd far larger and more enthusiastic than the group of well-wishers who had seen her off from Croydon when she made her start.

For by this time Amy Johnson's name was known to almost everyone amongst civilized nations; her fame had spread and the world was anxiously hoping for her success, but there were still more dangers and difficulties ahead, and after sixteen days and nights, of strain and stress, Amy's pluck had already been put hard to the test.

But she meant to get on to Australia, and she set off for the last stage of her journey, as undaunted as before, even though ahead of her stretched the wide dangers of the lonely Timor Sea.

The world almost held its breath when after her start across that dangerous thousand miles of ocean there came a silence, and no news of the world's wonderful flying girl!

Had she perished—after so much pluck and daring? It was not until after a day and night had gone by, and hope had given place to anxiety for Amy's sake, that news at last came through.

Away amongst small islands, in a little-known village called Haliloelik, Amy had arrived. She had missed the aerodrome at Atambua, and in her out-of-the-way foothold, there were no 'phones or possibilities of communication with the outside world. Preparations had been made to search for her when news of her arrival came through, and Amy flew her machine over the aerodrome at Atambua.

And then came the very last stage of all. She flew on, and it seemed as though not only the world of people but the world of weather decided that nothing could daunt this girl, and that instead of winds and tempests, sunshine and clear skies should herald her towards her goal. From early dawning until afternoon Amy flew on and on, across the ocean under conditions which were serene and clear, and on her nineteenth day's flight she reached Port Darwin, itself.

"She's *here*," blared the posters as Amy completed her flight.

Yes, the girl who meant to reach Australia had realized her ambition; she had travelled twelve thousand miles in nineteen days and had faced peril and difficulty, and had come through. She was the first girl to attempt and to carry out the solo flight between England and the other side of the world.

—Ethel Talbot

STUDY AND ENJOYMENT

1. Why did Amy Johnson choose to fly to Australia instead of America?
2. "A gruelling flight that in many ways was also a fight." Select details that show the truth of this description.
3. Alcock and Brown were two young Englishmen who made the first non-stop flight across the Atlantic. You will find their story in *The First Knights of the Air* in this Reader. Who was the American who made the first solo flight across the Atlantic? Do you know the name of his plane?
4. Amelia Earhart is another famous woman flyer. She was lost on one of her solo flights.
5. Amy Johnson lost her life while serving with the British Air Transport Auxiliary on January 5, 1941.

READ A BOOK

Treasure Island. By R. L. Stevenson. Dent. Jim Hawkins searches for Captain Flint's buried treasure.

Thirteen Bears. Edited by Ethel Hume Bennett. Ryerson. A collection of Sir Charles G. D. Roberts' best bear stories.

Castle Blair. By Flora L. Shaw. Little. Uncle Blair entertains nieces and nephews in his Irish castle.

Swallow and Amazons, Coot Club, Peter Duck and *Great Northern?* By Arthur Ransome. Cape. The Walker children have various adventures in the *Swallow*, their sail boat.

Adam of the Road. By Elizabeth Jane Gray. Viking. Adventure in the thirteenth century, in England.

Gulliver's Travels. By Jonathan Swift. Dent. Gulliver meets the little people of Lilliput and the giants of Brobdingnag.

Rebecca of Sunnybrook Farm. By Kate Douglas Wiggin. Rebecca's exciting experiences on the farm with her aunts.

The Arabian Nights. Edited by Padraic Colum. Macmillan. The best rendering of these famous stories of Oriental flavour.

East of the Sun and West of the Moon. By Peter C. Abjörnsen. Hodder and Stoughton. Popular Norse folk-tales well illustrated.

Robinson Crusoe. By Daniel Defoe. Dent. Crusoe's adventures on a desert island, alone except for Friday.

He Went with Marco Polo and *He Went with Vasco da Gama.* By Louise A. Kent. Houghton. In each, a young boy accompanies the famous explorer to the fabulous East.

Klondike Gold. By Herbert V. Coryell. Macmillan. Travel and adventure during the gold rush.

Off to the Game

WHEN ALL THE WORLD IS YOUNG

When all the world is young, lad,
   And all the trees are green;
And every goose a swan, lad,
   And every lass a queen;
Then hey for boot and horse, lad,
   And round the world away;
Young blood must have its course, lad,
   And every dog his day.

When all the world is old, lad,
   And all the trees are brown;
And all the sport is stale, lad,
   And all the wheels run down;
Creep home, and take your place there,
   The spent and maimed among:
God grant you find one face there
   You loved when all was young.

              —Charles Kingsley

STUDY AND ENJOYMENT

1. You will like the first stanza of this poem, for it is written for young folk. It is a poetic way of saying that young people look at the world through rosy spectacles. What lines suggest the idea of adventure?
2. The second stanza is written for older folk. Everything has slowed down and the bright colours are gone. Is there any suggestion of happiness left?

BEAN BALL BILL

I. A NEW PITCHER

From the very beginning Bill Stockton took a violent dislike to Jerry Ames. The cold, disapproving way in which Jerry spoke of his pitching roused him to a furious pitch of anger. Had Jerry been somewhere near his size, there would have been an adequate and primitive way in which to express his anger, but Jerry was small and slight. You could not hit him without feeling yourself something of a bully. And yet, though Bill kept control of himself, Jerry made him chafe with the raw feeling that he had been placed upon the defensive.

They met the afternoon of Bill's arrival at Hastings High. Bill, as soon as classes were over, went down to take a look at the gym. Over in a corner by the lockers, a group of students talked in low, dispirited voices. Things had gone to pot. Haynes, gym director and general coach, had been run down by a skidding taxi and would be in the hospital many months with a fractured hip. Hastings High was a small town school; there was none in the faculty to take the coach's place. And Wally Woods, the captain, lacked the resolution and the strength to handle the situation alone.

Bill breezily introduced himself to the group. "My name's Stockton. I suppose it isn't often a junior drops in here right after mid-year exams, but I didn't flunk where I came from. Dad's business came East, and he didn't want to leave me out on the Coast with a continent between us. He brought me with him and here I am. Any other questions?"

Jerry Ames was the first to answer. "Who asked the first question?" he queried mildly. "I must have missed it."

Bill reddened. He had meant to establish himself on an easy footing; now he saw that they were rating him as fresh. The short spell of silence that followed was awkward. Wally Woods, to save the situation, went off on a new tack.

"You don't happen to know any news that might cheer up a baseball captain, do you?"

"I can pitch a bit if that would help you any," suggested Bill.

Wally brightened. "Curves? What wouldn't we give for one dependable curve ball pitcher!"

"Not curves," said Bill. "Control. The ball goes where I tell it to go."

They looked at him dubiously.

"I dust them off," he explained. "It's a nice way of stopping a batter from becoming too eager."

It was characteristic of Wally that he should glance at his friends with eyes that showed indecision. It was characteristic, too, that it should be Jerry Ames who answered.

"Hastings doesn't go in for that sort of stuff," Jerry said evenly.

Bill stiffened. "What sort of stuff?"

"Knocking batters cold."

"Who said anything about hitting them? I just breeze it past them—sometimes their chests, sometimes their chins. After I drive them from the plate I work the outside corners. How many hits do you think I allowed per game last year?"

"How many batters did you bean?"

"I tell you I have control," Bill repeated angrily. "When I dust them it's merely a threat."

"Suppose you do sock one of them?"

"Well—" Bill shrugged his shoulders. "It wouldn't be intentional. Anyway, I've never hurt a batter—not much, I mean. I've winged them on the arm, but that's likely to happen if a pitcher is just wild."

"I see," Jerry said thoughtfully. "If a fellow's skull gets caved in some day—well, you didn't mean it. A regular 'Bean Ball Bill'."

Bill's fists clenched. "I don't like that name."

"You gave it to yourself," retorted Jerry.

This quarrelling with a boy who might be a star and the team's salvation was not to Wally's liking. "Oh, cut it out, Jerry. We'll turn out for baseball in about two weeks, Stockton, and then you can show us what you have."

"You're going to stand for this bean ball stuff?" Jerry asked in surprise. He saw the captain's eyes waver. Same old story, he told himself. Wally would swing this way and that.

"I'm due home to write some copy," he said abruptly, and disappeared through the gym doorway.

"What position does he play?" Bill demanded. "I hope he's not a catcher."

"He's not with the nine."

"And you let him put in his oar and rock the boat? What does he do anyway? How does it happen that he's such a big shot around here?"

"He writes the school news for the Hastings *Courier*."

Bill digested this with a scowl. "What does he do, scalp his enemies and pat his friends on the back? Everybody afraid of him because of what he'll say in print? Well, if he starts rapping me there's going to be trouble."

And yet, as the trouble slowly developed, it came not because of what Jerry wrote, but because of what he did not write.

II. The *Courier* Reports

The call went out for baseball early in March and Bill, among the first to respond, soon proved that his control of a baseball was real, and beautiful to behold.

Bill saw little of Jerry while the squad was hardening up with handball and throwing a baseball around the gym floor. Twice there had been stories of the practice, and once he was mentioned as among those there, and once he was not mentioned at all. Bill pondered this. His control was now a matter of school gossip; its sharp-shooting qualities became a favourite topic for discussion; he was a school celebrity before he had so much as pitched an inning of a game. Bill thought there ought to be a story in this—but the story did not appear.

He watched the *Courier* closely after the squad began to play on the grass of High School Field. When Wally made the first cut, Bill found his name published as one of the survivors. Just that, and no more. Later in the week, he pitched part of the first practice game of the year, and did not allow a hit or a base on balls.

"We'll see what our sour friend says of that," Bill told himself gleefully.

And all he read next day concerning his feat was:

Stockton was on the mound for the last three innings.

Bill saw red. If he was doing good work for Hastings wasn't he entitled to his measure of credit?

He carried his wrongs to the locker room that afternoon. Roberts, the first baseman, gave him scant sympathy.

"Do you know, you almost beaned me yesterday."

"Oh, keep a grip on your nerve," Bill said irritably. "I knew just where that ball was going. I grazed you only once."

"Twice," said Roberts. "I'm not anxious to have a couple of teeth knocked out. Make sure you don't get them any closer."

"He's sore," Bill reflected, "because he didn't get a hit." It was disappointing to find the players indifferent to his woes, but he was used to boys who grew peeved when he drove them from the plate and made them look foolish. He took his troubles to the captain. There, at least, he ought to find a friendly ear. But even Wally defended the reporter.

"Everybody rates Jerry as being pretty square," Wally told him. "He wouldn't be small enough to boycott a fellow."

"Then why is it he never writes a good word about me?"

"Why don't you talk to him?"

"I wouldn't talk to him," blurted Bill.

But he changed his mind just before the opening game with Raleigh High. Jerry had written a half column for the *Courier* setting forth what might be expected of the team. Bill read it eagerly. Here was where he ought to get his due. Instead, he found this:

Last year Brail and Thomas were the team's best pitchers. This year, again, they hold their places at the head of the hurling corps. They are not spectacular; they burn no red fires and set off no fireworks; they are simply dependable twirlers whose efforts are always smooth and even. Stockton, a newcomer, will also work in some of the games.

Bill choked. This was the limit—and Wally had told him that Jerry was square!

He had bought the *Courier* at a little store across the street from the high school. Now, through the doorway of the store, he saw Jerry come down the high school steps. Acting on impulse he stepped outside to meet the school reporter.

"Look here, Ames. What have you against me?"

"I have nothing against *you*," said Jerry.

The strong accent that fell on the "you" puzzled Bill and left him somewhat dampened. He shook out the *Courier*.

"What's the idea of this? You know what I've been doing in practice."

"I know."

"Then why this—this lie? Brail and Thomas are not the stars. Where do you leave me?"

"Out of it," Jerry said calmly. "You're not a pitcher; you're an intimidator. Pitchers use what skill they have; you use threats. They use a baseball as a tool with which to match their cunning against the batter's eye. You use a baseball as a weapon. The fellow who does that is not a baseball pitcher at all. He's a baseball gunman."

The tide of denunciation overwhelmed Bill and left him momentarily dazed. "Is that what you think?" he asked weakly.

"I think," said Jerry, "that it's a pity you don't shoot a clean game. With your control you could do the kind of pitching that Hastings could be proud of. Against the free swinger you could keep the ball high on the inside corner, and he wouldn't have a chance. Against the fellow who chokes his bat—the chop hitter—you could keep it low and on the outside. The inside corner for the batters who crowd the plate, and the outside corner for those who stand back. You have enough curve; any fast ball has a natural curve. And with your control—"

Bill was recovering from his shock. "Who made you an authority on baseball?"

"You asked me what I thought."

"I don't care what you think," Bill cried in a passion, and went raging down the street. And yet, even in the height of his temper, something told him that he did care what Jerry thought and that, once more, as in their first meeting, he had been strangely placed upon the defensive.

He pitched the Raleigh game. The wounds that Jerry had rubbed with salt were still smarting. He determined to show just how good he was. Before the first inning was over, with that wicked "duster" zipping past their chins, the Raleigh boys were backing away from the plate and consternation was settling over the Raleigh bench. Bill won the game 6 to 0 and gave only two hits.

Wally, captain, and Gunn, catcher, babbled blissfully. The others were queerly silent. Bill was nettled.

He had seen Jerry at the game; he wondered what the reporter would write. Next day's *Courier* brought him the answer:

Raleigh's batters, afraid to crowd the plate for fear of being hit, got only two safe blows. Raleigh, under the circumstances, never had a chance.

Never had a chance! Ordinarily that phrase would mean that the losing team had been hopelessly outclassed, but in this case it meant something else. There was a quality about the paragraph that suggested a victory that was shady and cheap. Bill found himself staring hard at the ground.

"This fellow Ames is a nut," he told himself at last. "He doesn't understand. It's my business to see that they have as little chance as possible. I'm out there to win."

Brail pitched the game against Jackson High. Two hits, a base on balls and a sacrifice bunt gave Jackson two runs in the first. Roberts came in with the pitcher.

"Attaboy, Brail. Nice work. That last hit was a scratch. You hold 'em and we'll get some runs for you."

Hastings tied it with two runs in the third, only to go behind again in the fourth when Jackson scored two more runs on a hit, a base on balls, another sacrifice and two errors. This time half the infield accompanied Brail to the bench after he had fanned a Jackson batter for the third out and had left three keenly disappointed runners on the bases.

"Pretty work, Brail, pretty. Heads up. We'll begin to play baseball now."

"Only four hits, old man, and about half the game gone. That's doing it."

Roberts patted the pitcher's shoulder and sat down beside him, and Brail began to smile.

Bill bit his lips. He had allowed only two hits and won by a shut-out, and Roberts had given him no praise whatever. Here was Brail with four runs chalked against him, and the team standing by him like buddies in battle. At that moment Bill was conscious of a gap, a bleak emptiness, a lack of warm and vital comradeship.

In the days that followed even as his string of victories lengthened, he could not shake off the feeling of being more or less alone. True, Gunn still sang an ardent song of admiration, but Bill began to see that Gunn was captivated by the mechanics of perfect control. As for Wally, Bill now saw that the captain was too variable, too lacking in moral fibre for his support to count for much.

Now and then, Jerry, with scorebook and pencil, sat upon the bench. More and more, Bill was surprised to find the weight that was apparently attached to Jerry's opinions. At first the pitcher kept himself aloof; but with everybody else on friendly terms with the school reporter he saw that he was making his own position of unfriendliness marked. He began to talk with Jerry—scraps of trivial conversation that meant nothing. And then he noticed that there was a slight coolness, a touch of constraint, whenever Wally and the reporter met.

"Did you have a row with Jerry?" he asked Wally.

The captain nodded. "He argued that your trick of dusting 'em off was against the spirit of the game and that you ought to be canned."

Bill was not surprised. "What did you tell him?"

"I told him to show me something that would win as many games for Hastings."

It was the same answer Bill would have made several weeks ago. Yet, coming from Wally, it stumped him. Jerry had been definite. "This thing," he said, "is wrong." Wally had neither defended nor denied. "Show me something better," he had argued—and Bill knew that that was no argument at all. For the first time, in his secret soul of souls, he was uneasy and doubtful.

Roberts, too, added to the force of his wistful longings. To have the first baseman pat his shoulder, to give him a cheery "That's working," as he gave it to Brail and to Thomas, would have made him feel that he belonged. He had grown used to finding himself slighted in the Courier. He wouldn't care so much about that if Jerry would only give him the slow, understanding smile he sometimes gave to Brail.

Bill was shaken with a sudden fit of fury. "I'm not a crook! They give me no credit for skill. I haven't hit a batter all season, and Jerry calls me a baseball gunman. If I can scare them away from the plate—" Scare! Scare! He had picked an unfortunate word. And Jerry had called him an intimidator.

III. HASTINGS *versus* ST. PETER'S PREP.

He pitched the game against St. Peter's Prep. After the warm-up, Gunn came to the bench shaking his head. Bill, the catcher confided to Wally, wasn't right.

"Control gone?" Wally asked anxiously.

"No; it isn't that. But he looks queer—as though he were under a strain. He isn't the same Bill."

Yet for three innings Bill held St. Peter's scoreless and in those three innings a home run by Roberts, with Wally on second, accounted for two Hastings runs. Gunn, coming to the bench after the third inning, sat down beside the pitcher.

"Lost your nerve?" he asked. "You're off today. I've signalled you a dozen times and you haven't put that duster ball over once. They'll begin to hit you the first thing you know."

"You're up next," said Bill. "We could use another run or two."

He was glad to be rid of the catcher. Roberts slid into the place that Gunn had vacated.

"Nice work, Bill," the first baseman said.

Bill glowed for just a moment. Nice work because it was clean work. Then all those other games— He winced.

For seven innings his control kept St. Peter's from even the threat of a score. He was pitching with his head, studying the batters, sending the ball where it was least welcome. And then, in the eighth, things went wrong. Gunn let a third strike go through him, and the batter got to first. The next boy hit to short. With a sure double play in front of him Wally fumbled, and there were two on and one out.

Bill began to sweat. To lose this game after he had tried so hard to win it! The batter at the plate had hit safely once before; if he hit now—

Roberts' voice came crooning from the direction of first

base. "Keep working, Bill old boy. We're with you. This is only a flurry. Keep working, Bill."

Bill pitched, and the batter drove a screaming liner toward left field. Bill's breath caught. But the ball was foul by inches.

"That's the first strike, Bill. You're getting him in the hole!" Roberts was pleading.

The shock of that hit had chilled the pitcher through and through. Gunn, with signalling fingers, was demanding the bean ball. With a sudden nod Bill let the ball go, and the batter leaped back to get away from the pitch.

Roberts' voice was silent.

After that the batter was easy. Two balls on the outside corner, and the umpire waved him to the bench. The next boy staggered back from a ball that dusted his chest, and on the next pitch rolled a weak grounder to the box. The game had been saved. Hastings shrilled a cheer as Bill came to the bench.

All through the last inning Bill used the bean ball, and St. Peter's didn't get a man to first. With the game over, the pitcher snapped his sweater up from the bench and strode toward the locker room. Next day the *Courier* printed this:

Despite the fact that he was touched up for eight hits, Stockton pitched his best game of the year. With crafty cunning he pitched to each batter's weakness, and his control never shone so brightly. The crowd, missing the real meaning of what was happening on the field, gave him a thundering cheer when he blanked St. Peter's in the eighth. It was the inning in which he was least entitled to acclaim.

Bill folded the paper and put it in his pocket. Eight hits, and yet his best game of the year! After all, with fellows like Jerry and Roberts, there was something greater than the mere winning of a game. You had to be white. If only he hadn't dusted the batter after that terrific, long foul—

"I did it," he said bitterly, "so what's the use of crying about it now?"

The St. Peter's game had been played on a Friday. Monday, Wally said to him:

"I'm going to save you for Jefferson High. That's our biggest shot; if we win that we win everything. I'll use Brail against Farragut High on Wednesday, and Thomas against Park High on Friday. That will give you a good rest. We want that Jefferson game, Bill."

"I'll try to get it," Bill assured him.

Brail sent Farragut down to defeat. Thomas lost the Park Hill game, 8 to 7. Gunn lamented the Park Hill defeat. If Thomas had had a good duster ball, Park Hill would not have scored four runs.

"Thank goodness," the catcher said fervently, "we have Bill for Jefferson. She won't get very far."

IV. The Game Against Jefferson

The day of the Jefferson game found Bill cold and hot by turns—trembling one moment, and tense the next. The game was played away from home. Hastings, first at bat, went out on six pitched balls.

"This is going to be a battle," predicted Gunn as he buckled on his protector. "Give them everything you have, Bill. Runs are going to be scarce."

Bill grew hot again. The first Jefferson batter did not like them high on the inside corner, and ended by popping to Roberts. The next boy had a good eye. With the count two and three, Bill gambled on an inside corner pitch and missed, the batter going to first. It was the third base on balls that Bill had given all season. He shook his head. Another slip like that might prove costly.

The boy on first had a good eye, but he was a poor base runner. In three or four apparent ways he showed that he intended to steal. Bill anticipated the move and sent Gunn a pitch-out. The catcher, over-eager, got a poor grip on the ball, tried to change the position of his fingers, and ended by making a bad throw. The runner was safe on second with only one out.

Roberts voice came to him like a prayer. "Bill! Oh, Bill!"

Bill's pitch was clean. The batter slashed it on the ground. Roberts came in on it like a ferret. A figure was dashing for third. From a crouched position the first baseman whipped the ball across the diamond. He could not hear the umpire's voice, but the upward wave of his hand was visible above the dust cloud that was raised by the slide.

"That's pitching, Bill," Roberts' voice carried a note of triumph.

Bill was conscious that his throat had been contracted and that the air, rushing to his lungs in great gulps, tasted good. Gunn had made a mess of that first runner. Perhaps the boy on first, counting on another sloppy throw, would also try to steal. He would have to go down before the batter was forced to hit, else a safe rap would merely move him around instead of scoring him. So Bill, with a slight signal to Gunn, sent another pitch-out.

The runner was away with the pitch. But this time Gunn got the ball securely. His whistling shot to Wally caught the runner by three feet.

All the way to the bench, Bill was conscious that something was pressing on him. Not until he sat down did he realize that it had been Roberts' hand patting his shoulder.

"I got through it," he kept muttering. "I got through it." Gunn was demanding why he had not dusted them. He did not hear the catcher's voice. Jerry, score book open, was watching the field and smiling that slow understanding smile.

For seven innings the game stayed a scoreless tie. Gunn had been a good prophet—runs were scarce. In the eighth inning, Wally, first up, was safe on an infield error. Bill, clutching his knees, prayed for a hit. Gunn, second up,

THE RUNNER WAS AWAY WITH THE PITCH

forced Wally at second. Jerry touched the pitcher with the score book.

"You're up, Bill."

He was so eager that he swung at bad balls. The Jefferson pitcher struck him out with the fifth pitch. As he stepped away from the plate he met Roberts going up for his turn.

"Rob!" he pleaded.

"I'll try to," the first baseman said grimly. "You deserve it."

He swung on the second ball and fired a three-bagger into the deep left centre.

"There's your game, Bill," cried Jerry.

Bill's heart pounded. One run in the eighth—and he hadn't pitched a dirty ball! The Jefferson pitcher, shaken by the disaster, threw a wild pitch, and Roberts dashed home with the second run. A moment later, after the third out, Hastings took the field.

"Dust them, Bill," Gunn pleaded. "You've got a lead now."

The pitcher's lips pressed tightly together. He didn't answer.

Jefferson was helpless before him in the eighth. Hastings was blanked in the ninth. And then Bill went out to face the fire for the last time.

"Not a dirty ball," he told himself. The batter dumped his first pitch in front of the plate. He raced in, picked it up, let it fall, made a blind stab for it and missed.

"Let it go," cried Roberts. Better a runner on first than a hurried, wild throw that would place him on second or third.

Gunn retrieved the ball and walked to the pitcher. "Dust them," he said in a fierce undertone. "Have you gone crazy? Dust them and save yourself."

Bill shook his head. As he pitched, the runner bluffed a start for second. Wally ran over to take the throw. And the batter, catching the ball, drove it through the spot where Wally had been a moment before. When the ball was returned to the infield, there were runners on second and third.

Twice Bill wiped the sweat from his hand. A little dusting and he would have this game where he wanted it. And yet, though the thought lured him, tempted him, tormented him, he shook his head to the signals that the catcher flashed. The boy at the plate, gripping the bat at its very end, held it far back over his shoulder. He would swing with all his power. Bill fed him a slow, tantalizing ball on the inside.

"Strike one."

The batter had been forced to swing and choke the bat against his body at the same time.

Again that slow ball on the inside.

"Strike two."

The batter was shortening his grip and moving back from the plate a bit. Bill pitched the third one outside.

It was a ball, and the batter unconsciously edged forward again. And then Bill zipped a fast one past him while he stood flat-footedly expecting another slow pitch.

"You're out!" marked the umpire.

Bill's nerves shook with an elation that was new and intoxicating. Never, while he had cowed batters and had mowed them down, had his heart sang as it sang now.

"That's showing them something, Bill, old boy," came from Roberts.

He flashed the first baseman a smile. Another batter was waiting, with stick gripped short. Holding the bat that way, he'd have a hard time reaching the outside corner. Bill tried the outside with a ball shoulder high.

"Strike one."

The boy at the plate stretched his arms the better to reach the next one. He was out of position for the inside, and Bill sent him a ball that came low and close.

"Strike two."

The batter was bewildered. In that state, Bill knew, he would be tense with anticipation and anxiety. Bill tried him with a floater and he swung before the ball reached the plate.

"You're out."

Bill saw Jerry, on the bench, toss his score book into the air. The third batter had Bill puzzled. He couldn't remember what he had hit at in earlier innings, and could not read his stand at the plate. He tried an experimental ball outside.

"Ball one!" ruled the umpire.

Jefferson took heart and began to cheer. But Bill had learned what he wanted to know. The batter was one who swung downward at the ball.

Bill served a pitch shoulder high. The boy at the plate hit into it and rapped it along the ground. Wally took three steps in, picked it out of the air as it bounded, and lined it across to Roberts. The game was over.

The nine made much of Bill in the dressing room, but

what he valued most was that slow smile of Jerry's and the rap across the shoulders from Roberts that knocked the breath out of his body. They seemed to gravitate together, these three who had never been friendly. On the way home in the train they monopolized two seats. Jerry worked out his box score for the *Courier*; Roberts hummed and beat time on the arm of his seat; Bill relaxed in contentment and stared out the train window.

Jerry looked up from the score book. "Bill, you sure were in a hole in the ninth."

"With two men on base, is that what you mean?" Bill asked.

Jerry nodded.

"The first inning," Bill differed, "was the toughest. Right then I learned something."

"What?"

"There are two ways of winning a ball game."

Roberts and Jerry looked their inquiry.

"Using a bean ball is one—" Bill hesitated before going on.

"And the other?"

The pitcher grinned. "Using your bean."

—*William Heyliger*

STUDY AND ENJOYMENT

1. How did Bill get the name of "Bean Ball Bill"?
2. What is a "duster"?
3. What made Bill change his way of pitching?
4. Which of these boys—Jerry Ames, Roberts, Gunn, Wally Woods—did you like best? Why?
5. On the trip home from the game against Jefferson High, Bill said there were two ways of winning a ball game—"using a bean ball" and "using your bean." What did he mean?
6. "After all, with fellows like Jerry and Roberts, there was something greater than the mere winning of a game." A foreign student studying at Oxford, England, was once asked what he felt was the most remarkable thing he had seen at Oxford University. He replied, "Three thousand young men who would rather lose a game than win it unfairly."

MR. WINKLE ON SKATES

Persons in this story:

SAMUEL PICKWICK, chairman and founder of the Club.

AUGUSTUS SNODGRASS, soft ⎫
TRACY TUPMAN, softer ⎭ who keep the Club records.

NATHANIEL WINKLE, a gay blade.

SAM WELLER, Mr. Pickwick's servant.

MR. WARDLE, host to the Pickwickians on Christmas Day.

EMILY WARDLE, daughter of Mr. Wardle.

THE FAT BOY, Mr. Wardle's sleepy page.

BENJAMIN ALLEN ⎫
BOB SAWYER ⎭ medical students.

ARABELLA ALLEN, sister of Benjamin.

TIME: *Christmas Day. The Club has been to church, and then eaten heartily.*

PLACE: *Mr. Wardle's home, Dingley Dell.*

On Christmas morning Mr. Wardle invited Mr. Pickwick, Mr. Snodgrass, Mr. Tupman, Mr. Winkle, and his other guests to go down to the pond.

"You skate, of course, Winkle?" said Mr. Wardle.

"Ye—s; oh, yes!" replied Mr. Winkle. "—I—am *rather* out of practice."

"Oh, *do* skate, Mr. Winkle," said Arabella. "I like to see it so much."

"Oh, it is so graceful," said another young lady.

A third young lady said it was "elegant," and a fourth expressed her opinion that it was "swanlike."

"I should be very happy, I am sure," said Mr. Winkle, reddening, "but I have no skates."

This objection was at once overruled. Trundle had a couple of pair, and the fat boy announced that there were half a dozen more downstairs; whereat Mr. Winkle expressed exquisite delight and looked exquisitely uncomfortable.

Mr. Wardle led the way to a pretty large sheet of ice; and the fat boy and Mr. Weller having shovelled and swept away the snow which had fallen on it during the night, Mr. Bob Sawyer adjusted his skates with a dexterity which to Mr. Winkle was perfectly marvellous, and described circles with his left leg, and cut figures of eight, and inscribed upon the ice, without once stopping for breath, a great many other pleasant and astonishing devices,—to the excessive satisfaction of Mr. Pickwick, Mr. Tupman, and the ladies,—which reached a pitch of positive enthusiasm when Mr. Wardle and Benjamin Allen, assisted by Bob Sawyer, performed some mystic evolutions which they called a reel.

All this time Mr. Winkle, with his face and hands blue with the cold, had been forcing a gimlet into the soles of his shoes, and putting his skates on, with the points behind, and getting the straps into a very complicated and entangled state, with the assistance of Mr. Snodgrass, who knew rather less about skates than a Hindoo. At length, however, with the assistance of Mr. Weller, the unfortunate skates were firmly screwed and buckled on, and Mr. Winkle was raised to his feet.

"Now, then, sir," said Sam, in an encouraging tone, "off with you, and show them how to do it."

"Stop, Sam, stop!" cried Mr. Winkle, trembling violently and clutching hold of Sam's arms with the grasp of a drowning man. "How slippery it is, Sam!"

"Not an uncommon thing upon ice, sir," replied Mr. Weller. "Hold up, sir!"

This last observation of Mr. Weller's bore reference to a demonstration Mr. Winkle made at the instant of a frantic desire to throw his feet in the air, and dash the back of his head on the ice.

"These—these—are very awkward skates; ain't they, Sam?" inquired Mr. Winkle, staggering.

"HOW SLIPPERY IT IS, SAM!"

"I'm afraid there's an orkard gen'l'm'n in 'em, sir," replied Sam.

"Now, Winkle," cried Mr. Pickwick, quite unconscious that there was anything the matter. "Come; the ladies are all anxiety."

"Yes, yes," replied Mr. Winkle, with a ghastly smile. "I'm coming."

"Just goin' to begin," said Sam, endeavouring to disengage himself. "Now sir, start off!"

"Stop an instant, Sam," gasped Mr. Winkle, clinging most affectionately to Mr. Weller. "I find I've got a couple of coats at home that I don't want, Sam. You may have 'em, Sam."

"Thank 'ee, sir," replied Mr. Weller.

"Never mind touching your hat, Sam," said Mr. Winkle, hastily. "You needn't take your hand away to do that. I meant to have given you five shillings this morning for a Christmas-box, Sam. I'll give it to you this afternoon, Sam."

"You're wery good, sir," replied Mr. Weller.

"Just hold me at first, Sam, will you?" said Mr. Winkle. "There—that's right. I shall soon get in the way of it, Sam. Not too fast, Sam; not too fast."

Mr. Winkle, stooping forward, with his body half doubled up, was being assisted over the ice by Mr. Weller, in a very singular and un-swan-like manner, when Mr. Pickwick most innocently shouted from the opposite bank: "Sam!"

"Sir?"

"Here. I want you."

"Let go, sir," said Sam. "Don't you hear the governor callin'? Let go, sir."

With a violent effort, Mr. Weller disengaged himself from the grasp of the agonized Pickwickian, and in so doing, administered a considerable impetus to the unhappy Mr. Winkle. With an accuracy which no degree of dexterity or practice could have insured, that unfortunate gentleman bore swiftly down into the centre of the reel at the very moment when Mr. Bob Sawyer was performing a flourish of unparalleled beauty. Mr. Winkle struck wildly against him, and with a loud crash they both fell heavily down. Mr. Pickwick ran to the spot. Bob Sawyer had risen to his feet, but Mr. Winkle was far too wise to do anything of the kind on skates. He was seated on the ice, making spasmodic efforts to smile; but anguish was depicted on every lineament of his countenance.

"Are you hurt?" inquired Mr. Benjamin Allen, with great anxiety.

"Not much," said Mr. Winkle, rubbing his back very hard.

"I wish you'd let me bleed you," said Mr. Benjamin, with great eagerness.

"No, thank you," replied Mr. Winkle hurriedly.

"I really think you had better," said Allen.

"Thank you," replied Mr. Winkle; "I'd rather not."

"What do *you* think, Mr. Pickwick?" inquired Bob Sawyer.

Mr. Pickwick was excited and indignant. He beckoned to Mr. Weller, and said in a stern voice, "Take his skates off."

"No; but really I had scarcely begun," remonstrated Mr. Winkle.

"Take his skates off," repeated Mr. Pickwick firmly.

The command was not to be resisted. Mr. Winkle allowed Sam to obey it in silence.

"Lift him up," said Mr. Pickwick. Sam assisted him to rise.

Mr. Pickwick retired a few paces apart from the bystanders; and, beckoning his friend to approach, fixed a searching look upon him, and uttered in a low, but distinct and emphatic tone, these remarkable words:

"You're a humbug, sir."

"A what?" said Mr. Winkle, starting.

"A humbug, sir. I will speak plainer, if you wish it. An impostor, sir."

With those words, Mr. Pickwick turned slowly on his heel, and rejoined his friends.

—*Charles Dickens*
From *The Pickwick Papers*

STUDY AND ENJOYMENT

Charles Dickens died some eighty years ago, but his books continue to be read and loved. He is one of England's great humorists. He had the knack of portraying, without bitterness, the oddities of human nature. Though the people of his novels may appear exaggerated types, they are real, nevertheless. He could detect oddities of human character, and having seen these clearly, he would exaggerate for humorous effect. *The Pickwick Papers*, from which this story is taken, was written when Dickens was only twenty-five. You will find two passages from his novel *David Copperfield* elsewhere in this Reader, as well as part of his book *A Christmas Carol*.

1. What part of this story amuses you the most? Read it aloud. Why did Mr. Winkle get into difficulty?

2. You may be puzzled over Mr. Allen wanting "to bleed" Mr. Winkle, but Benjamin Allen was a medical student, you will remember, and one remedy long ago for almost any ache or sickness was taking blood from the patient.

CASEY AT THE BAT

The outlook wasn't brilliant for the Mudville nine that
  day;
The score stood two to four, with but an inning left to play.
So, when Cooney died at second, and Burrows did the
  same,
A sickly silence fell upon the patrons of the game.

A straggling few got up to go, leaving there the rest,
With that hope that springs eternal within the human
  breast,
For they thought, "If only Casey could get a whack at
  that,"
They'd put up even money now, with Casey at the bat.

But Flynn preceded Casey, and likewise so did Blake,
And the former was a puddin', and the latter was a fake,
So on that stricken multitude the death-like silence sat,
For there seemed but little chance of Casey's getting to
  the bat.

But Flynn let drive a "single," to the wonderment of all,
And the much-despisèd Blakey "tore the cover off the
  ball."
And when the dust had lifted and they saw what had
  occurred,
There was Blakey safe at second, and Flynn a-huggin'
  third.

Then from the gladdened multitude went up a joyous yell,
It rumbled in the mountain-tops, it rattled in the dell;
It struck upon the hillside and rebounded on the flat;
For Casey, mighty Casey, was advancing to the bat.

There was ease in Casey's manner as he stepped into his
    place;
There was pride in Casey's bearing, and a smile on Casey's
    face,
And when, responding to the cheers, he lightly doffed his
    hat,
No stranger in the crowd could doubt 'twas Casey at the
    bat.

Ten thousand eyes were on him as he rubbed his hands
    with dirt,
Five thousand tongues applauded when he wiped them on
    his shirt;
Then while the New York pitcher ground the ball into his
    hip,
Defiance gleamed in Casey's eye, a sneer curled Casey's lip.

And now the leather-covered sphere came whirling through
    the air,
And Casey stood a-watching it in haughty grandeur there.
Close by the sturdy batsman the ball unheeded sped—
"That ain't my style," said Casey. "Strike one!" the
    umpire said.

From the benches, black with people, there went up a
    muffled roar,
Like the beating of storm waves on a stern and distant
    shore.
"Kill him! Kill the umpire!" shouted some one on the
    stand.
And it's likely they'd have killed him had not Casey
    raised a hand.

With a smile of Christian charity great Casey's visage
    shone;
He stilled the rising tumult; he bade the game go on;

He signalled to the pitcher, once more the spheroid flew;
But Casey still ignored it, and the umpire said: "Strike
    two!"

"Fraud!" cried the maddened thousands, and echo
    answered "Fraud!"
But one scornful look from Casey and the audience was
    awed.
They saw his face grow stern and cold, they saw his
    muscles strain,
And they knew that Casey wouldn't let that ball go by
    again.

The sneer is gone from Casey's lip, his teeth are clenched
    in hate;
He pounds with cruel violence his bat upon the plate.
And now the pitcher holds the ball, and now he lets it go,
And now the air is shattered by the force of Casey's blow.

Ah, somewhere in this favoured land the sun is shining
    bright;
The band is playing somewhere, and somewhere hearts are
    light.
And somewhere men are laughing, and somewhere
    children shout:
But there is no joy in Mudville—mighty Casey has
    struck out.

—*Ernest L. Thayer*

STUDY AND ENJOYMENT

1. In a survey made among many thousands of school children to discover
   their favourite poem, this poem stood first.   It is not really good poetry
   at all; why, then, did they like it?
2. When did you first begin to wonder if Casey was as good as he and the
   crowd thought he was?
3. How does Thayer make Casey's failure seem funny?   Do you like the last
   stanza?   Why?

THE YAK

For hours the princess would not play or sleep
  Or take the air;
Her red mouth wore a look it meant to keep
  Unmelted there;
(Each tired courtier longed to shriek, or weep,
  But did not dare.)

Then one young duchess said: "I'll to the King,
  And short and flat
I'll say, 'Her Highness will not play or sing
  Or pet the cat;
Or feed the peacocks, or do anything—
  And that is that.'"

So to the King she went, curtsied, and said,
  (No whit confused):
"Your Majesty, I would go home! The court is dead.
  Have me excused;
The little princess still declines,"—she tossed her head—
  "To be amused."

Then to the princess stalked the King: "What ho!" he
      roared,
"What may you lack?
Why do you look, my love, so dull and bored
  With all this pack
Of minions?" She answered, while he waved his sword:
  "I want a yak."

"A yak!" he cried (each courtier cried "Yak! Yak!"
  As at a blow)—
"Is that a figure on the zodiac?
  Or horse? Or crow?"
The princess sadly said to him: "Alack
  I do not know."

"We'll send the vassals far and wide, my dear!"
　　Then quoth the King:
"They'll make a hunt for it, then come back here
　　And bring the thing;—
　But warily,—lest it be wild, or queer,
　　Or have a sting."

So off the vassals went, and well they sought
　　On every track
Till by and by in old Tibet they bought
　　An ancient yak.
Yet when the princess saw it, she said naught
　　But: "Take it back!"

And what the courtiers thought they did not say
　　(Save soft and low),
For that is surely far the wisest way
　　As we all know;
While for the princess?　She went back to play!
　　　　Tra-rill-a-la-lo!
　　　　Tra-rill-a-la-lo!
　　　　Tra-rill-a-la-lo!

　　　　　　　　　　　—Virna Sheard

STUDY AND ENJOYMENT

1. What is your opinion of the little princess?　What well-chosen verbs help us to picture the king?　Why did the courtiers not say openly what they thought?

2. A *yak* is a wild or domesticated ox found on the plateau of Thibet (Tibet) in central Asia.　It is humped, it grunts, and it has long hair hanging from its shoulders, sides, and tail.　The *zodiac* is an imaginary belt in the heavens.　It is divided into twelve parts with a strange creature as the sign of each part.　You will find it pictured in any almanac.

3. This poem may be read chorally.　Choose three pupils to take the solo parts of duchess, princess, and king.　The background and connecting parts of the story may be read by two groups, one of dark or low voices, and one of light voices.　In the last stanza, the dark voices may read lines 1, 3, and 4, while the light voices should read lines 2, 5, 6, 7, and 8. Do your best to bring out the humour of the characters and situation.

HOLIDAYING IN THE WOODS

This selection comes from *The Living Forest*, a book about two boys and a half-breed hunter who live by their wits in the forests of Manitoba. Mr. Heming has made his own illustrations for the book. You may wish to look it up in the library.

Now for a number of days we spent most of our time at work on our canoe, but when we grew tired of one job we turned to another. Every day old Bill taught us something new, either in the way of woodcraft or natural history, and every day, too, we grew more fond of our life in the North Woods. What with our daily work, and the surprises and adventures it often brought us, so much of interest was crowded into our lot that neither Link nor I had time to think of the life we had left in civilization, or to brood over the catastrophe that had befallen Perkins and his party. Every day seemed to bring us more contentment and pleasure, and thus we boys were as happy as any boys could be who were living a life of adventure in an enchanting and mystery-haunted forest.

One evening after supper Link said:

"Bill, you've tol' us a lot about other animals but nothing about beavers. I've heard they're about the most interesting animals in the North Woods."

"That's true, Link. An' here they're right at your very door, yet neither of you boys've had courage or ambition to do a little investigatin' on your own account. I sometimes wonder what boys are made of nowadays. Any night you want you can slip over to Beaver Creek an' watch 'em. They may be workin' every night now. Perhaps the newly-weds've started buildin'. Or some old one may be doin' a bit o' work on the dam. An' when you go over there, stay quiet, and keep down wind, an' only move when they're not lookin' your way. You boys ought to be good at spyin' on animals, because you've less bulk an' better sight than ole Bill. I'll take you over an' leave you there."

We struck the creek just below the dam, and that was the first thing Bill explained to us.

"They built it to raise the water o' the stream high enough to protect their island-like homes by coverin' th' entrances to their lodges; also to form enough water below the winter's ice to allow o' swimmin' to the grub cache, as well as to flood the little valley until the water reached the surroundin' poplars, so that after cuttin' 'em down, they'd float 'em to their lodges."

"But how on earth did they build a big dam like this?" Lincoln asked. "It must be seventy or eighty feet long and at least five feet deep in the middle."

"They began by cuttin' brush an' layin' it in the water, butts up stream. On the brush they placed mud an' sod an' stones, or any handy stuff that'd weight the brush down and help block back the water. That's the way the work went on, until finally it raised the water as high as they wanted it. But this isn't a big dam. Sometimes they build 'em hundreds of feet long."

"I've heard they dig canals, too," I remarked.

"I haven't seen any 'round here," Bill replied. "If I had I'd show you one. They're usually dug for the purpose o' floatin' home the branches they've cut from trees beyond the reaches of their pond. Some of their canals are even provided with several little dams for the purpose o' raisin' the water to a number o' different levels."

"The canals are from two to three feet wide an' about eighteen inches deep an' sometimes run for hundreds of feet. Now I'm goin' to leave you boys here to do a little scoutin' of your own. Don't stay too late, an' when you get back to camp I'll be glad to hear what you've seen."

But after remaining a dark hour or two, and hearing nothing but an occasional noise that nearly frightened the life out of us—it sounded as if a moose had jumped off a hill into the water—we decided to go home. On the way Link twisted his ankle, and soon after arriving at camp it began to swell badly. Though the old hunter looked worried he merely remarked:

"I'll be back in a little while."

About a quarter of an hour later he returned with some branches of dwarf juniper. How he found them in the dark was a mystery to me. Breaking off the tips of the twigs in lengths about three inches long, he peeled off the outer bark; then with his knife scraped off the inner bark, which looked like the scrapings from new potatoes. Putting the pulpy stuff in his mouth he chewed it until it formed a mass like oatmeal porridge; then, plastering it around Link's ankle, he used soft willow bark to bind it there. In a couple of hours the pain left him, and by next morning the swelling had disappeared.

It was then that Bill asked us what we had learned about beaver, and when we told him what an awful noise we had heard, he laughingly remarked:

"Why, that was only the beavers slappin' the water with their tails when they dived. They did it to give warnin' to their comrades that danger was near. You're great boys, you are. However, when I finish the canoe I'll show you what beavers really do in the way o' work."

Later, when I asked the old hunter if he would make bows and arrows for Link and me, he replied:

"You're right, my son. You should both have 'em. An' you should be able to make 'em yourselves. Not only that, but you must learn what to do if you haven't even a knife. No man is a real woodsman unless he can hunt an' fish an' travel without even a gun, or an axe, or a knife. A real woodsman doesn't need anything from the outside world. He can live absolutely independent o' civilization. An' I might just as well show you right now how to make a bow an' arrows without the aid o' even a knife. Then as soon as you learn to do it for yourselves, I'll make each of you a proper bow, strung with a string o' twisted deer sinews."

After breakfast the old hunter led us down by the

shore, where a few days before we had seen part of the
skeleton of a wolf that must have been lying there for
several years, so hard and white were the weather-bleached
bones.   Choosing a bone about the thickness and roundness
of his little finger and the length of his hand, he then set out
in search of some milk-white quartz.   I remembered we had
seen quartz in a number of places, especially as jagged
lining to open pockets in the rocky wall of the cliff.   Sure
enough, we soon found it there; and with the aid of broken
stone, Bill smashed several pieces of quartz free and
carried them away.

"My boys, I'm now goin' to teach you how to make
knives, an' spears, an' axes, an' bows an' arrows just as
they were made by our ancestors fifty or a hundred thousand years ago.   A flinty stone would be better than this
quartz, but the quartz is handy an' it'll do.   When you've
learned how to make flint knives, an' spears, an' arrow-heads
without the aid of any tools, an' when you've learned how
to support yourselves independent o' civilization, an'
when you've spent the rest o' your lives livin' in the woods
learnin' the ways o' beasts and birds, then you'll be worthy
of bein' called real woodsmen.   Then you'll be the real
thing—real men o' the livin' forest.

"Now, my lads, with this bone I'll be able to chip
quartz or flint an' make it into knives or spears just as our
ancestors did in the old stone age.   Watch me do it."

Gripped firmly between the fingers and palm of his
left hand he held the quartz, and against its blunt edge he
steadily pressed the edge of the bone with all the force he
could command.   Suddenly a small piece of quartz flaked
off.   He kept on thus for about half an hour, chipping off
the flakes of stone until he had formed the quartz into a
sharp-pointed, double-edged spear-head, much after the
pattern of the ancient flints found on the sites of old Indian
burial grounds.   As he worked Bill explained:

"This is the way the Indians made their flint arrow-
an' spear-heads an' their skinnin' knives.   The Walkin'

Wonder taught me how to do it when I was a boy. Now, you said you wanted to be great hunters. Try it yourselves. You've got to learn. First you've got to make your own stone knives. Then you've got to use 'em to make your bows an' arrows. When you've done that, and when you've killed game with your own homemade huntin' implements, and when you've skinned the game too with your own homemade stone knives, then I'll make for each of you the finest bow and arrows I can, and I'll teach you how to use 'em as the Indian hunters used to do."

"You're a wise man, Uncle," Lincoln smiled.

"Link, my boy, common sense is so rare that it often creates surprise. An' don't forget, my son, wisdom's always worth more today than tomorrow."

That day, while resting Lincoln's ankle, we boys spent most of our time learning how to make stone arrowheads, and spear-heads, and knives, how to use willow bark, twisted into cord, for our bowstrings, and how to prevent our bowstrings from breaking by placing them in a birchbark tube along with wet moss to keep them moist. Then we practised with the bows and arrows that we had made with our stone knives, and as a reward, that evening the old hunter set about making us the best bows and arrows he could with the aid of his steel knife. But somehow or other we really took more pride in the rough bows and arrows we had made ourselves, though we had to lay them aside when it came to a choice for real hunting.

—Arthur Heming
From *The Living Forest*.

STUDY AND ENJOYMENT

1. What does the hunter tell the boys they must do before they become real woodsmen?

2. If you are a boy scout or a girl guide, you have learned some woodcraft. What knowledge have you that is not mentioned in this story?

3. What is another way of saying "wisdom's always worth more today than tomorrow"?

WEATHERS

This is the weather the cuckoo likes,
  And so do I;
When showers betumble the chestnut spikes,
  And nestlings fly:
And the little brown nightingale bills his best,
And they sit outside at "The Travellers' Rest,"
And maids come forth sprig-muslin drest,
And citizens dream of the south and west,
  And so do I.

This is the weather the shepherd shuns,
  And so do I;
When beeches drip in browns and duns,
  And thresh, and ply;
And hill-hid tides throb, throe on throe,
And meadow rivulets overflow,
And drops on gate-bars hang in a row,
And rooks in families homeward go,
  And so do I.
                              —*Thomas Hardy*

STUDY AND ENJOYMENT

1. Thomas Hardy was an Englishman, and the birds and landscape in his poem are
   English. What details in stanza one make us feel the gladness of the season? Why do shepherd, rooks, and poet shun the outdoors in stanza two?
2. In the two stanzas what contrasts in (a) weathers, (b) colours, (c) sounds,
   (d) feelings, are brought out by the poet?
3. *The Travellers' Rest*, an inn; *south and west*, seacoasts where people holiday;
   bills, sings.

THE STAMP-COLLECTOR

Three months ago he did not know
  His lessons in geography;
Though he could spell and read right well,
And cipher, too, he could not tell
  The least thing in topography.

But what a change! How passing strange!
This stamp-collecting passion
Has roused his zeal, for woe or weal,
And lists of names he now can reel
Off, in amazing fashion.

I hear him speak of Mozambique,
Heligoland, Bavaria,
Cashmere, Japan, Tibet, Soudan,
Sumatra, Spain, Waldeck, Kokan,
Khaloon, Siam, Bulgaria.

Schleswig-Holstein (oh, boy of mine,
Genius without a teacher!)
Wales, Panama, Scinde, Bolivar,
Cabul, Deccan, Helvetia.

And now he longs for more Hong-Kongs,
A Rampur, a Mauritius,
Greece, Borneo, Fernando Po—
And how much else no one can know;
But be, kind Fates, propitious!

—*Mary L. B. Branch*

STUDY AND ENJOYMENT

1. Stamp collectors early learn to identify stamps by names printed on them that are unknown to boys and girls who are not collectors. To what countries do stamps belong which bear these labels: Belgique, Danmark, Republique Francaise, Deutsches Reich, Helvetia, Sverige, Norge? If you do not know them all, ask a stamp collector.

2. Sometimes hobbies help in school work. How did this boy's hobby help him?

3. This poem shows how much music and glamour may be found in geographical names. Draw up a list of cities, towns, and rivers in Canada, the names of which seem musical to you. There is a list in *The Unknown Country* by Bruce Hutchison that might interest you.

THE FOX HUNT

Fox hunting is a sport closely associated with country life in the British Isles. Most of you have seen pictures of huntsmen, in their gay coats, mounted on fine horses, and with a pack of hounds beside them, all ready for the chase. Many poems and stories have been written in praise of the hunt, with its merry din of horn, baying hounds, and clattering hoofs.

Mr. Masefield in this exciting poem, only a part of which is given here, presents a vivid picture of the rural England, the huntsmen, people about the cottages, churches and inns, and above all Reynard himself. Crafty the fox is, but he is no quitter, and the poet's sympathy is with him as he runs for his life. This poem is abridged from *Reynard the Fox*.

The fox was strong, he was full of running,
He could run for an hour and then be cunning,
But the cry behind him made him chill,
They were nearer now and they meant to kill.

And all the way to that blinding end
He would meet with men and have none his friend:
Men to holloa and men to run him,

With stones to stagger and yells to stun him,
Men to head him, with whips to beat him,
Teeth to mangle and mouths to eat him.

And all the way, that wild high crying,
To cold his blood with the thought of dying,
The horn and the cheer, and the drum-like thunder
Of the horse hooves stamping the meadows under.
He upped his brush and went with a will
For the Sarsen Stones on Wan Dyke Hill.

Past Tineton Church over Tineton Waste,
With the lolloping ease of a fox's haste,
The fur on his chest blown dry with the air,
His brush still up and his cheek-teeth bare.
Over the Waste where the ganders grazed,
The long swift lift of his loping lazed,
His ears cocked up as his blood ran higher,
He saw his point, and his eyes took fire.
The Wan Dyke Hill with its fir tree barren,
Its dark of gorse and its rabbit warren.
The Dyke on its heave like a tightened girth,
And holes in the Dyke where a fox might earth.
He had rabbited there long months before,
The earths were deep and his need was sore,
The way was new, but he took a bearing,
And rushed like a blown ship billow-sharing.

Off Tineton Common to Tineton Dean,
Where the wind-hid elders pushed with green;
Through the Dean's thin cover across the lane,
And up Midwinter to King of Spain.
Old Joe, at digging his garden grounds,
Said "A fox, being hunted; where be hounds?

O lord, my back, to be young again,
'Stead a zellin zider in King of Spain.
O hard, I hear 'em, O sweet, O sweet.
Why there be redcoat in Gearge's wheat,
And there be redcoat, and there they gallop.
Thur go a browncoat down a wallop.
Quick, Ellen, quick, come Susan, fly.
Here'm hounds.　I zeed the fox go by,
Go by like thunder, go by like blasting,
With his girt white teeth all looking ghasting."

Ellen and Susan came out scattering
Brooms and dustpans till all was clattering;
They saw the pack come head to foot
Running like racers nearly mute;
Robin and Dansey quartering near,
All going gallop like startled deer.
A half-dozen flitting scarlets shewing
In the thin green Dean where the pines were growing.
Black coats and brown coats thrusting and spurring
Sending the partridge coveys whirring,
Then a rattle up hill and a clop up lane,
It emptied the bar of the King of Spain.

There they were coming, mute but swift,
A scarlet smear in the blackthorn rift,
A white horse rising, a dark horse flying,
And the hungry hounds too tense for crying.

The fox knew well, that before they tore him,
They should try their speed on the down before him.
There were three more miles to the Wan Dyke Hill,
But his heart was high, that he beat them still.
The wind of the downland charmed his bones,
So off he went for the Sarsen Stones.

On he went with a galloping rally
Past Maesbury Clump for Wan Brook Valley,
The blood in his veins went romping high
"Get on, on, on to the earth or die."
The air of the downs went purely past,
Till he felt the glory of going fast,
Till the terror of death, though there indeed,
Was lulled for a while by his pride of speed;
In one mile more he would lie at rest
So for one mile more he would go his best.
He reached the dip at the long droop's end
And he took what speed he had still to spend.

Within, as he reached that soft green turf,
The wind, blowing lonely, moaned like surf,
Desolate ramparts rose up steep,
On either side, for the ghosts to keep.
He raced the trench, past the rabbit warren,
Close grown with moss which the wind made barren,
He passed the Spring where the rushes spread,
And there in the stones was his earth ahead.
One last short burst upon failing feet,
There life lay waiting, so sweet, so sweet,
Rest in a darkness, balm for aches.

The earth was stopped.   It was barred with stakes.

Then for a moment, his courage failed,
His eyes looked up as his body quailed,
Then the coming of death, which all things dread,
Made him run for the wood ahead.

The taint of fox was rank on the air,
He knew, as he ran, there were foxes there.
His strength was broken, his heart was bursting
His bones were rotten, his throat was thirsting.

He thought as he ran of his old delight
In the wood in the moon in an April night,
His happy hunting, his winter loving,
The smells of things in the midnight roving;
The look of his dainty-nosing, red
Clean-felled dam with her footpad's tread,
Of his sire, so swift, so game, so cunning
With craft in his brain and power of running,
Their fights of old when his teeth drew blood.
Now he was sick, with his coat all mud.

He crossed the covert, he crawled the bank,
To a meuse in the thorns and there he sank,
With his ears flexed back and his teeth shown white,
In a rat's resolve for a dying bite.
And there as he lay and looked, the cry
Of the hounds at head came rousing by;
He bent his bones in the blackthorn dim.
But the cry of the hounds was not for him.

The fox lay still in the rabbit-meuse,
On the dry brown dust of the plumes of yews.
In the bottom below a brook went by
Blue, in a patch, like a streak of sky.

There, one by one, with a clink of stone,
Came a red or dark coat on a horse half blown.
And man to man with a gasp for breath
Said, "Lord, what a run.   I'm fagged to death."

After an hour, no riders came,
The day drew by like an ending game;
A robin sang from a pufft red breast,
The fox lay quiet and took his rest.

The stars grew bright as the yews grew black,
The fox rose stiffly and stretched his back.
He flaired the air, then he padded out
To the valley below him dark as doubt,

The stars grew bright in the winter sky,
The wind came keen with a tang of frost,
The brook was troubled for new things lost,
The copse was happy for old things found,
The fox came home and he went to ground.

And the hunt came home and the hounds were fed,
They climbed to their bench and went to bed,
The horses in stable loved their straw.
"Good-night, my beauties," said Robin Dawe.

—*John Masefield*

STUDY AND ENJOYMENT

1. Are you glad the fox got away? Why?
2. What is the most exciting part of the poem?
3. When Betsy read Scott's poem about the escape of the stag, her uncle advised her not to worry too much about the meanings of words. In this poem, too, the story is the important thing, but the following explanations may clear up some points that are puzzling:

   Sarsen Stones, Sarsen comes from Saracen, and probably is used to mean strange or foreign. The stones might have been used by the Druids; *zellin zider*, selling cider; *gorse*, low prickly shrub; *King of Spain*, name of an inn or tavern; *girt*, great; *ghasting*, frightful; *desolate ramparts*, possibly remains of an old Roman camp; *meuse*, a gap in a hedge.

THE WILL

A "will" is a written legal form by which a person disposes of his property after death. How does this will differ from that which most people would leave?

I, Charles Lounsbury, being of sound mind and disposing memory, do hereby make and publish this, my last will and testament, in order as justly as may be to distribute my interest in the world among succeeding men.

That part of my interest which is known in law and recognized in the sheep-bound volumes as "my property," being inconsiderable and of no account, I make no disposal of in this, my last will.

My right to live, being but a life estate, is not at my disposal; but these things excepted, all else in the world I now proceed to devise and bequeath.

(*Item*) I give to the good Fathers and Mothers, in trust for their children, all good little words of praise and encouragement and all quaint pet names and endearments; and I charge said parents to use them justly and generously as the needs of their children may require.

(*Item*) I leave to children exclusively, but only for the terms of their childhood, all and every flower of the fields, and the blossoms of the woods, with the right to play among them freely according to the custom of children, warning them at the same time against thistles and thorns.   And I devise to children the banks of the brooks and the golden sands beneath the waters thereof, and the odour of the willows that dip therein; and the white clouds that float high over the giant trees.   And I leave the children, long, long days in which to be merry in a thousand ways; and the night; and the Moon; and the train of the Milky Way to wonder at; but subject, nevertheless, to the rights hereinafter given to lovers.

(*Item*) I devise to boys jointly the use of the idle fields and commons where ball may be played; all pleasant waters where one may swim; all snow-clad hills where one may coast; and all streams and ponds where one may fish, or where, when grim winters come, one may skate; to have and to hold the same for the period of their boyhood.   And all meadows, with the clover blossoms and the butterflies thereof; the woods and their appurtenances, the squirrels and birds, the echoes of strange noises, and all distant places which may be visited, together with the adventures there found.   And I give to said boys each his own place at the fireside at night, with all pictures that may be in the burning wood, to enjoy without let or hindrance and without incumbrance or care.

(*Item*)   To lovers, I devise their imaginary world, with whatever they may need as to the stars of the sky, the red roses by the wall, the bloom of the hawthorn, the sweet strains of music, and aught else by which they may desire to figure to each other the lastingness and beauty of their love.

(*Item*)   To young men, jointly, I devise and bequeath all boisterous, inspiring sports of rivalry, and I give to them the disdain of weakness and undaunted confidence in their own strength though they are rude.   I give them the power to make lasting friendships, and of possessing companions; and to them exclusively I give all merry songs and brave choruses to sing with lusty voices.

(*Item*)   And to those who are no longer children or youths or lovers, I leave memory; and I bequeath to them the volumes of the poems of Burns and Shakespeare, and of other poets—if there be others—to the end that they may live over the old days again freely and fully, without tithe or diminution.

(*Item*)   To our loved ones with snowy crowns I bequeath the happiness of old age, the love and gratitude of their children, until they fall asleep!

—Williston Fish

STUDY AND ENJOYMENT

1. Wills are written in legal language, all very particular and solemn and high sounding.   What are some of the words and phrases that make this unusual will sound a little like the usual kind?

2. "We own what we appreciate."   An artist once told a very rich man on whose land he was sketching that the fields and woods really belonged to him much more than to the man who owned them.   What did he mean?

3. If you were drawing up a will of this sort, what would be the chief items of *your* wealth?

4. Glossary: *sheep-bound*, parchment-bound, as legal documents; *life-estate*, something that lasts only as long as the holder's life; *devise*, grant, leave, bequeath, give; *subject . . . to the rights . . . given to lovers.*   Lovers and children both enjoy the beauties of moon and stars; *appurtenances*, that which goes with them; *let*, obstacle, interference; *tithe or diminution*, tax or lessening.

"HE SHOOTS! HE SCORES!"

An Overseas Hockey Broadcast

The next best thing to seeing a hockey game is to hear it broadcast. This is an account of a hockey broadcast that went not only across Canada but to our troops overseas during the Second Great War. Can you follow some episodes in the game?   What magic this is, that turns back the hands of the clock and plunges us into the excitement of a game now almost forgotten.

McKNIGHT: This is Canada calling!

Hello, Canadian troops, and our new British and American hockey fans. . . . This is Wes McKnight pinch-hitting for Foster Hewitt with the story of the game between Montreal Canadiens and the Toronto Maple Leafs.

Tonight was the fourth time this season that these two teams clashed on Toronto ice. . . . In their previous three games, the power-house from Montreal failed to win a game. . . . And so, tonight, Canadiens were all out to show close to 15,000 Toronto fans that they deserved the top spot in the National Hockey League standing.

Perhaps the most talked-about player before the game was Maurice Richard. . . . "Rocket" Richard—Canadiens' high scoring right winger—had an opportunity tonight to equal the all-time scoring mark set by Joe Malone as far back as 1918. . . . Although Richard has led the League in goal-scoring practically all season, the "Rocket" has so far failed to gather a point on the Maple Leafs' home ice. . . . In last season's playoffs in Montreal, Richard snowed the Leafs under with five goals in one game . . . and this season he has proved to be one of hockey's greatest marksmen.

So with Maurice Richard just one goal away from tying the all-time scoring record—and with Canadiens out for their first win of the season in Maple Leaf Gardens—tonight's game got under way.

In the first twenty minutes both Canadiens and the
Maple Leafs failed to score. . . . It was not until the
thirty-six second mark of the second period that Canadiens
finally drove home, with Lach scoring unassisted. . . .
Then, four minutes later, the Toronto team came right back
with a goal by Metz, after Bodnar set up the play. . . .
With the score tied, one-to-one, Canadiens came back
strong with Gauthier poking one past McCool in the
Toronto net . . . and that's the way the second period
ended—Canadiens 2—Maple Leafs 1.

Then here's the way Foster Hewitt called the third and
final period.

HEWITT: . . . he zigzagged himself right out of position. . . . A forward pass ends up at centre ice, where Reg
Hamilton of the Leafs clears over. . . . Bodnar going in
with Nick Metz. . . . Here's a shot—and Nick Metz just
missed the corner by inches! . . . Lorne Carr got the
rebound on the right board. . . . Stopped by Getliffe. . . .
The Leafs keep that puck in the Montreal zone . . . it's
back to Reg Hamilton at the blue line . . . a flip pass is
wide of the Canadien goal. . . . Here comes the puck to
Carr, and it's knocked to the blue line and out—then in
again for an offside.

Hap Day is going to change the line again, and Dick
Irwin promptly counters. . . . They're changing players
now. . . . Two-to-one is the score for Montreal Canadiens,
with 13 minutes and 32 seconds left in the play.

Boston leading New York Rangers four-to-one at
Boston.

It's Kennedy, Hill and Davidson for the Leafs—and
Davidson is back on duty again after a temporary rest. . . .
Kennedy takes the pass on the left wing. . . . He forward-
passes one to Davidson. . . . Davidson is covered by Lach,
who is out there with Richard and Blake. . . . It's Lach
coming in—and it's grabbed off by the Leafs . . . then lost
again to Blake. . . . Here's a shot—and it's wide, with two
Canadien players standing in front of that net. . . . Toe

Blake on the left board clears over here on the right side, and Canadiens are keeping that puck in. . . . Here's a pass by Richard, and it slides right on to the Leaf goal . . . Richard is knocked sideways by Kennedy . . . Kennedy fails to get out . . . Lach battling right in there . . . he's been a tower of strength to the Canadiens at all times . . . Kennedy side-steps Blake—goes over on the right side. . . . A bad pass ends up at the Canadien defense—and Canadiens, with Richard, shoot it in, and Lach is Johnny-on-the-spot again in the Leaf zone. . . . He tries to centre it out . . . it hits the back of the net. . . . Then Blake has his pass blocked by Kennedy. . . . Kennedy, Hill and Pratt come racing up for the Leafs at centre . . . Pratt goes over the line . . . back to Kennedy . . . he's right in . . . he shoots—he SCORES!

Hill seemed to deflect that puck into the net—and they've tied the score again!

It was Pratt who started it . . . then over to Kennedy, and Hill seemed to sink it. . . . Hill from Kennedy and Pratt will likely be the scoring play. . . . Hill was the last man to touch the puck, and deflected it into the short side past Durnan. . . . The time of that goal—7:37 in the third period. . . . The score is now tied 2-2. There will likely be two assists on that play . . . (Pause for Gardens speaker system announcement) . . . Yes—Hill from Kennedy and Pratt. . . . Hill went in on the right side . . . Pratt fed it to Kennedy . . . Kennedy flipped it over, and it went right to the corner where Hill tipped it in, and Durnan had no chance. . . .

That goal was scored against the Blake-Richard-Lach line. Now here's Pratt again forward-passing one to Davidson. . . . Davidson leaves it for Kennedy, who moves to centre. . . . He's across the line . . . Bouchard gets a piece of Kennedy and falls with him, and he's going to get a penalty for dragging Kennedy against the boards and holding him at the same time. . . . Bouchard of Canadiens will get a penalty. . . . He dragged Kennedy against the boards hanging on to him—and—Bouchard is off. (End of first cut.)

McKNIGHT: With the Leafs putting on the pressure, and the score tied again, let's see what happens.

HEWITT: . . . it rolls in front of the defense, and Art Jackson of the Leafs is away with O'Connor, trailing him up to the centre line. . . . He shoots it into the Montreal zone. . . . Lamoureux, on the Canadien defense with Bouchard, failed to get out in the first try. . . . Here's a rolling puck, as Pratt moves up to try to get hold of it, and it slides past him to centre ice. . . . Babe Pratt of the Leafs is being watched by O'Connor of Canadiens. . . . He's chased all the way back to the Leaf blue line—then flips a forward pass over the centre line that's away offside. . . . Seven minutes and 40 seconds left. . . . Score tied 2-2.

O'Connor facing Art Jackson of the Leafs. . . . Heller's on the left wing and Gauthier on the right wing for Canadiens. . . . Bouchard and Lamoureux the defense, playing up near centre. . . . The Leafs fail to clear it out of their own zone, and Pratt is going into the corner for it— going slowly back of his own net. . . . O'Connor tries to stick with him. . . . Heller cuts in front of him . . . Gauthier is coming in front of the net—but the pass didn't arrive, and it's knocked off to the corner and cleared out to centre ice. . . . Now Lamoureux takes it on the right wing and shoots it into the Leaf zone again. . . . It slides back of the net. . . . Johnston, on the defense with Pratt, is squeezed off into the corner on the first try . . . then Pratt goes behind his own net—changes his mind—is knocked over—and Hill finally comes out across the line with Jackson and Davidson. . . . They're over the line, and Bouchard blocks it nicely, covering the Leaf players as they try to swerve in on him. . . . Canadiens shoot it out to centre ice.

Jackson passes to Davidson on the left boards—who carries it into the Montreal zone. . . . He shoves Lamoureux out of position—centres out in front—and the pass comes right back to the blue line to Johnston, who shoots it around the boards back of the net to Jackson. . . . It's centred to Hill, who shoots—hits the post! . . . Hill shot and hit the post. . . . Here it's out in front again—he shoots—he SCORES!

Jackson shot in front of the net, putting the Leafs on top for the first time. . . . Jackson got a loose puck in front of the Canadien goal and fired it—a backhand, without even looking at the net—to give the Leafs the lead for the first time in the game. . . . 13:25 is the time of that Maple Leaf score—a rather unexpected one. . . . The puck came out in front. . . . Art Jackson was right in position, but he had his back turned . . . so he just let one go anyway, and it went right in the bottom left hand corner. . . . Durnan had no chance to move on the shot.

Pratt seemed to be the last man to assist Jackson. . . . He passed it in front so it will likely be Jackson from Pratt.

Here's a rolling puck from the face-off. . . . It goes into the Leaf zone, as Canadiens desperately try to come back. . . . The Leafs fail to clear out. . . . Harmon takes a long shot. . . . He shoots—he SCORES!

Harmon took a long shot from the blue line. . . . Whether the Canadien player who cut in front—Lach—actually touched it or not, it's hard to say . . but Harmon appeared to get credit for that goal. . . . He let a long shot go from the blue line, as Canadiens surged to the attack—and they tied it up again 3-3, just to show what a great team they are. . . . 13:48 is the time of that goal.

Now Canadiens are coming in again, as Richard, Lach and Blake are the forward line. . . . A pass on the left wing . . . (Yes, Harmon got the goal—a long shot. . . . He was just inside the Leaf blue line when he let it go . . . Lach went whizzing in front of McCool to block his vision, and it bounced off McCool's right leg into the corner of the net, tying the score 3-3—and that was a matter of about 23 seconds after the Leafs had taken the lead. . . . It was immediately after the face-off . . . they carried it right down and Harmon let it go.)

Now the Leafs with Stanowski are coming back to centre. . . . It's cleared over to Bodnar. . . . Bodnar deflects it into the Montreal zone, and Eddols was right on the spot to clear back of his own net. . . . He forward-passes one to Lach. . . . Lach is covered at centre ice . . . then a try by Eddols, moving in on the right side—over to Richard. . . . Richard is checked, and Blake tries to centre out, and Stanowski knocks it back of the Leaf goal. . . . A cleared pass goes ahead to Bodnar, who misses it. . . . It slides down the ice into the Montreal zone, to the left, and they have five minutes and five seconds left as Carr backhands one wide.

Bodnar, attempting to centre out, fails—and Richard and Lach come racing out together like a team . . . Richard goes to centre . . . over the Leaf line . . . coming in on goal . . . he's right in close . . . he SCORES!

It rolls right into the net—and Richard has finally got that all-important goal. . . . The Canadien players rush over to pat him on the back.

It's a great one, too. . . . The puck slid into the net after the Canadien player appeared to have fallen and was almost out of the play. . . . It had enough momentum to carry over the line and give the Canadien player the goal he's been aiming for for some time. . . . It was a real effort—his first goal on Toronto ice this year. . . . That makes it 4-3 for the Montreal Canadiens. . . . The time of that goal was 15:05—and Richard was the hero of the piece. . . . Four to three now for Montreal Canadiens . . . (End of cut.)

McKnight: And that was the game-winning goal. . . . The Maple Leafs pressed hard from there until the final bell—even taking Frank McCool out of the net and throwing out six forwards for the last 25 seconds . . . but to no avail. . . . Maurice Richard gave Canadiens their first victory on Toronto ice this season, and equalled the oldest existing record in the League—the one set by Joe Malone in the very first season of the N.H.L., when he scored 44 goals. . . . This one tonight was Richard's 44th goal. It bettered by one the modern record of Cooney Weiland— 43 goals in 1929-30.

Elmer Lach set Richard up for his big goal after getting one on a solo effort himself earlier. . . . These two stars are now tied for the N.H.L. point-scoring leadership—each with 65 points.

Chosen as the three stars of the game tonight were Elmer Lach and Vern Gauthier of Canadiens, and young Ted Kennedy of the Maple Leafs. . . . The game marked Canadiens' 15th win in their last 16 starts—one tie marring a great string of wins. . . . The final score tonight— Montreal Canadiens 4—Toronto Maple Leafs 3.

In Boston tonight the veteran defenceman, Dit Clapper, scored 3 goals to lead the Boston Bruins to a 6 to 1 victory over the New York Rangers—to take a very firm grip on the 4th playoff spot.

Next week, Canada will call again with highlights of the game between the New York Rangers and the Toronto Maple Leafs.

This is the Canadian Broadcasting Corporation.

—Foster Hewitt and Wes McKnight

READ A BOOK

Pickwick Papers. By Charles Dickens. Nelson.

The Adventures of Tom Sawyer and *Huckleberry Finn.* By Mark Twain. Musson. Exciting boy's life near the Mississippi a century ago.

Hans Brinker, or The Silver Skates. By Mary Mapes Dodge. Scribner. Hans and Gretel, in Holland, and the winning of the silver skates.

The Birds' Christmas Carol. By Kate Douglas Wiggin. Carol Bird gives a real Christmas party for the Ruggles family.

Games & Parties the Year Round. By Nellie M. Lewis. Ryerson. What to play, whenever games are required.

The Canadian Book of Games. By W. G. Brandreth. Ryerson. How to arrange programmes of games.

Strike-Out Story. By Bobby Feller. McLeod. A great baseball story.

Games of Every Day. By G. Elliot and A. R. Forbush. Macmillan. A good collection of games for every possible occasion, indoors and out.

IV

Outdoors Calling

BE STRONG, O PADDLE! BE BRAVE, CANOE!

THE SONG MY PADDLE SINGS

Pauline Johnson was the daughter of an Indian chief who lived near Brantford. In 1892 she recited one of her poems to an audience in Toronto. So delighted were her hearers that she was asked to give a programme entirely from her own poems two weeks later. For that programme Miss Johnson wrote *The Song My Paddle Sings*. Why do you think it makes a good recitation?

Pauline Johnson wrote many poems that you would enjoy. You will find them in *Flint and Feather*.

West wind, blow from your prairie nest,
Blow from the mountains, blow from the west.
The sail is idle, the sailor too;
O wind of the west, we wait for you!
Blow, blow,

137

I have wooed you so,
But never a favour you bestow.
You rock your cradle the hills between,
But scorn to notice my white lateen.

I stow the sail, unship the mast;
I wooed you long but my wooing's past;
My paddle will lull you into rest.
O drowsy wind of the drowsy west,
Sleep, sleep,
By your mountain steep,
Or down where the prairie grasses sweep!
Now fold in slumber your laggard wings,
For soft is the song my paddle sings.

August is laughing across the sky,
Laughing while paddle, canoe and I,
Drift, drift,
Where the hills uplift
On either side of the current swift.

The river rolls in its rocky bed;
My paddle is plying its way ahead;
Dip, dip,
While the waters flip
In foam as over their breast we slip.

And oh, the river runs swifter now,
The eddies circle about my bow!
Swirl, swirl!
How the ripples curl
In many a dangerous pool awhirl!

And forward far the rapids roar,
Fretting their margin for evermore.
Dash, dash,
With a mighty crash,
They seethe, and boil, and bound, and splash.
Be strong, O paddle! be brave, canoe!
The reckless waves you must plunge into.
Reel, reel,
On your trembling keel,—
But never a fear my craft will feel.

We're raced the rapid, we're far ahead;
The river slips through its silent bed.
Sway, sway,
As the bubbles spray
And fall in tinkling tunes away.

And up on the hills against the sky,
A fir tree rocking its lullaby,
Swings, swings,
Its emerald wings,
Swelling the song that my paddle sings.

—*Pauline Johnson*

STUDY AND ENJOYMENT

1. In the second stanza the song the paddle sings is like a lullaby, reflecting the delightfully drowsy mood of the author. What other words besides "drowsy" does the author use to suggest this mood?

2. Describe the picture of a canoeist that the fourth stanza calls to your mind.

3. From the fifth, sixth, and seventh stanzas, select words: (a) that show the quickened movement; (b) that indicate danger.

THE HOUSE OF McGINNIS

Grey Owl was a trapper. One day the sight of two young beaver, left desolate because he had trapped their parents, made him resolve to give up trapping. He adopted the beaver, and succeeded in taming them, something that had never been done before. Here he tells of his pets.

When Grey Owl gave up trapping, he turned to writing of Nature for a livelihood. "The House of McGinnis" was the first article he sold to a magazine. Later he became a leader in conserving the fast-disappearing wild life of the Canadian forests. He wrote several books: *The Men of the Last Frontier, Pilgrims of the Wild, Sajo and Her Beaver People,* and *Tales of an Empty Cabin.*

Only those who have had the opportunity of studying living specimens of the beaver, over an extended period, can obtain any idea of the almost human mentality of these likeable little creatures.

They roam around the camp, and, with no evil intent but apparently from just sheer joy of living, take large slices out of table-legs, and chairs, and nice long splinters out of the walls, and their progress is marked by little piles and strings of chips. This in the fore part of the evening. After "lights out" the more serious work commences, such as the removal of deerskin rugs, the transferring of firewood from behind the stove into the middle of the floor, or the improvement of some waterproof footwear by the addition of a little openwork on the soles. They will gnaw a hole in a box of groceries to investigate, and are very fond of toilet soap, on brand in particular preferred, owing, no doubt, to the flavour incident to its schoolgirl complexion-giving qualities!

In winter they will not leave the camp, and I sink a small bath tub in the floor for them, as they need water constantly. They make a practice of lying in the tub eating their sticks and birch tops, later climbing into the bunk to dry themselves. To accomplish this they sit upright and squeeze and scrub the entire body. The water never penetrates beyond the guard hairs into the fur, but I suppose half a pint is no exaggeration of the amount of water one of them will squeeze out of his coat.

Tiring of this performance, I once removed the bench by which they climbed into the bunk and prepared for a good night's rest at last. I had got so used to the continuous racket they created all night, between the drying-off periods, that, like the sailor who hired a man to throw pails of water against the sides of his house all night while on shore, I could not sleep so well without the familiar sounds, and during the night I awoke to an ominous silence. With a premonition of evil I lit the lamp, and on taking stock saw one of my much-prized Hudson's Bay blankets hanging over the edge of the bunk, and cut into an assortment of fantastic patterns, the result of their efforts to climb into the bed. The regularity of the designs startled me, and I began to wonder if I had gone suddenly insane, as nothing short of human agency, it seemed, could have cut those loops and triangles so symmetrically. Closer examination showed that the effect had been produced by their gathering the blanket in bunches with their forepaws, and cutting out a few pieces from the pucker, with more or less pleasing results.

Apparently realizing, by the tone of certain carelessly worded remarks which I allowed to escape me, that they had gone a little too far this time, the guilty parties had tactfully retired to their trench under the wall, awaiting developments. This excavation they had made themselves. In building the camp I had made an aperture in the bottom log, and constructed outside it, at great trouble, what was, I considered, a pretty good imitation of a beaver house. The first night in they had inspected my work, found it unsuitable, and proceeded to block up the entrance with sacking. They then commenced operations under the bunk, cutting a hole in the floor for the purpose, and digging out the soil. This dirt they trundled up from the depths, pushing it ahead of them, walking with the hind feet only, the forepaws and chin being used to hold the mass together.   They brought up, on each journey, perhaps the full of a two-quart measure apiece of earth, which was painstakingly spread on the floor as it accumulated.   They eventually got pretty well organized, one sleeping and the other working in shifts of two or three hours each.

After about a week of this a large mound of earth was eventually patted down smooth and solid near the water supply, and operations apparently brought to a satisfactory conclusion; so I considered that we should all now take a good rest.   But the beaver is not a restful animal.   Doubtless they had been warned by those advertisements that remind us that "those soft foods are ruining our teeth," for anything that offered resistance enough was bitten, the harder the better.   Anything that gave good tooth-holds was hauled, and everything that could be pushed was pushed high, west, and sideways.   Quantities of birch-bark were carried into the bunk and shredded, this contribution to the sleeping accommodation supposedly entitling them to a share of the blankets.

Some mornings, at daylight, I would awaken to find one on each side of me sleeping, lying on their backs snoring like any human.   At intervals during sleep they sharpened their teeth, in readiness for the next onslaught. When working, if the teeth do not seem to be in good shape, they pause for half a minute or so and sharpen them, repeating this until they are suited.   The skull is fitted with a longitudinal slot which allows for the necessary motion of the jaws, and the resultant grinding is much like the whetting of an axe.   The sound of an axe or knife being filed struck them with terror, and they would drop everything and run to me for protection, evidently thinking the noise came from some large animal whetting its teeth.

Beaver are the most persevering creatures I know of,

man not excepted, and any job which they undertake is never abandoned until completed or proved impossible. They conduct their operations with all the serious intentness and economy of movement of trained artisans, and at the conclusion of each stage, small adjustments are made, and little pats and pushes given, either expressing satisfaction with the work or testing its solidity, I know not which.

They seem capable of great affection, which they show by grasping my clothing with their strong forepaws, very hands in function, pushing their heads into some corner of my somewhat angular person, bleating and whimpering. At times they clamour for attention, and if taken notice of they shake their heads from side to side, rolling on their backs with squeals of joy. If left alone for as long as twenty-four hours, on my return they are very subdued until I talk to them, when they at once commence their uncouth gambols and their queer wrestling.

They conduct these wrestling matches—for they can be called nothing else—by rising on their hind feet, supported by the tail, while the forepaws are locked in neck and under-arm holds, looking like dancers. In this position they strain and push, each striving to overcome the other, until one begins to give way, walking backwards, still erect, pushed by his adversary. Then, perhaps by the judicious use of his tail, he recovers, prevails, and the walk commences in the opposite direction. They go at this for all they are worth, and the changes in the expression of their voices, according to the luck they are having, are remarkably plain. This performance resembles a violent fox-trot about as closely as it does anything else, and is continued until one or the other allows his tail to double under him and is bowled over, protesting loudly.

One peculiarity they have is that, when hungry, they do not fawn as most domestic animals do, but complain loudly, standing on their hind legs and grasping at the dish.

If the food is withheld they scold shrilly, beating the air with their forepaws. Also, if in their work they fail in some object such as the placing of a stick, they jerk the limbs and head violently and show every sign of irritation, resuming the attempt with an impetuous violence that either makes or breaks.

The male beaver has, to a certain extent, the protective instinct that dogs possess, but not of course so highly developed. I had no knowledge of this until one day I happened to be resting on my blankets on the floor after a trip—a common custom in the woods—and lying with his head on my shoulder was a six-months-old buck beaver. An Indian friend came in, and busied himself in some way that brought him close to my head, on the opposite side from my furry chum. Immediately the latter crossed over and stationed himself between the man's feet and my person. My friend found it necessary to pass around me, and the beaver made a quick shortcut across my face, and again took post between us. Noticing this, and thinking it might be coincidence, my companion returned to his former position, and the beaver returned also, again using my face for a runway, blowing and hissing his disapproval.

Beaver are far from being the dumb creatures that most animals are. While working they are continually murmuring and muttering, even if alone, and if some distance apart occasionally signal their position by short, sharp cries. It is very rarely that speaking to them does not elicit some kind of answer.

They have a large range of distinctly different sounds. The emotions of rage, sorrow, fear, joy and contentment are expressed quite differently, and are easily recognized after a short period of observation. Often when a conversation is being carried on they will join in with their vocal gymnastics, and the resemblance to the human voice is almost uncanny to those not accustomed to hearing it, and has been partly the cause of their undoing, as they are a very easy animal to imitate. When in trouble they whimper in the most dolorous fashion, and become altogether disconsolate.

In common with most animals when tamed, beaver will answer to a name. In Canada an Irishman is known as "a Mick," and the Indian word for beaver, Ahmik, is identical in pronunciation. So I gave them Irish names, of which the two most notable were McGinty and McGinnis, names they got to know very well, and they were suitable in more ways than one, as they both had peppery tempers, and would fight at the drop of the hat anything or anybody, regardless of size, always excepting each other or myself.

My camp became known as "The House of McGinnis," although McGinty, whimsical, mischievous as a flock of monkeys, being the female, was really the boss of the place; and although I am deficient in the art of making the best mouse-traps, all the world hereabouts has made a beaten path to my door on their account.

Today I kill no more beaver, but am bent on repairing in some small measure the damage done in younger and more thoughtless days; replacing at least a part of what I have destroyed, restoring dried-out lakes to their fulness of contented families, bringing life where is nought but desolation. That I may hear in the long evenings, as in the old days, the splash of huge flat tails on the water as the working parties change shift; the queer child-like cries as they wrestle on the leaves beneath the silvery poplars that are their life; the crooning of the mothers within the lodges tending their young. That I may see the dark and gloomy forest shores shining again with Wasacsena,[1] the brightness of newly-peeled sticks, and visit and marvel over the carefully-dug canals and the sand pits. And

[1]PRONOUNCE: Wăh-săk'-să-nă, Indian word for the shining of peeled timber on the shore; the peeling of the bark is caused by beaver, or the erosion of ice or water.

perhaps at times I may glimpse a wise old head, the head of Mishomis, the Old Man, as a pair of bright black eyes, not unfriendly, but always cautious, watch covertly my every move from out the shadows near the shore. And I shall know that I am not, after all, alone in this mighty wilderness, whilst I have for neighbours the happy colonies of Ahmik, the Beaver People.

—*Grey Owl*
From *The Men of the Last Frontier*

STUDY AND ENJOYMENT

1. How does this account help us to understand why the beaver was chosen as a Canadian emblem?
2. What is the House of McGinnis? What prank of the beaver seemed to you the cleverest? the most destructive?

THE MERCHANTS

From which of these merchants would you buy?

I am the Frost.
I'll show you diamonds, laces, and tapestries
Of all variety
At lowest cost;
Weavings of chaste design
Perfect in every line;
Connoisseurs surely will buy of the Frost.

I am the Dew.
Notice my elegant bracelets and necklaces,
All of rare quality;
Pearls not a few;
Emeralds and amethyst;
Opals all rainbow kissed;
Ladies rise early to buy of the Dew.

I am the Snow.
Let me display for you carpets most exquisite.
Choicest of bordering
Also I show,
Heavy and soft and white,
Spread in a single night;
Folks who have wisdom will buy of the Snow.

I am the Rain.
Something I'll show you priceless and wonderful,
Making these offers seem
Tawdry and vain!
'Tis but a cloak of grey
Wrapping the world away—
Happy the few who will buy of the Rain.

—*Isabel Ecclestone Mackay*

STUDY AND ENJOYMENT

1. Why are the Rain's customers happy? Several readers were asked this question, and here are some of their answers:
   (a) because they see beauty in common things;
   (b) because every cloud has a silver lining, and things that at first seem unpleasant often turn out well;
   (c) because the rain falls like a quiet curtain, cutting off the hurly-burly of the world.
   You may agree with one of these answers. If not, what do you suggest?
2. These four stanzas describe various aspects of Nature. A single word will describe the prevailing note of each stanza. Thus the first three might be:

   Stanza 1. Design
   Stanza 2. Colour
   Stanza 3. Softness

   Find words in each stanza that develop these ideas. Begin with the second stanza; it will be easy to find colour words there. Think of one word that will describe the thought of the last stanza.
3. Think of as many words as you can (shining, for example), that describe dew in the sunlight.
4. The word "tawdry" has a very distinguished ancestry. It comes from the name of the patron saint of Ely, a cathedral town of England. The Saint's name was St. Etheldrida, whom the peasants called St. Awdrey, which easily became "tawdry." Find out from one of the larger dictionaries how tawdry came to have the idea of cheapness associated with it.

THE WILD GEESE OF WYNDYGOUL

Ernest Thompson Seton was born in England in 1860. When five years old he came to Canada, and attended school in Toronto. Later he studied art, and, like Arthur Heming, illustrated many of his own books. Mr. Seton became naturalist to the Government of Manitoba when he was only twenty-six. Long before that, he began to make notes and keep a journal, with drawings of birds and animals. He has written splendid books on the out-of-doors.

I

THE BUGLING ON THE LAKE

Who that knows the wild Northland of Canada can picture that blue and green wilderness without hearing in his heart the trumpet "honk" of the wild geese? Who that has ever known it there can fail to get again, each time he hears, the thrill it gave when first for him it sounded on the blue lake in the frame of green? Older than ourselves is the thrill of the gander-clang. For without a doubt that trumpet note in springtime was the inspiring notice to our far-back forbears in the days that were, that the winter famine was at end—the wild geese come, the snow will melt, and the game again be back on the browning hills. The ice of the wintertime is gone; the warm bright heaven of the green and perfect land is here. This is the tidings it tells, and when I hear the honker-clang from the flying wedge in the sky, that is the message it brings me with a sudden mist in the eyes and a choking in the throat, so I turn away, if another be there, unless that other chance to be one like myself, a primitive, a "hark-back" who, too, remembers and who understands.

So when I built my home in the woods and glorified a marshy swamp into a deep blue, brimming lake, with muskrats in the water and intertwining boughs above, my memory, older than my brain, harked hungry for a sound that should have been. I knew not what; I tried to find by subtle searching, but it was chance in a place far off that gave the clue. I wanted to hear the honkers call; I longed for the clang of the flying wedge, the trumpet note of the long-gone days.

So I brought a pair of the blacknecks from another lake, pinioned to curb the wild roving that the seasons bring, and they nested on a little island, not hidden, but open to the world about. There in that exquisite bed of soft grey down were laid the six great ivory eggs. On them the patient mother sat four weeks unceasingly, except each afternoon she left them half an hour. And round and round that island, night and day, the gander floated, cruised, and tacked about, like a warship on patrol. Never once did the gander cover the eggs; never once did the mother mount on guard. I tried to land and learn about the nest one day. The brooding goose it was that gave the danger call. A short quack, a long, sharp hiss, and before my boat could touch the shore the gander splashed between and faced me. Only over his dead body might my foot defile their isle—so he was left in peace.

The young ones came at length. The six shells broke and the six sweet golden downlings "peeped" inspiringly. Next day they quit the nest in orderly array: the mother first; the downlings closely bunched behind, and last the warrior sire. And this order they always kept, then, and all other times that I have knowledge of. It gave me food for thought. The mother always leads, the father, born a fighter, follows—yes, obeys. And what a valiant guard he was; the snapping turtle, the henhawk, the black snake, the coon, and the vagrant dog might take their toll of duckling brood or chicken yard, but there is nothing alive the gander will not face for his little ones, and there are few things near his bulk can face him.

So the flock grew big and strong. Before three months

NEXT DAY THEY QUIT THE NEST IN ORDERLY ARRAY

they were big almost as the old ones, and fairly fledged; at four their wings were grown; their voices still were small and thin—they had not got the trumpet note, but seemed the mother's counterparts in all things else. Then they began to feel their wings, and take short flights across the lake. As their wings grew strong their voices deepened, till the trumpet note was theirs, and the thing I had dreamed of came about: a wild-goose band that flew and bugled in the air, and yet came back to their home water that was also mine. Stronger they grew, and long and high their flights. Then came the moon of falling leaves, and with its waning flocks of small birds flew, and in the higher sky the old loud clang was heard. Down from the north they came, the arrowheads of geese. All kinsmen these, and that ahead without a doubt the mother of the rest.

II

THE MOTHER'S CALL

The wild geese on my lake turned up their eyes and answered back, and lined up on the lake. Their mother led the way and they whispered all along the line. Their mother gave the word, swimming fast and faster, then quacked, then called, and then their voices rose to give the "honk"; the broad wings spread a little, while they spattered on the glassy lake, then rose to the measured "Honk, honk"; soaring away in a flock, they drifted into line, to join those other honkers in the southern sky.

"Honk, honk, honk!" they shouted as they sped. "Come on! Come on!" they inspired each other with the marching song; it set their wings aquiver. The wild blood rushed still faster in their excited breasts. It was like a glorious trumpet. But—what! Mother is not in the line. Still splashed she on the surface of the lake, and father, too—and now her strident trumpet overbore their clamorous "On, on! Come on!" with a strong "Come back! Come back!" And father, too, was bugling there: "Come back! Come back!"

So the downlings wheeled, and circling high above the woods came sailing, skirting, kiting, splashing down at the mother's call.

"What's up? What's up?" they called lowly all together, swimming nervously. "Why don't we go?" "What is it, mother?"

And mother could not tell. Only this she knew, that when she gave the bugle note for all to fly, she spattered with the rest, and flapped, but it seemed she could not get the needed send-off. Somehow she failed to get well under way; the youngsters rose, but the old ones, their strong leaders, had strangely failed. Such things will come to all. Not quite run enough, no doubt. So mother led them to the northmost arm of the lake, an open stretch of water now, and long. They here lined up again, mother giving a low, short double "honk" ahead, the rest aside and yet in line, for the long array was angling.

Then mother passed the word "Now, now," and nodding just a little swam on, headed for the south; the young ones passed the word "Now, now," and nodding swam; and father at the rear gave his deep, strong, "Now, now," and swam. So swam they all, then spread their wings, and spattered with their feet, as they put on speed, and as they went they rose, and rising bugled louder till the marching song was ringing in full chorus. Up, up, and away, above the tree tops. *But again*, for some strange reason, mother was not there, and father, too, was left behind on the pond, and once again the bugle of retreat was heard, "Come back! Come back!"

And the brood, obedient, wheeled on swishing wings to sail and slide and settle on the pond, while mother and father both expressed in low, short notes their deep perplexity.

Again and again this scene took place. The autumn message in the air, the flying wedges of their kin, or the impulse in themselves lined up that flock on the water. All the law of ceremony was complied with, and all went well but the climax.

When the mad moon came the mania was at its height; not once but twenty times a day I saw them line up and rise, but ever come back to the mother's call, the bond of love and duty stronger than the annual custom of the race. It was a conflict of their laws indeed, but the strongest was *obey*, made absolute by love.

After a while the impulse died and the flock settled down to winter on the pond. Many a long, far flight they took, but the allegiance to the older folk was strong and brought them back. So the winter passed.

Again, when the springtime came, the blacknecks flying north stirred up the young, but in a less degree.

That summer came another brood of young. The older ones were warned away whenever near. Snapper, coon, and ranging cur were driven off, and September saw the young ones on the lake with their brothers of the older brood.

Then came October, with the southward rushing of the feathered kinds. Again and again that line upon the lake and the bugle sound to "fly," and the same old scene, though now there were a dozen flyers who rose and circled back when mother sounded the "retreat."

III

MOTHER OR FATHER

So through the moon it went. The leaves were fallen now, when a strange and unexpected thing occurred. Making unusual effort to meet this most unusual case, good Mother Nature had prolonged the feathers of the pinioned wing and held back those of the other side. It was slowly done, and the compensating balance not quite made till near October's end. Then on a day, the hundredth time at least that week, the bugle sang, and all the marchers arose. Yes! mother, too, and bugling louder till the chorus was complete, they soared above the trees, and mother marshalled all her brood in one great arrow flock, so they sailed, and clamouring, sailed away, to be lost in the southward blue—and all in vain on the limpid lake behind the gander trumpeted in agony of soul, "Come back! Come back!" His wings had failed him, and in the test, the young's allegiance bound them to their mother and the seeking of the southern home.

All that winter on the ice the gander sat alone. On days a snow-time hawk or some belated crow would pass above, and the ever-watchful eye of Blackneck was turned a little to take him in and then go on unheeding. Once or twice there were sounds that stirred the lonely watcher to a bugle call, but short and soon suppressed. It was sad to see him then, and sadder still as we pondered, for this we knew: his family would never come back. Tamed, made trustful by life where men were kind, they had gone to the land of gunners, crafty, pitiless, and numberless; they would learn too late the perils of the march. Next, he never would take another mate, for the wild goose mates for life, and mates but once; the one surviving has no choice —he finishes his journey alone.

Poor old Blackneck, his very faithfulness it was that made for endless loneliness.

The bright days came with melting snow. The floods cut through the ice, and again there were buglers in the sky, and the gander swam on the open part of the lake and answered back:

> Honk, honk, come back,
> Come back. Come back!

but the flying squads passed on with a passing "Honk!"

Brighter still the days, and the gander paddled with a little exultation in the opening pond. How we pitied him, self-deluded, faithful, doomed to a long, lone life.

Then balmy April swished the woods with green; the lake was brimming clear. Old Blackneck never ceased to cruise and watch, and answer back such sounds as touched him. Oh, sad it seemed that one so staunch should find his burden in his very staunchness.

But on a day when the peeper and the woodwall sang, there came the great event! Old Blackneck, ever waiting, was astir, and more than wont. Who can tell us whence the tidings came? With head at gaze he cruised the open pond, and the short, strong honk seemed sad, till some new excitation raised the feathers on his neck. He honked and honked with a brassy ring. Then long before we heard a sound, he was bugling the marching song, and as he bugled answering sounds came—from the sky—and grew—then swooping, sailing from the blue, a glorious array of thirteen wild geese, to sail and skate and settle on the pond; and their loud honks gave place to softer chatter as they crowded round and bowed in grave and loving salutation.

There was no doubt of it. The young were now mature and they seemed strange, of course, but this was surely the missing mate; the mother had come back, and the faithful pair took up their life—and live it yet.

The autumn sends the ordered flock afar, the father stays on guard, but the bond that binds them all and takes them off and brings them back is stronger than the fear of death. So I have learned to love and venerate the honker wild goose whom Mother Nature dowered with love unquenchable, constructed for her own good ends a monument of faithfulness unchanging, a creature heir of all the promises, so master of the hostile world around that he lives and spreads, defying plagues and beasts, and I wonder if this secret is not partly that the wise and patient mother leads. The long, slow test of time has given a minor place to the valiant, fearless, fighting male; his place the last of all, his mode of open fight the latest thing they try. And by a law inexorable, the young obey the mother. Wisdom their guide, not force. Their days are long on earth, and the homeland of their race grows wide while others pass away.

—*Ernest Thompson Seton*

STUDY AND ENJOYMENT

1. "Windygoul" was the author's farm in Connecticut. Pinioning the geese means clipping the longer wing-feathers, so that they are unable to fly away. The "moon of falling leaves" is the Indian name for October.
2. What is a sentinel? a "mad moon"? a "flying wedge"?

THE DAFFODILS

I wandered lonely as a cloud
That floats on high o'er vales and hills,
When all at once I saw a crowd,
A host, of golden daffodils;
Beside the lake, beneath the trees,
Fluttering and dancing in the breeze.

Continuous as the stars that shine
And twinkle on the milky way,
They stretched in never-ending line
Along the margin of a bay:
Ten thousand saw I at a glance,
Tossing their heads in sprightly dance.

The waves beside them danced; but they
Out-did the sparkling waves in glee;
A poet could not but be gay,
In such a jocund company:
I gazed—and gazed—but little thought
What wealth the show to me had brought:

For oft, when on my couch I lie
In vacant or in pensive mood,
They flash upon that inward eye
Which is the bliss of solitude;
And then my heart with pleasure fills,
And dances with the daffodils.

—William Wordsworth

STUDY AND ENJOYMENT

1. Wordsworth once said that he did not care for a landscape unless he could tell from it at once the season of the year and the kind of day. In this poem Wordsworth is painting a landscape in words. What details tell you the kind of day it is?
2. What words are used to give the idea of the great number of daffodils? Which expression best brings out this idea?

3. Wordsworth believed flowers were like people—that they felt joy, too. How has he suggested this idea?

4. What does "wealth" mean in the third stanza?   Express the thought of the last stanza in your own words.

5. Glossary: *jocund*, merry, happy, jolly; *vacant or in pensive mood*, day-dreaming or thoughtful; *that inward eye*, memory; *the bliss of solitude*, the joy of being alone.

DOROTHY'S DAFFODILS

You have read Wordsworth's poem *The Daffodils*. The poet spent his whole life amid rural English scenes of great beauty. Much of his best poetry was composed on walks with his sister. William would return to write out the poems, while Dorothy would make an entry in her diary.

One of the most interesting entries in Dorothy Wordsworth's diary was made after she had been walking with her brother near their English cottage home at Grasmere. What they saw that day has been remembered through these many years, and all because of the daffodils.

"When we were in the woods beyond Gowbarrow Park, we saw a few daffodils close to the waterside. We fancied that the sea had floated the seeds ashore and that the little colony had so sprung up. But as we went along there were more and yet more; and at last under the boughs of the trees we saw that there was a long belt of them along the shore, about the breadth of a country turnpike road.

"I never saw daffodils so beautiful. They grew among the mossy stones about and above them; some rested their heads upon these stones as on a pillow for weariness; and the rest tossed and reeled and danced, and seemed as if they verily laughed with the wind that blew upon them from the lake, they looked so gay, ever glancing, ever changing. The wind blew directly over the lake to them. There was here and there a little knot, and a few stragglers higher up, but they were so few as not to disturb the simplicity, unity, and life of the one busy highway."

All the dancing beauty of the spring day the brother and sister enjoyed together. If she had written simply, "Went to walk with William," as a less observing, less sensitive soul might have done, we should never have had this poem of his that lets us share their delight.

Wordsworth once wrote of his sister—

> She gave me eyes, she gave me ears,
> And humble cares, and delicate fears;
> A heart, the fountain of sweet tears,
> And love and thought and joy.

So in his daffodil poem you will see how he used many of Dorothy's own words and ideas. She gave him the key for the music of his stanzas, which have as graceful a motion as the waving flowers themselves.

—Frances Avery Faunce

TOM SAWYER: WORK AND PLAY

This story is from *The Adventures of Tom Sawyer*. One of Tom's friends of whom Aunt Polly did not approve was Huck Finn. In *Huckleberry Finn* Mark Twain gives us further adventures of Tom and Huck. Their story has also been told in movies.

Saturday morning was come, and all the summer world was bright and fresh, and brimming with life. There was a song in every heart; and if the heart was young the music issued at the lips. There was cheer in every face, and a spring in every step. The locust trees were in bloom, and the fragrance of the blossoms filled the air.

Cardiff Hill, beyond the village and above it, was green with vegetation, and it lay just far enough away to seem a Delectable Land, dreamy, reposeful, and inviting.

Tom appeared on the sidewalk with a bucket of whitewash and a long-handled brush. He surveyed the fence, and all gladness went out of Nature, and a deep melancholy settled down upon his spirit. Thirty yards of board-fence nine feet high! It seemed to him that life was hollow, and existence but a burden. Sighing, he dipped his brush and passed it along the topmost plank; repeated the operation;

did it again; compared the insignificant whitewashed streak
with the far-reaching continent of unwhitewashed fence,
and sat down on a tree-box discouraged. Jim came skip-
ping out at the gate with a tin pail, and singing "Buffalo
Gals." Bringing water from the town pump had always
been hateful work in Tom's eyes before, but now it did not
strike him so. He remembered that there was company
at the pump. White, mulatto, and negro boys and girls
were always there waiting their turns, resting, trading
playthings, quarrelling, fighting, skylarking. And he
remembered that, although the pump was only a hundred
and fifty yards off, Jim never got back with a bucket of
water under an hour; and even then somebody generally
had to go after him.

(*Tom offers Jim certain things if Jim will do some whitewashing while Tom goes to the pump for water. While they
are coming to terms Aunt Polly appears.*)

In another moment Jim was flying down the street with
his pail, Tom was whitewashing with vigour, and Aunt Polly
was retiring from the field with a slipper in her hand and
triumph in her eye.

But Tom's energy did not last. He began to think of
the fun he had planned for this day, and his sorrows multi-
plied. Soon the free boys would come tripping along on all
sorts of delicious expeditions, and they would make a world
of fun of him for having to work—the very thought of it
burnt him like fire. He got out his worldly wealth and
examined it—bits of toys, marbles and trash; enough to buy
an exchange of work, maybe, but not half enough to
buy so much as half-an-hour of pure freedom. So he
returned his straitened means to his pocket, and gave up
the idea of trying to buy the boys. At this dark and
hopeless moment an inspiration burst upon him! Nothing
less than a great, magnificent inspiration. He took up his
brush and went tranquilly to work. Ben Rogers hove in

sight presently—the very boy of all boys whose ridicule he had been dreading.   Ben's gait was the hop-skip-and-jump —proof enough that his heart was light and his anticipations high.   He was eating an apple, and giving a long, melodious whoop at intervals, followed by a deep-toned ding-dong-dong, ding-dong-dong, for he was personating a steamboat. As he drew near, he slackened speed, took the middle of the street, leaned far over to starboard, and rounded-to ponderously and with laborious pomp and circumstance— for he was personating the *Big Missouri*, and considered himself to be drawing nine feet of water.   He was boat, and captain, and engine-bells combined, so he had to imagine himself standing on his own hurricane-deck, giving the orders and executing them—

"Stop her, sir!   Ling-a-ling-ling."   The head-way ran almost out, and he drew up slowly toward the sidewalk.

"Ship up to back!   Ling-a-ling-ling!"   His arms straightened and stiffened down his sides.

"Set her back on the stabboard!   Ling-a-ling-ling!" His right hand meantime describing stately circles, for it was representing a forty-foot wheel.

"Let her go back on the labboard!   Ling-a-ling-ling!" The left hand began to describe circles.

Tom went on whitewashing—paid no attention to the steamboat.   Ben stared a moment, and then said—"Hi-yi! You're up a stump, ain't you?"

No answer.   Tom surveyed his last touch with the eye of an artist; then he gave his brush another gentle sweep, and surveyed the result, as before.   Ben ranged up along-side of him.   Tom's mouth watered for the apple, but he stuck to his work.

Ben said—

"Hello, old chap; you got to work, hey?"

Tom wheeled suddenly and said—

"Why, it's you, Ben!   I warn't noticing."

"Say—I'm going in a-swimming, I am.   Don't you

wish you could? But of course you'd druther work—wouldn't you? Course you would!"

Tom contemplated the boy a bit, and said—

"What do you call work?"

"Why, ain't that work?"

Tom resumed his whitewashing, and answered carelessly—

"Well, maybe it is, and maybe it ain't. All I know is, it suits Tom Sawyer."

"Oh, come now, you don't mean to let on that you like it?"

The brush continued to move.

"Like it? Well, I don't see why I oughtn't to like it. Does a boy get a chance to whitewash a fence every day?"

That put the thing in a new light. Ben stopped nibbling his apple. Tom swept his brush daintily back and forth—stepped back to note the effect—added a touch here and there—criticized the effect again—Ben watching every move, and getting more and more interested, more and more absorbed. Presently he said—

"Say, Tom, let me whitewash a little."

Tom considered—was about to consent; but he altered his mind—

"No, no; I reckon it wouldn't hardly do, Ben. You see, Aunt Polly's awful particular about this fence—right here on the street, you know—but if it was the back fence I wouldn't mind, and she wouldn't. Yes, she's awful particular about this fence; it's got to be done very careful; I reckon there ain't one boy in a thousand, maybe two thousand, that can do it the way it's got to be done."

"No—is that so? Oh, come now; lemme just try, only just a little. I'd let you, if you was me, Tom."

"Ben, I'd like to; honest Injun; but Aunt Polly—well, Jim wanted to do it, but she wouldn't let him. Sid wanted to do it, and she wouldn't let Sid. Now, don't you see how I'm fixed? If you was to tackle this fence, and anything was to happen to it—"

"Oh! Shucks; I'll be just as careful. Now lemme try. Say—I'll give you the core of my apple."

"Well, here—No, Ben; now don't; I'm afeard—"

"I'll give you all of it!"

Tom gave up the brush with reluctance in his face but alacrity in his heart. And, while the late steamer *Big Missouri* worked and sweated in the sun, the retired artist sat on a barrel in the shade close by, dangled his legs, munched his apple, and planned the slaughter of more innocents. There was no lack of material; boys happened along every little while; they came to jeer, but remained to whitewash. By the time Ben was fagged out, Tom had traded the next chance to Billy Fisher for a kite in good repair; and when he played out, Johnny Miller bought in for a dead rat and a string to swing it with; and so on, and so on, hour after hour. When the middle of the afternoon came, from being a poor, poverty-stricken boy in the morning, Tom was literally rolling in wealth. He had, beside the things before mentioned, twelve marbles, part of a jew's harp, a piece of blue bottle-glass to look through; a spool-cannon, a key that wouldn't unlock anything, a fragment of chalk, a glass stopper of a decanter, a tin soldier, a couple of tadpoles, six fire-crackers, a kitten with only one eye, a brass door-knob, a dog-collar—but no dog—the handle of a knife, four pieces of orange-peel, and a dilapidated old window-sash. He had had a nice, good, idle time all the while—plenty of company—and the fence had three coats of whitewash on it! If he hadn't run out of whitewash, he would have bankrupted every boy in the village.

Tom said to himself that it was not such a hollow world, after all. He had discovered a great law of human action, without knowing it—namely, that in order to make a man or a boy covet a thing, it is only necessary to make the thing difficult to attain. If he had been a great and wise philosopher, like the writer of this book, he would now have comprehended that Work consists of whatever a body is obliged to do, and that Play consists of whatever a body is not obliged to do. And this would help him to understand why constructing artificial flowers or performing on a treadmill is work, while rolling ten-pins or climbing Mont Blanc is only amusement. There are wealthy gentlemen in England who drive four-horse passenger-coaches twenty or thirty miles on a daily line in the summer, because the privilege costs them considerable money; but, if they were offered wages for the service, that would turn it into work, and then they would resign.

—Mark Twain

STUDY AND ENJOYMENT

1. What work once seemed like play to you because it was difficult to get permission to do it? If you can't think of a case, perhaps you can make up one.

2. How does Mark Twain explain the difference between work and play?

3. What is your idea of "rolling in wealth"? What was Tom's? Tom lived on the banks of the Mississippi a long time ago. Is he very different from boys you know today?

TREES

I think that I shall never see
A poem lovely as a tree;

A tree whose hungry mouth is prest
Against the earth's sweet-flowing breast;

A tree that looks at God all day
And lifts her leafy arms to pray;

A tree that may in summer wear
A nest of robins in her hair;

Upon whose bosom snow has lain;
Who intimately lives with rain.

Poems are made by fools like me,
But only God can make a tree.

—Joyce Kilmer

STUDY AND ENJOYMENT

1. It is said that the poet lived near an American Beauty elm, and it was this tree that inspired the poem. Which lines best show Kilmer's love of trees?
2. What seasons are represented in the poem? Read lines to support your answer.
3. What picture in the poem do you like best?
4. This poem has been set to music. You may know the song. If not, perhaps someone could get it for the class.

TREES

In the Garden of Eden, planted by God,
There were goodly trees in the springing sod—
Trees of beauty and height and grace,
To stand in splendour before His face:

Apple and hickory, ash and pear,
Oak and beech, and the tulip rare,
The trembling aspen, the noble pine,
The sweeping elm by the river line;

Trees for the birds to build and sing,
And the lilac tree for a joy in spring;
Trees to turn at the frosty call
And carpet the ground for their Lord's footfall;

Trees for fruitage and fire and shade,
Trees for the cunning builder's trade;
Wood for the bow, the spear, and the flail,
The keel and the mast of the daring sail—

He made them of every grain and girth
For the use of man in the Garden of Earth.
Then lest the soul should not lift her eyes
From the gift to the Giver of Paradise,
On the crown of a hill, for all to see,
God planted a scarlet maple tree.

—Bliss Carman

STUDY AND ENJOYMENT

1. This poem has been called a catalogue of trees. Why is this a rather good description of the first four stanzas? What striking picture lingers in our memory from the fifth stanza?
2. Carman has classified the trees in several different ways. One way is for beauty, another is for use. Which tree do you think is the most useful? the most beautiful?
3. Different poets treat similar topics in different ways: Which of the two poems on trees do you like the better? Why?
4. Find and read "The Scarlet Maple," by Carman. *Ballads and Lyrics* contains poems from six of Carman's early books.

COALY-BAY, THE OUTLAW HORSE

Coaly-Bay, once the cunning lord of an outlaw herd, as beautiful as he was haughty, suffers the humiliation of captivity, but not for ever.

I. COALY-BAY, OUTLAW

Five years ago in the Bitterroot Mountains of Idaho there was a beautiful little foal. His coat was bright bay; his legs, mane, and tail were glossy black—coal black and bright bay—so they named him Coaly-Bay.

"Coaly-Bay" sounds like "Kolibey," which is an Arab title of nobility, and those who saw the handsome colt, and did not know how he came by the name, thought he must be of Arab blood. No doubt he was, in a far-away sense; just as all our best horses have Arab blood, and once in a while it seems to come out strong and show in every part of the creature, in his frame, his power, and his wild, free, roving spirit.

Coaly-Bay loved to race like the wind; he gloried in his speed and his tireless legs; when he was careering with the herd of colts, if they met a fence or ditch it was as natural for Coaly-Bay to overleap it as it was for the others to sheer off.

So he grew up strong of limb, restless of spirit, and rebellious at any thought of restraint. Even the kindly curb of the hay-yard or the stable was unwelcome, and he soon showed that he would rather stand out all night in a driving storm than be locked in a comfortable stall where he had no vestige of the liberty he loved so well.

He became very clever at dodging the horse wrangler whose job it was to bring the horseherd to the corral. The very sight of that man set Coaly-Bay going. He became what is known as a "Quit-the-bunch"—that is, a horse of such independent mind that he will go his own way the moment he does not like the way of the herd.

So each month the colt became more set on living free, and more cunning in the means he took to win his way. Far down in his soul, too, there must have been a streak of cruelty, for he stuck at nothing and spared no one that seemed to stand between him and his one desire.

When he was three years of age, just in the perfection of his young strength and beauty, his real troubles began, for now his owner undertook to break him to ride. He was as tricky and vicious as he was handsome, and the first day's experience was a terrible battle between the horse-trainer and the beautiful colt.

But the man was skilful. He knew how to apply his power, and all the wild plunging, bucking, rearing, and rolling of the wild one had no desirable result. With all his strength the horse was hopelessly helpless in the hands of the skilful horseman, and Coaly-Bay was so far mastered at length that a good rider could use him. But each time the saddle went on he made a new fight. After a few months of this the colt seemed to realize that it was useless to resist; it simply won for him lashings and spurrings, so

EACH TIME THE SADDLE WENT ON HE MADE A NEW FIGHT

he pretended to reform. For a week he was ridden each day, and not once did he buck, but on the last day he came home lame.

His owner turned him out to pasture. Three days later he seemed all right; he was caught and saddled. He did not buck, but within five minutes he went lame as before. Again he was turned out to pasture, and after a week, saddled, only to go lame again.

His owner did not know what to think, whether the horse really had a lame leg or was only shamming, but he took the first chance to get rid of him, and though Coaly-Bay was easily worth fifty dollars, he sold him for twenty-five. The new owner felt he had a bargain, but after being ridden half a mile Coaly-Bay went lame. The rider got off to examine the foot, whereupon Coaly-Bay broke away and galloped back to his old pasture. Here he was caught, and the new owner, being neither gentle nor sweet, applied spur without mercy, so that the next twenty miles was covered in less than two hours, and no sign of lameness appeared.

Now they were at the ranch of this new owner. Coaly-Bay was led from the door of the house to the pasture, limping all the way, and then turned out. He limped over to the other horses. On one side of the pasture was the garden of a neighbour. This man was very proud of his fine vegetables and had put a six-foot fence around the place. Yet the very night after Coaly-Bay arrived, certain of the horses got into the garden somehow and did a great deal of damage. But they leaped out before daylight and no one saw them.

The gardener was furious, but the ranchman stoutly maintained that it must have been some other horses, since his were behind a six-foot fence.

Next night it happened again. The ranchman went out very early and saw all his horses in the pasture, with Coaly-Bay behind them. His lameness seemed worse now instead of better. In a few days, however, the horse was seen walking all right, so the ranchman's son caught him and tried to ride him. But this seemed too good a chance to lose; all his old wickedness returned to the horse; the boy was bucked off at once and hurt. The ranchman himself now leaped into the saddle; Coaly-Bay bucked for ten minutes, but finding he could not throw the man, he tried to crush his leg against a post, but the rider guarded himself well. Coaly-Bay reared and threw himself backward; the rider slipped off, the horse fell, jarring heavily, and before he could rise the man was in the saddle again. The horse now ran away, plunging and bucking; he stopped short, but the rider did not go over his head, so Coaly-Bay turned, seized the man's boot in his teeth, and but for heavy blows on the nose would have torn him dreadfully. It was quite clear now that Coaly-Bay was an "outlaw"—that is, an incurably vicious horse.

The saddle was jerked off, and he was driven, limping, into the pasture.

The raids on the garden continued, and the two men began to quarrel over them. But to prove that his horses were not guilty the ranchman asked the gardener to sit up with him and watch. That night as the moon was brightly shining they saw, not all the horses, but Coaly-Bay, walk straight up to the garden fence—no sign of a limp now—easily leap over it, and proceed to gobble the finest things he could find. After they had made sure of his identity, the men ran forward. Coaly-Bay cleared the fence like a deer, lightly raced over the pasture to mix with the horseherd, and when the men came near him he had—oh, such an awful limp.

"That settles it," said the rancher. "He's a fraud, but he's a beauty, and good stuff, too."

"Yes, but it settles who took my garden truck," said the other.

"Wal, I suppose so," was the answer; "but luk a here, neighbour, you haven't lost more'n ten dollars in truck.

That horse is easily worth—a hundred. Give me twenty-five dollars, take the horse, an' call it square."

"Not much I will," said the gardener. "I'm out twenty-five dollars' worth of truck; the horse isn't worth a cent more. I'll take him and call it even."

And so the thing was settled. The ranchman said nothing about Coaly-Bay being vicious as well as cunning, but the gardener found out, the very first time he tried to ride him, that the horse was as bad as he was beautiful.

Next day a sign appeared on the gardener's gate:

> FOR SALE
> FIRST-CLASS HORSE,
> SOUND AND GENTLE
> $10.00

II. The Bear Bait

Now at this time a band of hunters came riding by. There were three mountaineers, two men from the city, and the writer of this story. The city men were going to hunt bear. They had guns and everything needed for bear-hunting, except bait. It is usual to buy some worthless horse or cow, drive it into the mountains where the bears are, and kill it there. So seeing the sign the hunters called to the gardener: "Haven't you got a cheaper horse?"

The gardener replied: "Look at him there, ain't he a beauty? You won't find a cheaper horse if you travel a thousand miles."

"We are looking for an old bear bait, and five dollars is our limit," replied the hunter.

Horses were cheap and plentiful in that country; buyers were scarce. The gardener feared that Coaly-Bay would escape. "Wal, if that's the best you can do, he's yourn."

The hunter handed him five dollars, then said: "Now,

stranger, the bargain's settled. Will you tell me why you sell this fine horse for five dollars?"

"Mighty simple. He can't be rode. He's dead lame when he'd going your way and sound as a dollar going his own; no fence in the country can hold him; he's a dangerous outlaw. He's wickeder nor old Nick."

"Well, he's an almighty handsome bear bait," and the hunters rode on.

Coaly-Bay was driven with the pack horses, and limped dreadfully on the trail. Once or twice he tried to go back, but he was easily turned by the men behind him. His limp grew worse, and toward night it was painful to see him.

The leading guide remarked: "That thar limp is no fake. He's got some deep-seated trouble."

Day after day the hunters rode farther into the mountains, driving the horses along and hobbling them at night. Coaly-Bay went with the rest, limping along, tossing his head and his long splendid mane at every step. One of the hunters tried to ride him and nearly lost his life, for the horse seemed possessed of a demon as soon as the man was on his back.

The road grew harder as it rose. A very bad bog had to be crossed one day. Several horses were mired in it, and as the men rushed to the rescue, Coaly-Bay saw his chance of escape. He wheeled in a moment and turned himself from a limping, low-headed, sorry, bad-eyed creature into a high-spirited horse. Head and tail aloft now, shaking their back streamers in the wind, he gave a joyous neigh, and, without a trace of lameness, dashed for his home one hundred miles away, threading each narrow trail with perfect certainty, though he had seen it but once before, and in a few minutes he had steamed away from their sight.

The men were furious, but one of them, saying not a word, leaped on his horse—to do what? Follow that free-ranging racer? Sheer folly. Oh, no!—he knew a better plan. He knew the country. Two miles around by the trail, half a mile by the rough cut-off that he took, was Panther Gap. The runaway must pass through that, and Coaly-Bay raced down the trail to find the guide below awaiting him. Tossing his head with anger, he wheeled on up the trail again, and within a few yards recovered his monotonous limp and his evil expression. He was driven into camp, and there he vented his rage by kicking in the ribs of a harmless little pack horse.

III. His Destined End

This was bear country, and the hunters resolved to end his dangerous pranks and make him useful for once. They dared not catch him; it was not really safe to go near him, but two of the guides drove him to a distant glade where bears abounded. A thrill of pity came over me as I saw that beautiful untamable creature going away with his imitation limp.

"Aren't you coming along?" called the guide.

"No, I don't want to see him die," was the answer. Then as the tossing head was disappearing I called: "Say, fellows, I wish you would bring me that mane and tail when you come back!"

Fifteen minutes later a distant rifle crack was heard, and in my mind's eye I saw that proud head and those superb limbs, robbed of their sustaining indomitable spirit, falling flat and limp—to suffer the unsightly end of fleshly things. Poor Coaly-Bay! he would not bear the yoke. Rebellious to the end, he had fought against the fate of all his kind. It seemed to me the spirit of an eagle or a wolf it was that dwelt behind those full, bright eyes—that ordered all his wayward life.

I tried to put the tragic finish out of mind, and had not long to battle with the thought, not even one short hour, for the men came back.

Down the long trail to the west they had driven him;

there was no chance for him to turn aside. He must go on, and the men behind felt safe in that.

Farther away from his old home on the Bitterroot River he had gone each time he journeyed. And now he had passed the high divide and was keeping the narrow trail that leads to the valley of bears and on to Salmon River, and still away to the open, wild Columbian Plains, limping sadly as though he knew. His glossy hide flashed back the golden sunlight, still richer than it fell, and the men behind followed like hangmen in the death train of a nobleman condemned—down the narrow trail till it opened into a little meadow, with rank, rich grass, a lovely mountain stream, and winding bear paths up and down the waterside.

"Guess this'll do," said the older man. "Well, here goes for a sure death or a clean miss," said the other confidently, and, waiting till the limper was out in the middle of the meadow, he gave a short, sharp whistle. Instantly Coaly-Bay was alert. He swung and faced his tormentors, his noble head erect, his nostrils flaring; a picture of horse beauty—yes, of horse perfection.

The rifle was leveled, the very brain its mark, just on the cross line of the eyes and ears, that meant sure, sudden, painless death.

The rifle cracked. The great horse wheeled and dashed away. It was sudden death or miss; and the marksman *missed*.

Away went the wild horse at his famous best, not for his eastern home, but down the unknown western trail, away and away; the pine woods hid him from view, and left behind was the rifleman vainly trying to force the empty cartridge from his gun.

Down that trail with an inborn certainty he went, and on through the pines, then leaped a great bog, and splashed an hour later through the limpid Clearwater, and on, responsive to some unknown guide that subtly called him from the farther west. And so he went till the dwindling pines gave place to scrubby cedars and these in turn were mixed with sage, and onward still, till the far-away flat plains of Salmon River were about him, and ever on, tireless as it seemed, he went, and crossed the cañon of the mighty Snake, and up again to the high, wild plains where the wire fence still is not, and on, beyond the Buffalo Hump, till moving specks on the far horizon caught his eager eyes, and coming on and near, they moved and rushed aside to wheel and face about. He lifted up his voice and called to them, the long shrill neigh of his kindred when they bugled to each other on the far Chaldean plain; and back their answer came. This way and that they wheeled and sped and caracoled, and Coaly-Bay drew nearer, called, and gave the countersigns his kindred know, till this they were assured—he was their kind, he was of the wild free blood that man had never tamed. And when the night came down on the purpling plain his place was in the herd as one who after many a long hard journey in the dark had found his home.

There you may see him yet, for still his strength endures, and his beauty is not less. The riders tell me they have seen him many times by Cedra. He is swift and strong among the swift ones, but it is that flowing mane and tail that mark him chiefly from afar.

There on the wild free plains of sage he lives; the storm-wind smites his glossy coat at night and the winter snows are driven hard on him at times; the wolves are there to harry all the weak ones of the herd, and in the spring the mighty grizzly, too, may come to claim his toll. There are no luscious pastures made by man, no grain-foods; nothing but the wild, hard hay, the wind and the open plains, but here at last he found the thing he craved—the one worth all the rest. Long may he roam—this is my wish, and this—that I may see him once again in all the glory of his speed with his black mane on the wind, the spur-galls gone from his flanks, and in his eye the blazing light that grew in his far-off forbears' eyes as they spurned Arabian plains to leave behind the racing wild beast and the

fleet gazelle—yes, too, the driving sandstorm that o'er-
whelmed the rest, but strove in vain on the dusty wake of
the desert's highest born.

—Ernest Thompson Seton

From *Wild Animal Ways*

STUDY AND ENJOYMENT

1. What is the most exciting moment in this story? What do you admire in
   Coaly-Bay? What were his weaknesses?

2. Look at the north-west section of the map of the United States. Find the
   State of Idaho, the Bitterroot Mountains, the Snake River, the Columbia
   River. What Canadian Provinces are neighbours of Idaho?

3. *Chaldean plains,* countryside in the vicinity of Arabia; *caracole,* to make half-
   turns to right or left; *countersigns,* pass-words, or signs common to a
   group.

4. If you enjoyed this story, you will be interested in two books by O'Hara:
   My Friend Flicka and *Thunderhead.* They tell of a wild horse and of a
   boy who loved him.

A THUNDERSTORM

A moment the wild swallows like a flight
Of withered gust-caught leaves, serenely high,
Toss in the windrack up the muttering sky.
The leaves hang still. Above the weird twilight,
The hurrying centres of the storm unite
And spreading with huge trunk and rolling fringe,
Each wheeled upon its own tremendous hinge,
Tower darkening on. And now from heaven's height,
With the long roar of elm-trees swept and swayed,
And pelted waters, on the vanished plain
Plunges the blast. Behind the wild white flash
That splits abroad the pealing thunder-crash,
Over bleared fields and gardens disarrayed,
Column on column comes the drenching rain.

—Archibald Lampman

STUDY AND ENJOYMENT

Archibald Lampman (1861-1899) was born in the village of Morpeth,
Ontario. His father was a clergyman, who wrote poetry for his own enjoyment.
Young Lampman grew up near lovely Rice Lake, and the beauty of this Ontario

lake region left a lasting impression upon him. He attended Cobourg High School and Trinity College School, Port Hope, and matriculated into the University of Toronto. Upon graduation he was appointed to a clerkship in the Post Office Department, Ottawa, and disliked the dull routine. He found escape in his great friendship with Duncan Campbell Scott, in his two growing children, and in the beauty of the Ottawa countryside.

1. In this poem the poet gives three pictures to indicate that a storm is near. They refer to the swallows, the leaves, and the clouds. Study the lines carefully and tell in your own words the pictures you have in mind.

2. In the last seven lines mention four or five pictures the poet gives to show the fury of the storm.

THE THUNDER STORM

Emily Dickinson (1830-1886) was born in Amherst, Mass. She lived a secluded life, concealing her talents, and publishing only four poems during her lifetime. Turning aside from her cooking, for she revelled in house-wifery, Emily Dickinson would jot down a poem. Eight hundred or more have been discovered and published. "If I read a book and it makes my whole body so cold no fire can even warm me, I know it is poetry. If I feel physically as if the top of my head were taken off, I know this is poetry. These are the only ways I know it." Her definition is as good as any.

The wind began to rock the grass
With threatening tunes and low—
He flung a menace at the earth,
A menace at the sky.

The leaves unhooked themselves from trees
And started all abroad;
The dust did scoop itself like hands
And throw away the road.

The wagons quickened on the streets,
The thunder hurried slow;
The lightning showed a yellow beak,
And then a livid claw.

The birds put up the bars to nests,
The cattle fled to barns;
There came one drop of giant rain,
And then, as if the hands

That held the dams had parted hold,
The waters wrecked the sky,
But overlooked my father's house,
Just quartering a tree.
                              —Emily Dickinson

STUDY AND ENJOYMENT

1. In this poem the storm is pictured as a monstrous bird threatening the earth. Quote lines from the poem that show this.
2. What were the first signs of the approaching storm? How does the author make you feel the fright of inanimate things like the leaves and the dust?
3. What does "put up the bars" make you think of? How could birds do this to their nests? What lines make you aware that the rain fell like a cloudburst? How close did the lightning come?
4. Here we have two more poems on the same theme. Which storm was the more terrifying, that described by Lampman or the one in Emily Dickinson's poem? Which poem do you like the better? Why?

BUDDY AND WAFFLES

I. Two of a Kind

They were two of a kind—Buddy and his dog, Waffles. "That child," declared Mrs. H. Orrison Finch, president of the Ladies' Village Improvement Society, "is a disgrace and a hurt to the community."

"Where did the boy come from, Madam President?" asked Mrs. Mary Amelia Sitt.

"He looks as if he had escaped from a rag-picker's bag," replied Mrs. Finch. "But I believe that he was born in the county poorhouse, and that an old widow, now dead, adopted him and left him, after her demise, to grow up like a rank and noxious weed."

"Who feeds him?" asked another member.

"He feeds himself somehow and also feeds his dog, who is as much a disgrace to the town as his master," the president informed the Society. "We should and must get rid of the two of them."

"I move, Madam President," said Mrs. Nales, "that the Committee on Beautification of Railroad Parks and Stations be instructed to take such action as is necessary to have this nuisance abated. If the dog has no license he may be easily disposed of. The boy might be placed in some institution."

"Second the motion!" came from all over the meeting room.

Meanwhile, Buddy sat on his favourite bench in the sun, making fast a cord to a slender branch of a tree laid across his knees, with a tin can filled with worms beside him, and, looking up into his face, his dog and only friend: a gaunt, shaggy cur, dingy brown in colour. Buddy was about twelve years old, and his eyes shone from a dirty face like two blue patches of summer sky through shower-promising clouds. One of his shoes was intended for a male person and the other, from which he had removed the high heel, had been made for a female. His coat and trousers had been cut for a man. He stopped fixing his fishing tackle to caress the dog—at the dog's own earnest and caudal beseeching.

Thinking that his friend was hungry, Buddy fished in a cavernous pocket, pulled out half a loaf of bread, and wrenched off a goodly piece. He emptied his bait from the can and filled it with water from a nearby rain barrel, placing it beside his pet and putting the wriggling, protesting worms in his coat pocket, stuffing a piece of newspaper on top of them to hold them captive.

Waffles did not beg often, for he was a good self-provider. By upsetting a boy and stealing the contents of a tray which he was carrying to a neighbour's home one morning,

Buddy's dog secured a breakfast that day of a dozen well-browned and buttered waffles, which not only gave him inner satisfaction, but also caused his christening by the other boys who saw him make the raid.

After the dog had finished his repast and quenched his thirst, Buddy filled his own mouth with bread, wet his own throat, and departed whistling with his rod, line, worms and four-footed friend in the direction of the brook. The heart of the lad was light within him. The winter had passed; the robins had come up from the south to steal all the worms they could from small boys who would a-fishing go; and the grackles were flying overhead in countless air squadrons, making a noise like crackling twigs in a brisk forest fire. Over the untilled fields the dandelions spread their golden carpets; the trees had well advanced in leafing, the fish were nibbling, and Buddy was no longer compelled to beg a shelter in barns or in the rear of village stores at the coming of night.

II. A WELL-EDUCATED DOG

It was probably the spirit of pride and responsibility in ownership which early determined Buddy thoroughly to educate his dumb friend. He knew nothing about praying, but he did know the posture for praying, so he taught Buddy to kneel down with his head between his forepaws and not stir until he heard the magic word "Amen." Waffles was taught to say "Good-morning" and "Good-night," and to ask for food and water when there were any with which to meet his request. Waffles, in time, also acquired the art of playing sick, writhing in great pain on the ground and then lying stiff and stark in death until the magic words "Git up!" brought him back to the living.

Buddy further taught his friend to be useful, having him carry his ragged cap or tattered shoes on hot days, or the fishing pole or the bait can. It was not necessary to teach him to love his master; that was born in his puppy soul when Buddy crawled under the freight-station platform one winter morning and saved him from death by cold and starvation.

So the sweetest season of the year began with a well-educated dog and a thoroughly happy and uneducated boy, neither asking anything of life save plenty of sunshine and a bite to eat. Nature offered them both, and a little later in the year Man would offer the lad the highest and greatest blessing that can come to a boy—the circus!

Buddy was already coping with the problem of acquiring enough money to pay his way through the gates of boyhood's heaven. He lived from circus to circus; and as each springtime came, he planned to gaze long and lovingly upon every freak in every side show, every animal in the menagerie; planned for a top seat in the big tent, where he could rub his back against the beloved canvas, and watch all three rings at once; and laid out appropriations for peanuts, lemonade, and the concert which always followed the regular show.

Buddy earned his circus money by fishing. A little piece of red flannel rag on his line served him for trout if they were running, and if they were not running, the wriggling worm on his hook and a light sinker brought up perch. He sold his catches to elaborately equipped fishermen who failed to fill their baskets. This money he hoarded, burying it, and marking the treasure trove against the time when the glittering caravans would pass from the dreams of childhood to the reality of the Fair Grounds in the nearest big town.

"How much ye got now, Buddy?" asked Tom McCue, the village constable, when circus rumours began to spread.

"Ninety-eight," the boy replied.

"Better'n last year, ain't it?" inquired the police arm of the village law.

"Ten cents better."

"Glad to hear it, Buddy, glad to hear it!" McCue, bearing a badge that was a shield to his whole big heart, was one person not among the absolutely poverty-stricken who would converse openly with the boy.

"You going to the circus, too, Chief?" Buddy asked.

"Sure; if everything is quiet and I can git off! Be you teaching Waffles any new tricks, Buddy?"

"I guess he knows *everything* now, Chief," the boy replied, rubbing his dog's ears. "He can walk on his hands, stand on his head, and turn the back flipflap."

"Is that so? He can, eh?" cried McCue. "You know you'd make a barrel of money with him if you joined the circus, Buddy. I have saw many a trick dog that couldn't tech him; no, sirree, not for a minute. And think of travelling all over the country, with a parade every day, the steam pianner just hittin' it up all the time, and feeding the animules every day!"

"Lawsy!" exclaimed Buddy, his eyes like two blue saucers.

"I'd try it when ye got a little bigger, Buddy. Dinged ef I wouldn't ef I was you."

III. Buddy Meets a Clown

At last the morning of the circus came, and Buddy had two dollars, every cent of which he was prepared to squander. The circus town was ten miles away across country and nearer a more profitable railroad line. To reach it on the cars he would have to spend one of his two precious dollars in a long and roundabout journey. With better shoes he could have made the journey easily in a little over three hours, for he was stout of legs and of fine wind. He prepared for the journey by having the village cobbler tack a heel on his "female" shoe.

The day was glorious and he felt very thankful over the prospects and was especially kind to Waffles when he chained him to a post under the freight-station platform where he would have plenty of shade. He fed his faithful friend with ten cents' worth of beef bones, placed a big can of water beside him, and kissed him good-bye.

"Chief" McCue was at the station on duty as usual, and he promised Buddy that if the freight house caught fire he would unchain the dog even before he turned in the alarm. "You leave him to me, Buddy," said the old constable. "When things is dull, about two o'clock, I'll give him fresh water and take him for a little walk to cheer him up. You go ahead and have a good time. I'm going to the show tonight—if nothing happens."

With a word of gratitude, Buddy was off down the road. It was eight o'clock and he counted on covering the ten miles by noon.

Only three times did Buddy stop to rest, and, as he had been unable to sleep the night before because of excitement, he rested either standing up or seated on a fallen log, for fear he might doze off. At the last resting place he found the newly nailed heel on his shoe had been lost. With two rocks, he hammered the tacks flat and was off in the stretch. The sun was directly overhead when he saw the waving banners above the tented city and then the softly gleaming white tops of the tents themselves.

When he reached the circus grounds, he found a pump and stuck his mouth under it, working the handle as only a thirsty boy can. Then he bought a big sandwich, and with this to nibble on luxuriously, he made a preliminary inspection of the tents.

Presently he personally met a Clown! At first it seemed that he was dreaming, but there stood the Clown, his white face and egglike head unmistakably real. He was speaking to him—speaking to Buddy Noname!

"Hi, kid," Buddy heard him say. "I'd like to buy them clothes from you. They'd do for a make-up, believe me."

"I ain't much on clothes, Mister Clown," Buddy finally managed to say, "but I'll betcher I got a dog that can beat any dog you got in this show."

"You have, eh? And wot might be his name?"

"Waffles."

"Waffles," cried the Clown. "It's a fine name. Wot's yours?"

"Buddy."

The Clown roared. "Say," he said, "if you ain't got no family ties and want to join the circus, come to see me. Ask for Smithy—Boob Smithy—and I'll take you along. I need a boy clown and a trick dog." Then he disappeared behind the canvas flap.

For the rest of the afternoon Buddy remained in a dream. Almost mechanically he carried out his programme of seeing all the freaks and getting his top seat for the big show, but all the time the thought of fetching Waffles to that dressing tent and showing Boob Smithy what that wonderful dog could do filled his mind.

He cut out the concert and started comparatively early on the long hike back to base. It was pitch black by the time he had covered the fifth homeward mile, and he found that, the shoe with the lost heel having given up trying to keep up with him, his foot was torn and bleeding. Sitting down in the road, he tore off half his shirt and bandaged the wounded member, starting off with a limp to do the next five miles. It was well after daybreak when he crawled into the village.

He dragged himself across the railroad tracks and groped beneath the freight platform for Waffles.

He was gone!

IV. Take Aim! Fire!

Nobody bothered about Buddy as he lay on the ground, half under the freight station, any more than anyone had bothered about him previously. He lay half-hidden and half-senseless, certain of only one friend—Waffles; and he was gone! Used to neglect, Buddy soon fell asleep against the breast of the only mother he had ever known. He was awakened by a familiar voice, and lifting himself on one elbow, was rejoiced to see Waffles tugging at the end of a chain held by McCue.

"Hi, Chief!" he called, scrambling to his feet and limping across the tracks. "Here I am! Did you think I was lost?" Waffles in paroxysm of joy howled at the top of his voice. "I was late getting back," continued Buddy as he reached for the leash of his friend, "Me feet give out on the way."

McCue did not surrender the chain to the boy. His face was a shade whiter than usual.

"Lemme take him now, Chief," the boy urged. "It's been mighty kind of you to look out for the old feller for me.'

"Ye can't take him, Buddy," the constable replied in a low voice. "Ten o'clock yestiddy the Mayor serves me with an order to kill him within twenty-four hours because he ain't got no license and a lot of ladies signed a complaint against him. I wanted to—"

"Kill me dawg!" cried Buddy. "Kill Waffles? Wot's he done? Did he bite anybody, Chief?" He fell on his knees and put his arms about his friend's neck.

"He ain't done nuthin'," replied McCue. "They ain't done said a word agin him 'ceptin' he was a nuisance."

A sob broke from Buddy's lips. "Ye can't kill him; ye can't kill him!" the boy moaned, pressing the cur to his breast. "Kill me, Chief, won't ye, please? Kill me 'stead of him. Please, Chief, don't you shoot me dawg!"

It was a job to be done in a hurry, and McCue was

BUDDY MANAGED TO CATCH UP WITH THEM

sorry that his ragged friend had come back. The old constable dragged the dog from the arms of his little master and started down the hard-beaten tracks beside the rails. Waffles struggled in vain, calling on Buddy to come along, too.

The boy rubbed the mud made by his tears clear of his eyes, and started after the constable and his dog. His bandaged foot dragged heavily; his sobs broke the quiet of the country air. Because of the struggles of Waffles, Buddy managed to catch up with them. A quarter mile down the track McCue stopped and pulled out a big, old-fashioned silver watch.

"In twenty-four hours, Buddy," he said solemnly. "They give me the order at ten o'clock yestiddy. It is nine-fifty now."

Buddy dropped to the ground, his arms about the neck

of his dog. "Don't kill him, don't kill him, Chief!" he begged.

"He's only got ten minutes, Buddy."

"I ain't never had another friend on earth," moaned Buddy. The dog whimpered and licked the chin and cheek of his master.

"Time's up, Buddy; you'd better go away now." The constable dropped his watch into his pocket and heaved forth an old-fashioned horse pistol. As he did so, Waffles yanked himself free, but only for a moment, for the big foot of McCue came down on the chain.

"You ain't going to shoot him chained up," begged Buddy. "He won't go away from me, and I can't run with a lame foot. Loosen him, won't you?"

"I don't mind doing that for ye, son," replied McCue. "There ain't nothing in the order about shooting him chained up. It says just shoot and kill him."

McCue unleashed the dog, and, with a word lifted on a sob, Buddy ordered his friend to stand at attention. Not a muscle, sinew, or hair of the brute moved after the word was spoken. But in his brown eyes came a message of affection, fidelity, and undying faith to the eyes of his master.

McCue was aiming his great pistol.

"Sit up!" came the command from the swollen lips of the boy. Waffles rose to his haunches, his forepaws pointed downward pathetically. "Take aim!" cried Buddy. "Fire!" As he shouted the last word he fell against the side of old Tom, the horse pistol roaring to the clear heavens, spitting a tongue of fire and a cloud of smoke.

Waffles dropped over on his side and lay stark and still in the path.

"By gum!" cried McCue. "I done it with one shot. I'm glad of that, Buddy." He slipped his pistol into its holster under his coat and turned to the boy, taking his dirty tear-stained face in his shaky hands. "Don't blame me, son," he said in a husky voice. "I had to obey orders. You take him and bury him. I know how you loved him."

"I'll put him away in the woods over yonder," replied Buddy.

McCue turned and trudged up the path beside the rails to the station, shaking his head sadly.

Buddy lifted his stark friend to a shoulder, and stole into the underbrush beside the tracks, burrowing deeper and deeper until his strength gave out. Now, fully screened from all eyes, he laid down his precious burden and uttered one magic word: "Waffles!"

The corpse stirred.

"Sit up!"

The corpse sat up.

Buddy pointed a finger at him and said slowly: "Take aim! Fire!"

Waffles flopped over on his side.

"Git up!"

The corpse got up again.

"Come over and kiss your boss."

Waffles needed no further invitation.

Buddy then cleared a spot in the underbrush and, with a grateful sigh, threw himself on the bare ground.

"Now we'll go to sleep," he said; and his dog coiled up close to the empty stomach of his master, warming it. "When we both git up we'll start after that circus," added Buddy drowsily. "We'll show—them—sumpin'—eeyah! won't we?"

—*John A. Moroso*

STUDY AND ENJOYMENT

1. Why were Buddy and his dog Waffles "two of a kind"?
2. What was the most important trick Buddy taught his dog?
3. Give three examples of Chief McCue's kindness.
4. How did Buddy meet the clown? What offer did the clown make him?

5. Show how Buddy managed to save Waffles from being killed. You will notice that both dog and boy were clever.
6. Did the ending of the story surprise you? As you read the last pages again what clues do you find that make the ending seem right and probable?

THE SONG OF THE SEA WIND

How it sings, sings, sings,
Blowing sharply from the sea-line,
With an edge of salt that stings;
How it laughs aloud, and passes,
As it cuts the close cliff-grasses:
How it sings again, and whistles
As it shakes the stout sea-thistles—
How it sings!

How it shrieks, shrieks, shrieks,
In the crannies of the headland,
In the gashes of the creeks;
How it shrieks once more, and catches
Up the yellow foam in patches;
How it hurls it out and over
To the corn-field and the clover—
How it shrieks!

How it roars, roars, roars,
In the iron under-caverns,
In the hollows of the shores;
How it roars anew, and thunders,
As the strong hull splits and sunders:
And the spent ship, tempest-driven,
On the reef lies rent and riven—
How it roars!

How it wails, wails, wails,
In the tangle of the wreckage,
In the flapping of the sails;
How it sobs away, subsiding,
Like a tired child after chiding;
And across the ground-swell rolling
You can hear the bell-buoy tolling—
How it wails.

—*Austin Dobson*

STUDY AND ENJOYMENT

1. The changing key-words in the four stanzas of this poem—"sings," "shrieks," "roars," and "wails"—show how the wind's song changes. But the poet has done more than this to make word music. In stanza one, notice all the *s's*. It might be fun to count them. In stanza two the *k's* and the hard *c's* and *g* give a harsh effect. And the vowels in stanza three, particularly the *o's*—what a fine uproar they contribute! Can you discover the sounds that make the wind wail in stanza four?
2. What picture is given in stanza three?
3. This is an excellent poem for choral reading. Divide your class into groups, with your lightest or highest voices for stanza two, and your deepest or darkest voices for stanza three. Be careful not to drop your voices at "whistles," "catches," and "over," though you should pause slightly at each, as you would at a rest in music.

ROADS OF THE AIR

Have you ever been up in the sky,
  sailing like a cloud over a far-away world
  where little trees cluster and little roads wind,
  where creased and mighty mountains look as if hand-
    moulded,
  where rivers shine and wander like tiny silver tracings?
Have you ever been up in the sky?

Have you ever been up in the sky,
　　moving with no sense of motion over the sea
　　where baby boats lie with back-trailing line of white,
　　where the wrinkled, crinkled ocean crawls like a live thing,
　　where the water stretches to the sky and the sky stretches
　　　　to the water?
Have you ever been up in the sky?

Have you ever been up in the sky,
　　scudding like a thing lost behind the clouds,
　　where the mists roll, part, and roll together again,
　　where the knife wind whistles and the swift rain stings,
　　where there is no up, no down, and you are all there is?
Have you ever been up in the sky?

　　　　　　　　　　　　　　　　　　—Lucy S. Mitchell

STUDY AND ENJOYMENT

1. Have you been up in an aeroplane? How did the countryside look below you? Describe the appearance of several things in particular. What could you see when you went through a cloud? Above the clouds? If you have not flown, ask someone who has. Then read him this poem to see if it rings true.

2. The first two stanzas describe what one can see from an aeroplane. What does the third stanza describe?

3. The words "little," "tiny," and "baby" are used to describe many things on the earth below. How are the mountains and ocean described? Why not use the word "little" there, too?

4. Why is there "no up, no down" in stanza three?

5. How does this poem differ from all the other poems in your book? One difference is that it hasn't a regular metre or beat. It has a rhythm like some modern music. If you look closely you will find a pattern which is the same for each stanza, a pattern that stands out because of repeated words and lines. What other differences do you notice?

6. Tennyson, before the age of aeroplanes, wrote a poem in which he described the world as seen from a lofty height. Is any picture in "The Eagle" found in "Roads of the Air"?

THE EAGLE

He clasps the crag with hookèd hands;
Close to the sun in lonely lands,
Ring'd with the azure world, he stands.

The wrinkled sea beneath him crawls.
He watches from his mountain walls,
And like a thunderbolt he falls.

　　　　　　　　　　　　　　—Alfred, Lord Tennyson

MOTI GUJ[1]—MUTINEER

Rudyard Kipling lived many years in India, and many of his best tales deal with life in that country. As you read this story you will realize that Kipling "knew his elephants," and had listened to and closely observed their trainers.

I. Stump Pulling in India

Once upon a time there was a coffee planter in India who wished to clear some forest land for coffee planting. When he had cut down all the trees and burned the underwood, the stumps still remained. Dynamite is expensive and slow fire slow. The happy medium for stump clearing is the lord of all beasts, who is the elephant. He will either push the stump out of the ground with his tusks, if he has any, or drag it out with ropes. The planter, therefore, hired elephants by ones and twos and threes, and fell to work. The very best of all the elephants belonged to the very worst of all the drivers or mahouts[2]; and this superior beast's name was Moti Guj. When Deesa gave Moti Guj a beating with a tent peg over the tender nails of the forefoot, Moti Guj never trampled the life out of Deesa, for he knew that after the beating was over, Deesa would embrace his trunk and weep and call him his love and his life and the liver of his soul. Then Deesa would go to sleep between Moti Guj's forefeet, and as Deesa generally chose the middle of the public road, and as Moti Guj mounted guard over him, and would not permit horse, foot, or cart to pass by, traffic was congested till Deesa saw fit to wake up.

There was no sleeping in the daytime on the planter's clearing; the wages were too high to risk. Deesa sat on Moti Guj's neck and gave him orders, while Moti Guj rooted up the stumps—for he owned a magnificent pair of tusks; or pulled at the end of a rope—for he had a magni-

[1]*Moti Guj*—(mō'tē gōōzh). [2]*Mahout*—A driver and trainer of elephants.

ficent pair of shoulders—while Deesa kicked him behind
the ears and said he was the king of elephants. Once a
week Deesa led Moti Guj down to the river, and Moti Guj
lay on his side luxuriously in the shallows, while Deesa
went over him with a coir swab[1] and a brick. Moti Guj
never mistook the pounding blow of the latter for the
smack of the former that warned him to get up and turn
over on the other side. Then Deesa would look at his feet
and examine his eyes, and turn up the fringes of his mighty
ears in case of sores. After inspection the two would
"come up with a song from the sea," Moti Guj, all black
and shining, waving a torn tree branch twelve feet long in
his trunk, and Deesa knotting up his own long wet hair.

II. THE URGE FOR AN ORGY

It was a peaceful, well-paid life till Deesa felt the
return of the desire to drink deep. He wished for an orgy.

He went to the planter, and "My mother's dead," said
he, weeping.

"She died on the last plantation, two months ago, and
she died once before that when you were working for me
last year," said the planter, who knew something of the
ways of nativedom.

"Then it's my aunt, and she was just the same as a
mother to me," said Deesa, weeping more than ever.
"She has left eighteen small children entirely without
bread, and it is I who must fill their little stomachs," said
Deesa, beating his head on the floor.

"Who brought you the news?" said the planter.

"The post," said Deesa.

"There hasn't been a post here for the past week.
Get back to your lines!"

"A devastating sickness has fallen on my village, and

---

[1] A coarse brush or sponge made of the fibre of cocoanut husks.

all my wives are dying," yelled Deesa, really in tears this time.

"Call Chihun, who comes from Deesa's village," said the planter.

"Chihun, has this man got a wife?"

"He?" said Chihun. "No. Not a woman of our village would look at him. They'd sooner marry the elephant."

Chihun snorted. Deesa wept and bellowed.

A flickering smile crossed the planter's face. "Deesa," said he, "I'd give you leave on the spot if anything could be done with Moti Guj while you're away. You know that he will only obey your orders."

"May the light of the heavens live forty thousand years. I shall be absent but ten little days. After that, upon my faith and honour and soul, I return. As to the inconsiderable interval, have I the gracious permission of the heaven-born to call up Moti Guj?"

Permission was granted, and in answer to Deesa's shrill yell, the mighty tusker swung out of the shade of a clump of trees where he had been squirting dust over himself till his master should return.

"Light of my heart, mountain of might, give ear!" said Deesa, standing in front of him.

Moti Guj gave ear, and saluted with his trunk. "I am going away," said Deesa.

Moti Guj's eyes twinkled. He liked jaunts as well as his master.

"But you, you fussy old pig, must stay behind and work."

The twinkle died out as Moti Guj tried to look delighted. He hated stump hauling on the plantation. It hurt his teeth.

"I shall be gone for ten days, oh, delectable one! Hold up your near forefoot and I'll impress the fact upon it, warty toad of a dried mud puddle." Deesa took a tent peg and banged Moti Guj ten times on the nails. Moti Guj grunted and shuffled from foot to foot.

"Ten days," said Deesa, "You will work and haul and root the trees as Chihun here shall order you. Take up Chihun and set him on your neck!" Moti Guj curled the tip of his trunk, Chihun put his foot there and was swung on to the neck. Deesa handed Chihun the heavy iron elephant goad.

Chihun thumped Moti Guj's bald head as a paver thumps a curbstone.

Moti Guj trumpeted.

"Be still, hog of the backwoods! Chihun's your mahout for ten days. And now bid me good-bye, beast after mine own heart. Oh, my lord, my king! Jewel of all created elephants, lily of the herd, preserve your honoured health; be virtuous. Adieu!"

Moti Guj lapped his trunk round Deesa and swung him into the air twice. That was his way of bidding him good-bye.

"He'll work now," said Deesa to the planter. "Have I leave to go?"

The planter nodded, and Deesa dived into the woods. Moti Guj went back to haul stumps.

Chihun was very kind to him, but he felt unhappy and forlorn for all that. Chihun gave him a ball of spices, and tickled him under the chin, and Chihun's little baby cooed to him after work was over, and Chihun's wife called him a darling; but Moti Guj was a bachelor by instinct, as Deesa was. He did not understand the domestic emotions. He wanted the light of his universe back again—the savage beatings and the savage caresses.

III. The Agreement Expires

None the less he worked well, and the planter wondered. Deesa had wandered along the roads till he met a marriage procession of his own caste, and had drifted with it past all knowledge of the lapse of time.

The morning of the eleventh day dawned, and there returned no Deesa. Moti Guj was loosed from his ropes for the daily stint.[1] He swung clear, looked round, shrugged his shoulders and began to walk away, as one having business elsewhere.

"Hi! ho! Come back, you!" shouted Chihun. "Come back and put me on your neck, misborn mountain. Return, splendour of the hillside! Adornment of all India, heave to, or I'll bang every toe off your fat forefoot!"

Moti Guj gurgled gently, but did not obey. Chihun ran after him with a rope and caught him up. Moti Guj put his ears forward, and Chihun knew what that meant, though he tried to carry it off with high words.

"None of your nonsense with me," said he. "To your pickets, devil son!"

"Hrrump!" said Moti Guj, and that was all—that and the forebent ears.

Moti Guj put his hands in his pockets, chewed a branch for a toothpick, and strolled about the clearing, making fun of the other elephants who had just set to work.

Chihun reported the state of affairs to the planter, who came out with a dog whip and cracked it furiously. Moti Guj paid the white man the compliment of charging him nearly a quarter of a mile across the clearing and "Hrrumping" him into his veranda. Then he stood outside the house, chuckling to himself and shaking all over with the fun of it, as an elephant will.

"We'll thrash him," said the planter. "He shall have the finest thrashing ever elephant received. Give Kala Nag and Nazim twelve feet of chain apiece, and tell them to lay on twenty."[2]

Kala Nag—which means Black Snake—and Nazim were two of the biggest elephants in the lines, and one of their duties was to administer the graver punishment, since no man can beat an elephant properly.

[1] Task. [2] Lay on twenty lashes with the whipping chains.

They took the whipping chains and rattled them in their trunks as they sidled up to Moti Guj, meaning to hustle him between them. Moti Guj had never, in all his life of thirty-nine years, been whipped, and he did not intend to begin a new experience. So he waited, waving his head from right to left and measuring the precise spot in Kala Nag's fat side where a blunt tusk could sink deepest. Kala Nag had no tusks; the chain was the badge of his authority; but for all that, he swung wide of Moti Guj at the last minute, and tried to appear as if he had brought the chain out for amusement. Nazim turned round and went home early. He did not feel in fighting trim that morning, and so Moti Guj was left standing alone with his ears cocked.

That decided the planter to argue no more, and Moti Guj rolled back to his amateur inspection of the clearing. An elephant who will not work and is not tied up is about as manageable as an eighty-one-ton gun loose in a heavy seaway. He slapped old friends on the back and asked them if the stumps were coming away easily; he talked nonsense concerning labour and the inalienable rights of elephants to a long "nooning"; and, wandering to and fro, he thoroughly demoralized the garden till sundown, when he returned to his picket for food.

"If you won't work you shan't eat," said Chihun, angrily. "You're a wild elephant, and no educated animal at all. Go back to your jungle."

Chihun's little brown baby was rolling on the floor of the hut, and stretching out its fat arms to the huge shadow in the doorway. Moti Guj knew well that it was the dearest thing on earth to Chihun. He swung out his trunk with a fascinating crook at the end, and the brown baby threw itself, shouting, upon it. Moti Guj made fast and pulled up till the brown baby was crowing in the air twelve feet above his father's head.

THE BROWN BABY WAS CROWING IN THE AIR TWELVE FEET ABOVE HIS
FATHER'S HEAD

"Great Lord!" said Chihun. "Flour cakes of the best,
twelve in number, two feet across, shall be yours on the
instant, and two hundred pounds' weight of fresh-cut
young sugar cane therewith. Deign[1] only to put down
safely that insignificant brat who is my heart and my
life to me!"

Condescend.

Moti Guj tucked the brown baby comfortably between his forefeet, that could have knocked into toothpicks all of Chihun's possessions, and waited for his food. He ate it, and the brown baby crawled away. Moti Guj dozed and thought of Deesa. One of many mysteries connected with the elephant is that his huge body needs less sleep than anything else that lives. Four or five hours in the night suffice—two just before midnight, lying down on one side; two just after one o'clock, lying down on the other. The rest of the silent hours are filled with eating and fidgeting, and long, grumbling soliloquies.

IV. The Joyful Reunion

At midnight, therefore, Moti Guj strode out of his pickets, for a thought had come to him that Deesa might be lying somewhere in the dark forest with none to look after him. So all that night he chased through the undergrowth, blowing and trumpeting and shaking his ears. He went down to the river and blared across the shallows where Deesa used to wash him, but there was no answer. He could not find Deesa, but he disturbed all the other elephants in the lines, and nearly frightened to death some gypsies in the woods.

At dawn Deesa returned to the plantation. He expected to get into trouble for outstaying his leave. He drew a long breath when he saw that the bungalow and the plantation were still uninjured, for he knew something of Moti Guj's temper, and reported himself with many lies and salaams.[1] Moti Guj had gone to his pickets for breakfast. The night exercise had made him hungry.

"Call up your beast," said the planter; and Deesa shouted in the mysterious elephant language that some

[1] Low bows of the head and body, with right palm on the forehead.

mahouts believe came from China at the birth of the world, when elephants and not men were masters. Moti Guj heard and came. Elephants do not gallop. They move from places at varying rates of speed. If an elephant wished to catch an express train he could not gallop, but he could catch the train. So Moti Guj was at the planter's door almost before Chihun noticed that he had left his pickets. He fell into Deesa's arms[1] trumpeting with joy, and the man and beast wept over each other and handled each other from head to heel to see that no harm had befallen.

"Now we will get to work," said Deesa. "Lift me up, my son and my joy!"

Moti Guj swung him up, and the two went to the coffee clearing to look for difficult stumps.

The planter was too astonished to be very angry.

—Rudyard Kipling

STUDY AND ENJOYMENT

1. Which description of Moti Guj do you prefer: Moti Guj the worker, or Moti Guj the idler? Why?

2. How does Deesa show his real nature (a) in the excuses he makes; (b) in the language he uses to Moti Guj?

3. What do you think of the punishments in this story? Were they just? Did they do any good?

4. Read aloud Deesa's farewell, then tell, without rereading, the details of Moti Guj's behaviour while Deesa was absent.

5. Moti is very human. Show where. Is he too human? Illustrate.

6. How can you account for the fact that Moti Guj loved Deesa?

7. You will enjoy *Stalky and Co.*, Kipling's story of Westward Ho, his boarding school. His *Jungle Books* and *Just So Stories* are also great favourites.

[1]"Deesa embraced the elephant's trunk."

RAIN

Rain is a maker of songs—the gay fellow—
　Rain is a maker of songs.
He may whisper a lullaby, "Hush-hush-hush,"
He can chuckle and gurgle as loud as a thrush;
His rollicking tune to the water-chute's gush
　Is of shouting, trampling throngs.
　Oh, Rain is a maker of songs.

Rain is a dancer of jigs—the quaint fellow—
　Rain is a dancer of jigs.
Hop-hop in a puddle you see him dance;
With stamp and clap on the roof he may prance;
Tap-tap, tip-toe off the leaves he'll glance,
　As gay as a hundred grigs.
　Oh, Rain is a dancer of jigs.

Rain is a weaver of spells—the strange fellow—
　Rain is a weaver of spells.
Streets gleam like mirrors, tiles glint like mail,
He springs shining beads along gate-bar and rail,
Jewelled flower-cup and cobweb he leaves in his trail
　And the incense of good earth smells.
　Oh, Rain is a weaver of spells.

—*E. M. Wilkie*

STUDY AND ENJOYMENT

1. In what three roles is Rain pictured? In which do you like him best? Why?
2. What three songs can he sing? What three jigs can he dance? What five magic spells does he weave?
3. The senses of hearing, seeing, and smelling are all appealed to in this poem. Select lines to show the truth of this statement.
4. *Grigs*, grasshoppers or crickets; *tiles*, thin slabs of baked clay used for roofing; *mail*, armour made of metal rings.

THE STORY OF KEESH

Jack London (1876-1916) was born in San Francisco and is at his best when describing ships and waters in the California region. His books are vivid and full of life, including stories of the South Seas and Alaska. Among his best books are *The Sea Wolf*, *The Call of the Wild*, and *White Fang*.

I. KEESH DEFIES THE COUNCIL

When Keesh stood up in the council of hunters and complained that the meat allotted to him and his mother was tough, old and full of bones, the men were aghast at his impertinence. Keesh was an orphan and lived with his mother, Ikeega, in the poorest igloo of this little Eskimo village, up on the rim of the polar sea. The father of Keesh had been a mighty hunter, who had sacrificed his life in trying to get food for the tribe in time of famine, but these things had been forgotten and Keesh and his mother were left to live in poverty. But Keesh was now thirteen years old, a strong and active lad, with his father's courage and spirit, and he was determined to stand for his rights. When the men at the council tried to shout him down, and threatened him with a beating for presuming to speak in the meeting of his elders, he sprang to his feet and retorted that never again would he speak in council until they came and asked him to. Moreover, from that time on he would do his own hunting, and would see to it that there should be a fair division of all that he killed, and that the weak members of the tribe should not be slighted because of their weakness. With this defiance he left the igloo.

Jeers and scornful laughter followed him out of the igloo, but his jaw was set and he went his way, looking neither to right nor left.

The next day he went forth along the shore line where the ice and the land met together. Those who saw him go noted that he carried his bow, with a goodly supply of bone-barbed arrows, and that across his shoulders was his

father's big hunting spear. And there was laughter, and
much talk, at the event. It was an unprecedented occurrence. Never did boys of his tender age go forth to hunt,
much less to hunt alone. Also were there shaking of heads
and prophetic mutterings, and the women looked pityingly
at Ikeega, and her face was grave and sad.

"He will be back ere long," they said cheeringly.

"Let him go; it will teach him a lesson," the hunters
said. "And he will come back shortly, and he will be
meek and soft of speech in the days to follow."

But a day passed, and a second, and on the third a
wild gale blew, and there was no Keesh. Ikeega tore her
hair and put soot of the seal oil on her face in token of her
grief; and the women assailed the men with bitter words
in that they had mistreated the boy and sent him to his
death; and the men made no answer, preparing to go in
search of the body when the storm abated.

II. Keesh Succeeds as a Hunter

Early next morning, however, Keesh strode into the
village. But he came not shamefacedly. Across his
shoulders he bore a burden of fresh-killed meat. And
there was importance in his step and arrogance in his speech.

"Go ye men, with the dogs and sledges, and take my
trail for the better part of a day's travel," he said. "There
is much meat on the ice—a she-bear and two half-grown
cubs."

Ikeega was overcome with joy, but he received her
demonstrations in manlike fashion, saying: "Come, Ikeega,
let us eat. And after that I shall sleep, for I am weary."

And he passed into their igloo and ate profoundly, and
after that slept for twenty running hours.

There was much doubt at first, much doubt and discussion. The killing of a polar bear is very dangerous, but
thrice dangerous is it, and three times thrice, to kill a
mother bear with her cubs. The men could not bring

themselves to believe that the boy Keesh, single-handed, had accomplished so great a marvel. But the women spoke of the fresh-killed meat he had brought on his back, and this was an overwhelming argument against their unbelief. So they finally departed, grumbling greatly that in all probability, if the thing were so, he had neglected to cut up the carcasses. Now in the north it is very necessary that this should be done as soon as the kill is made. If not, the meat freezes so solidly as to turn the edge of the sharpest knife, and a three-hundred-pound bear, frozen stiff, is no easy thing to put upon a sled and haul over the rough ice. But arrived at the spot, they found not only the kill, which they had doubted, but that Keesh had quartered the beasts in true hunter fashion, and removed the entrails.

III. The Mystery of Keesh

Thus began the mystery of Keesh, a mystery that deepened and deepened with the passing of the days. His very next trip he killed a young bear, nearly full grown, and on the trip following, a large male bear and his mate. He was ordinarily gone from three to four days, though it was nothing unusual for him to stay away a week at a time on the ice field. Always he declined company on these expeditions, and the people marvelled.

"How does he do it?" they demanded of one another. "Never does he take a dog with him, and dogs are of such great help, too."

"Why dost thou hunt only bear?" Klosh-Kwan once ventured to ask.

And Keesh made fitting answer. "It is well known that there is more meat on the bear," he said.

But there was also talk of witchcraft in the village. "He hunts with evil spirits," some of the people contended, "Wherefore his hunting is rewarded. How else can it be, save that he hunts with evil spirits?"

"Mayhap they be not evil, but good, these spirits," other said. "It is known that his father was a mighty hunter. May not his father hunt with him so that he may attain excellence and patience and understanding? Who knows?"

None the less, his success continued, and the less skilful hunters were often kept busy hauling in his meat. And in the division of it he was just. As his father had done before him, he saw to it that the least old woman and the last old man received a fair portion, keeping no more for himself than his needs required. And because of this, and of his merit as a hunter, he was looked upon with respect, and even awe; and there was talk of making him chief after old Klosh-Kwan. Because of the things he had done, they looked for him to appear again in the council, but he never came, and they were ashamed to ask.

"I am minded to build me an igloo," he said one day to Klosh-Kwan and a number of the hunters. "It shall be a large igloo, wherein Ikeega and I can dwell in comfort."

"Aye," they nodded gravely.

"But I have no time. My business is hunting, and it takes all my time. So it is but just that the men and women of the village who eat my meat should build me my igloo."

And the igloo was built accordingly, on a generous scale which exceeded even the dwelling of Klosh-Kwan. Keesh and his mother moved into it, and it was the first prosperity she had enjoyed since the death of Bok. Nor was material prosperity alone hers, for, because of her wonderful son and the position he had given her she came to be looked upon as the first woman in all the village; and the women were given to visiting her, to asking her advice, and to quoting her wisdom when arguments arose among themselves or with the men.

But it was the mystery of Keesh's marvellous hunting that took chief place in all their minds. And one day Ugh-Gluk taxed him with witchcraft to his face.

"It is charged," Ugh-Gluk said ominously, "that thou dealest with evil spirits, wherefore thy hunting is rewarded."

"Is not the meat good?" Keesh made answer. "Has one in the village yet to fall sick from the eating of it? How dost thou know that witchcraft be concerned? Or dost thou guess, in the dark, merely because of the envy that consumes thee?"

IV. THE SPIES REPORT

And Ugh-Gluk withdrew discomfited, the women laughing at him as he walked away. But in the council one night, after long deliberation, it was determined to put spies on his track when he went forth to hunt, so that his methods might be learned. So, on his next trip, Bim and Bawn, two young men, and of hunters the craftiest, followed after him, taking care not to be seen. After five days they returned, their eyes bulging and their tongues atremble to tell what they had seen. The council was hastily called in Klosh-Kwan's dwelling, and Bim took up the tale.

"Brothers! As commanded, we journeyed on the trail of Keesh, and cunningly we journeyed, so that he might not know. And midway of the first day he picked up with a great he-bear. It was a very great bear."

"None greater," Bawn corroborated, and went on himself. "Yet was the bear not inclined to fight, for he turned away and made off slowly over the ice. This we saw from the rocks of the shore, and the bear came toward us, and after him came Keesh, very much unafraid. And he shouted harsh words after the bear, and waved his arms about, and made much noise. Then did the bear grow angry, and rise up on his hind legs and growl. But Keesh walked right up to the bear."

"Aye," Bim continued the story. "Right up to the bear Keesh walked. And the bear took after him, and Keesh ran away. But as he ran he dropped a little round ball on the ice, and the bear stopped and smelled of it, and then swallowed it up. And Keesh continued to run away and drop little round balls, and the bear continued to swallow them up."

Exclamations and cries of doubt were being made, and Ugh-Gluk expressed open unbelief.

"With our own eyes we saw it," Bim affirmed.

And Bawn—"Aye, with our own eyes. And this continued until the bear stood suddenly upright and cried aloud in pain, and thrashed his forepaws madly about. And Keesh continued to make off over the ice to a safe distance. But the bear gave him no notice, being occupied with the misfortune the little round balls had wrought within him."

"Aye, within him," Bim interrupted. "For he did claw at himself, and leap about over the ice like a playful puppy; save from the way he growled and squealed, it was plain it was not play but pain. Never did I see such a sight!"

"Nay, never was such a sight seen," Bawn took up the strain. "And furthermore, it was such a large bear."

"Witchcraft," Ugh-Gluk suggested.

"I know not," Bawn replied. "I tell only of what my eyes beheld. And after a while the bear grew weak and tired, for he was very heavy and he had jumped about with exceeding violence, and he went off along the shore ice, shaking his head slowly from side to side and sitting down ever and again to squeal and cry. And Keesh followed after the bear, and we followed after Keesh, and for that day and three days more we followed. The bear grew weak, and never ceased crying from his pain."

"It was a charm!" Ugh-Gluk exclaimed. "Surely it was a charm!"

"It may well be."

And Bim relieved Bawn. "The bear wandered, now this way and now that, doubling back and forth and crossing his trail in circles, so that at the end he was near where Keesh had first come upon him. By this time he was quite sick, the bear, and could crawl no farther, so Keesh came up close and speared him to death."

"And then?" Klosh-Kwan demanded.

"Then we left Keesh skinning the bear, and came running that the news of the killing might be told."

V. The Mystery Explained

And in the afternoon of that day the women hauled in the meat of the bear while the men sat in council assembled. When Keesh arrived a messenger was sent to him, bidding him come to the council. But he sent reply, saying that he was hungry and tired; also that his igloo was large and comfortable and could hold many men.

And curiosity was so strong on the men that the whole council, Klosh-Kwan to the fore, rose up and went to the igloo of Keesh. He was eating, but he received them with respect and seated them according to their rank. Ikeega was proud and embarrassed by turns, but Keesh was quite composed.

Klosh-Kwan recited the information brought by Bim and Bawn, and at its close said in a stern voice: "So explanation is wanted, O Keesh, of thy manner of hunting. Is there witchcraft in it?"

Keesh looked up and smiled. "Nay, O Klosh-Kwan. It is not for a boy to know aught of witches, and of witches I know nothing. I have but devised a means whereby I may kill the ice bear with ease, that is all. It be headcraft, not witchcraft."

"And may any man?"

"Any man."

There was a long silence. The men looked in one another's faces, and Keesh went on eating.

"And—and—and wilt thou tell us, O Keesh?" Klosh-Kwan finally asked in a tremulous voice.

"Yea, I will tell thee." Keesh finished sucking a marrow-bone and rose to his feet. "It is quite simple. Behold!"

He picked up a thin strip of whalebone and showed it to them. The ends were sharp as needle points. The strip he coiled carefully, till it disappeared in his hand. Then, suddenly releasing it, it sprang straight again. He picked up a piece of blubber.

"So," he said, "one takes a small chunk of blubber, thus, and thus makes it hollow. Then into the hollow goes the whalebone, so, tightly coiled, and another piece of blubber is fitted over the whalebone. After that it is put outside where it freezes into a little round ball. The bear swallows the little round ball, the blubber melts, the whalebone with its sharp ends stands out straight, the bear gets sick, and when the bear is very sick, why, you kill him with a spear. It is quite simple."

And Ugh-Gluk said, "Oh!" and Klosh-Kwan said, "Ah!" And each said something after his own manner, and all understood.

And this is the story of Keesh, who lived long ago on the rim of the polar sea. Because he exercised headcraft and not witchcraft, he rose from the meanest igloo to be head man of his village, and through all the years that he lived, it is related, his tribe was prosperous, and neither widow nor weak one cried aloud in the night because there was no meat.

—*Jack London*
From *Brown Wolf and Other Stories*

STUDY AND ENJOYMENT

1. Do you think Keesh was "impertinent"?
2. What was "the mystery of Keesh"?

3. What report did the spies bring?

4. How did Keesh explain his "witchcraft"? What lines explain his success?

5. *Unprecedented occurrence*, an event with no happening like it in the past; *corroborated*, backed the truth of the statement; *ominously*, in a threatening manner.

GYPSIES

Perhaps you have not seen a gypsy band. The gypsies used to roam about the country in covered wagons, camping by the road-side for a day or two, and then moving on to another camping site. The men traded horses, and the women sold laces, baskets, and trinkets. And there was always a gypsy ready to tell a fortune whenever her palm was crossed with silver! Gypsy fires have always spelled romance.

Last night the gypsies came—
Nobody knows from where.
Where they've gone to nobody knows,
And nobody seems to care!

Between the trees on the old swamp road
I saw them round their fire:
Tattered children and dogs that barked
As the flames leaped high and higher;
There were black-eyed girls in scarlet shawls,
Old folk wrinkled with years,
Men with handkerchiefs round their throats
And silver loops in their ears.
Ragged and red like maple leaves
When frost comes in the fall,
The gypsies stayed but a single night;
In the morning gone were all—
Never a shaggy gypsy dog.
Never a gypsy child;
Only a burnt-out gypsy fire
Where danced that band so wild.

All gone and away,
Who knows where?
Only the wind that sweeps
Maple branches bare.

—Rachel Field

STUDY AND ENJOYMENT

1. You will enjoy this poem more if you fancy the "I" mentioned in line six as a girl or boy who is very interested in, but a little afraid of, gypsies. What does he or she find most fascinating about the gypsies?

2. What two contrasting pictures are presented in this poem? Be sure to catch the brilliant colours in the first picture. Why is "ragged and red like maple leaves when frost comes in the fall" an excellent simile?

3. This is a good selection to memorize. Try repeating it aloud, either as a solo or in chorus.

READ A BOOK

Flint and Feather. By Pauline Johnson. Musson. Narrative poems by an Indian princess of the Mohawk tribe.

The Two Jungle Books. By Rudyard Kipling. Macmillan. Stories of the jungle life of Mowgli, who was adopted by the wolf pack.

The Feet of the Furtive, Red Fox, Kings in Exile and *Thirteen Bears.* By Sir Charles G. D. Roberts. Ryerson. Animal life in the Canadian wilds.

Two Little Savages. By Ernest Thompson Seton. Grosset. This tale is of woodcraft and Indian lore.

Bambi. By Felix Salten. Grosset. The delightful life story of Bambi from the days when he was a timid fawn until he became a powerful stag.

The Adventures of Sajo and Her Beaver People. By Grey Owl. Macmillan. Two Indian children learn of the daily lives of the little People of the forest.

Tom Sawyer. By Mark Twain. Grosset. This idle, thoughtless, mischievous boy has plenty of escapades.

Silver Pennies. Edited by Blanche Jennings Thompson. Macmillan. Modern verse for children.

The Wind in the Willows. By Kenneth Grahame. Scribner. A delightful fantasy about the adventures of Toad, Mole, Ratty and their friends.

Lassie-Come-Home. By Eric Knight. Lippincott. A collie finds her way home at last, after an adventurous trip from northern Scotland.

High Courage. By C. W. Anderson. Macmillan. A fine horse story written especially for girls.

Kak, the Copper Eskimo. By Stefansson and Irwin. Macmillan. The exciting life of the Eskimos.

Rufus Redtail. By Helen Garrett. Macmillan. The story of a hawk.

V

Actors All

Long ago, when the human race was in its childhood, the art of "let's pretend," of dressing up to represent somebody quite different from themselves, was a favourite pastime of primitive peoples. Perhaps it should not be called a pastime, for it was regarded as of such importance as to become the very central act of their religious ceremonies. Out of this primitive religious drama, which was more like dancing and chanting than our drama of today, at length arose in Greece, more than four hundred years before Christ was born, the most noble dramatic performances yet known to man. These great Greek plays were presented in open-air theatres, not unlike modern football stadiums, seating twenty to a hundred thousand spectators.

The Romans borrowed the theatre and its dramas from the Greeks, and developed Greek comedy until it became something like the plays we know today. Then the Romans seemed to get tired of the theatre, and favoured the circus, gladiators fighting, and wild beasts tearing criminals to death.

The early leaders of the Christian Church could see little difference between the Roman theatre and the bloody sports of the Roman arena, and frowned on all theatrical performances as of the devil. But the play-making instinct was too strong. After the fall of Rome, plays and theatres were unknown for nearly a thousand years, and then, suddenly, in the thirteenth century, they began to spring up again. And the interesting thing is, that they began to spring up in the Church which had once banned them completely. Few people in those days could read, and the priests started to put on little plays illustrating the Bible stories.

These religious plays were first presented in the churches and cathedrals, on the altar steps, but soon proved so popular that they were transferred to the steps outside. In time they came to be presented annually at a great religious festival, by the Trade Guilds, as an act of devotion, well-pleasing to the Church. Each guild would take one incident in the Bible, make it into a short play, and present it on a sort of wagon or float, which moved through the streets of the town, stopping at every corner and in front of the houses of the chief citizens. Early morning saw the first wagon pass, with the story of the creation, and Adam and Eve in the Garden of Eden, and twilight brought the last wagon of all, with the play of the Last Judgment. Perhaps as many as fifty floats took part in one of these great dramatic pageants. The competition between the various guilds was keen as to which could present the best play and stage it most elaborately.

In these plays, the main outlines of the Bible stories were closely followed, but whenever possible, minor characters were introduced, who were easily recognized by the delighted audiences as people just like themselves. One of the most delightful plays of this sort was one about the shepherds who came with gifts to the infant Christ, which was played in a town in Yorkshire. Now Yorkshire, then as now, was a great county for sheep-raising, and, being not far from the Scottish border, was doubtless troubled at times by Scottish sheep-stealers. In this play of the adoration of the shepherds, then, these shepherds are made into Yorkshire folk. One grumbles at the weather, another at the high taxes the nobles make them pay, and a third complains that his wife talks too much all the time. They lie down to sleep. Mac, a notorious sheep-stealer, appears on the scene, and makes off with a ewe. They suspect him, and go off to search his house. By a clever trick he succeeds in hiding the sheep, disguising it as a new-born babe, lying in a cradle. The shepherds decide to give the new baby a sixpence, because they have suspected its father unjustly, the sheep is found, and the fat is in the fire. Mac is let off lightly, because the shepherds are so amused at his clever trick, and this part of the play ends with their tossing Mac in a blanket! Tired after their exertions, they lie down to sleep again, to be awakened by a great multitude of the heavenly host, singing "Glory to God in the Highest!" They hasten to Bethlehem, and the last scene shows these simple Yorkshire country-folk offering the child Christ their humble gifts: a ball, a little cap, and a bird in a cage.

Gradually more and more popular material was introduced into these plays, until at last the religious side was forgotten, and a native English drama began to emerge, about the time of Henry VIII. Bands of strolling players, classed by law as "rogues, vagabonds, and masterless men," wandered the country in the summer, presenting plays on temporary out-of-door stages, when and how they could. In the winter, they would stick to the courtyard of an inn in some large city. Some of them would be fortunate enough to get permission to join the household of some great noble, in return for entertaining him and his guests whenever required. There were as yet no regular theatres, or proper "professional" actors. In many villages, however, there seem to have been various amateur attempts at putting on plays, generally modelled on some old half-remembered legend. It is such a troop of amateur actors, with all their ignorance, vanity, and earnestness, that Shakespeare good-naturedly makes fun of in the little play which follows.

The first real theatre in England was built just outside London, in the reign of Queen Elizabeth, who was very fond of plays. It was erected by a carpenter turned actor, James Burbage. James's son afterwards became the most famous actor of his time, and played the leading rôle in most of Shakespeare's plays when first presented. This theatre was built in 1576, when Shakespeare was only twelve years old. It proved so popular, that by the time Shakespeare himself came to London, there were several theatres in existence, and the leading writers of the day were developing the art of writing plays. By the time Shakespeare was thirty, he was acknowledged as the greatest dramatist England had yet seen. He is still, after more than three hundred years, our greatest dramatist, perhaps the greatest writer the world has ever known.

The stage where Shakespeare's plays were first acted was very different from ours. There was no "picture frame" and curtain between actors and audience, and the main stage was a bare platform projecting into the midst of the spectators. At the back was an inner stage, which could be curtained off. The theatre was open to the sky, and performances took place in the afternoons. There was no painted scenery. Instead, the spectators were invited to use their imaginations. Our Elizabethan ancestors could make an enchanted wood out of a bare platform, for it was a glorious game of "Let's Pretend!" as the theatre should be. To change from the wood to Theseus' palace, the curtains on the inner stage were pulled aside, and there was a throne. A throne meant a palace, and there you were! The players' costumes were elaborate and colourful, and as the marriage celebrations of Theseus and his bride proceeded, the stage must have been a succession of dazzling pictures. With the aid of a few properties: a throne, a stump, a "grassy bank," was created that magic wood, still ready to cast its spell on us. There is only one thing requisite: imagination.

Today we have Dominion Drama Festivals in which hundreds of teams compete, from Vancouver to Halifax; every big city has its theatres and movie houses. Scores

of new plays are produced every year, hundreds of movies.
How many of them would we want to see twice? How
many would our grandchildren be likely to see? And yet
I am very sure that our grandchildren, and our grandchildren's children, will still be seeing and enjoying the
plays of William Shakespeare.

—*W. S. Milne*

THE COMEDY OF PYRAMUS AND THISBE

This play is taken from Shakespeare's *A Midsummer Night's Dream*.
In order to get the comedy in its proper setting, you might read Charles
and Mary Lamb's account of *A Midsummer Night's Dream* in their
Tales from Shakespeare.

Theseus, Duke of Athens, is marrying Hippolyta, Queen of the
Amazons. Philostrate, Master of the Revels for Theseus, is arranging
for an evening's entertainment in honour of the marriage. For this
programme the tradesmen of the town, "hard-handed men that work in
Athens here, which never laboured in their minds till now," decide to
put on a play. They choose the romance of *Pyramus and Thisbe* as a
theme well suited to the pleasure of lords and ladies. The courtiers
find the comedy amusing because the tradesmen take the play very seriously, although they act it in a ridiculous way.

In Scene I, the tradesmen are rehearsing in town. In Scene II,
the rehearsal continues in a nearby wood, where Puck, a mischievous
sprite, puts an ass's head on Bottom. In Scene III, the tradesmen make
final preparations for the play, Bottom having returned, free of the
ass's head. In Scene IV, the play is presented before the Duke and
Duchess and two other newly married couples—Lysander and Hermia,
and Demetrius and Helena.

PYRAMUS AND THISBE

Pyramus and Thisbe is a very old story. If you know it, you will
better understand the tradesmen's play. One version, from *Old Greek
Folk Stories Told Anew* by Josephine Peabody, is as follows:

There once lived in Babylonia two lovers named Pyramus and Thisbe,
who were parted by a strange mischance. For they lived in adjoining
houses; and although their parents had forbidden them to marry, these
two had found a means of talking together through a crevice in the wall.

Here, again and again, Pyramus on his side of the wall and Thisbe
on hers, they would meet to tell each other all that had happened during
the day, and to complain of their cruel parents. At length they decided
that they would endure it no longer, but that they would leave their homes

and be married, come what might. They planned to meet, on a certain evening, by a mulberry tree near the tomb of King Ninus, outside the city gates. Once safely met, they were resolved to brave fortune together.

So far all went well. At the appointed time, Thisbe, heavily veiled, managed to escape from home unnoticed, and after a stealthy journey through the streets of Babylon, she came to a grove of mulberries near the tomb of Ninus. The place was deserted, and once there she put off the veil from her face to see if Pyramus waited anywhere among the shadows. She heard the sound of a footfall and turned to behold—not Pyramus, but a creature unwelcome to any tryst—none other than a lioness crouching to drink from a pool hard by.

Without a cry, Thisbe fled, dropping her veil as she ran. She found a hiding place among the rocks at some distance, and there she waited, not knowing what else to do.

The lioness, having quenched her thirst after some ferocious meal, turned from the spring and, coming upon the veil, sniffed at it curiously, tore and tossed it with her reddened jaws—as she would have done with Thisbe herself—then dropped the plaything and crept away to the forest once more.

It was but a little after this that Pyramus came hurrying to the meeting place, breathless with eagerness to find Thisbe and tell her what had delayed him. He found no Thisbe there. For a moment he was confounded. Then he looked about for some sign of her, some footprint by the pool. There was the trail of a wild beast in the grass, and nearby a woman's veil, torn and stained with blood! He caught it up, and knew it for Thisbe's!

So she had come at the appointed hour, true to her word; she had waited there for him alone and defenceless, and she had fallen a prey to some beast from the jungle! As these thoughts rushed upon the young man's mind, he could endure no more.

"Was it to meet me, Thisbe, that you came to such a death!" cried he. "And I followed all too late. But I will atone. Even now I come lagging, but by no will of mine!"

So saying, the poor youth drew his sword and fell upon it, there at the foot of that mulberry tree which he had named as the trysting-place, and his life-blood ran about the roots.

During these moments, Thisbe, hearing no sound and a little reassured, had stolen from her hiding-place and was come to the edge of the grove. She saw that the lioness had left the spring, and, eager to show her lover that she dared all things to keep faith, she came slowly, little by little, back to the mulberry tree.

She found Pyramus there, according to his promise. His own sword was in his heart, the empty scabbard by his side, and in his hand he held her veil still clasped. Thisbe saw these things as in a dream, and suddenly the truth awoke her. She saw the piteous mischance of all;

and when the dying Pyramus opened his eyes and fixed them upon her, her heart broke. With the same sword she stabbed herself, and the lovers died together.

There the parents found them, after a weary search, and they were buried together in the same tomb. But the berries of the mulberry tree turned red that day, and red they have remained ever since.

SCENE I. *Athens.* QUINCE'S *House.*
Enter QUINCE, SNUG, BOTTOM, FLUTE, SNOUT, *and*
STARVELING.

QUINCE: Is all our company here?

BOTTOM: You were best to call them generally, man by man, according to the scrip.

QUINCE: Here is the scroll of every man's name, which is thought fit, through all Athens, to play in our interlude before the Duke and Duchess, on his wedding-day at night.

BOTTOM: First, good Peter Quince, say what the play treats on; then read the names of the actors, and so grow to a point.

QUINCE: Marry, our play is, The most lamentable comedy, and most cruel death of Pyramus and Thisby.

BOTTOM: A very good piece of work, I assure you, and a merry. Now, good Peter Quince, call forth your actors by the scroll. Masters, spread yourselves.

QUINCE: Answer as I call you. Nick Bottom, the weaver.

BOTTOM: Ready. Name what part I am for, and proceed.

QUINCE: You, Nick Bottom, are set down for Pyramus.

BOTTOM: What is Pyramus? a lover or a tyrant?

QUINCE: A lover, that kills himself most gallant for love.

BOTTOM: That will ask some tears in the true performing of it. If I do it, let the audience look to their eyes; I will move storms; I will condole in some measure. To the rest:

—yet my chief humour is for a tyrant; I could play Ercles rarely, or a part to tear a cat in, to make all split.

> *The raging rocks*
> *And shivering shocks*
> *Shall break the locks*
>   *Of prison-gates;*
> *And Phibbus' car*
> *Shall shine from far,*
> *And make and mar*
>   *The foolish Fates.*

This was lofty!   Now name the rest of the players.   This is Ercles' vein, a tyrant's vein; a lover is more condoling.

QUINCE: Francis Flute, the bellows-mender.

FLUTE: Here, Peter Quince.

QUINCE: Flute, you must take Thisby on you.

FLUTE: What is Thisby? a wandering knight?

QUINCE: It is the lady that Pyramus must love.

FLUTE: Nay, faith, let not me play a woman; I have a beard coming.

QUINCE: That's all one: you shall play it in a mask, and you may speak as small as you will.

BOTTOM: If I may hide my face, let me play Thisby too! I'll speak in a monstrous little voice, *Thisne, Thisne; Ah! Pyramus, my lover dear! thy Thisby dear, and lady dear!*

QUINCE: No, no, you must play Pyramus: and, Flute, you Thisby.

BOTTOM: Well, proceed.

QUINCE: Robin Starveling, the tailor.

STARVELING: Here, Peter Quince.

QUINCE: Robin Starveling, you must play Thisby's mother.—Tom Snout, the tinker.

SNOUT: Here, Peter Quince.

QUINCE: You, Pyramus' father; myself, Thisby's father.

Snug, the joiner, you the lion's part; and, I hope, here is a play fitted.

SNUG: Have you the lion's part written? pray you, if it be, give it me, for I am slow of study.

QUINCE: You may do it extempore, for it is nothing but roaring.

BOTTOM: Let me play the lion too: I will roar, that I will do any man's heart good to hear me; I will roar, that I will make the Duke say, *Let him roar again, let him roar again.*

QUINCE: If you should do it too terribly, you would fright the Duchess and the ladies, that they would shriek; and that were enough to hang us all.

ALL: That would hang us, every mother's son.

BOTTOM: I grant you, friends, if you should fright the ladies out of their wits, they would have no more discretion but to hang us: but I will aggravate my voice so, that I will roar you as gently as any sucking dove; I will roar you as if 'twere any nightingale.

QUINCE: You can play no part but Pyramus; for Pyramus is a sweet-faced man; a proper man, as one shall see in a summer's day; a most lovely, gentleman-like man: therefore you must needs play Pyramus.

BOTTOM: Well, I will undertake it.   What beard were I best to play in?

QUINCE: Why, what you will.

BOTTOM: I will discharge it in either your straw-colour beard, your orange-tawny beard, your purple-in-grain beard, or your French-crown-colour beard, your perfect yellow.

QUINCE: Masters, here are your parts: and I am to entreat you, request you, and desire you, to con them by tomorrow night; and meet me in the palace wood, a mile without the town, by moonlight: there will we rehearse; for if we meet in the city, we shall be dogged with company, and our devices known.   In the meantime, I will draw a bill of properties, such as our play wants.   I pray, you, fail me not.

BOTTOM: We will meet; and there we will rehearse most courageously.   Take pains; be perfect; adieu.   [*Exeunt.*

SCENE II.   *The Wood.*   TITANIA, *the Fairy Queen, lying asleep.*

Enter QUINCE, SNUG, BOTTOM, FLUTE, SNOUT, *and* STARVELING.

BOTTOM: Are we all met?

QUINCE: Pat, pat; and here's a marvellous convenient place for our rehearsal.   This green plot shall be our stage, this hawthorn-brake our tiring-house; and we will do it in action as we will do it before the Duke.

BOTTOM: Peter Quince—

QUINCE: What sayest thou, bully Bottom?

BOTTOM: There are things in this comedy of *Pyramus and Thisby* that will never please.   First, Pyramus must draw a sword to kill himself; which the ladies cannot abide. How answer you that?

SNOUT: By'r lakin, a parlous fear.

STARVELING: I believe we must leave the killing out, when all is done.

BOTTOM: Not a whit: I have a device to make all well. Write me a prologue; and let the prologue seem to say, we will do no harm with our swords and that Pyramus is not killed indeed; and for the more better assurance, tell them that I Pyramus am not Pyramus, but Bottom, the weaver; this will put them out of fear.

QUINCE: Well, we will have such a prologue.

SNOUT: Will not the ladies be afeared of the lion?

STARVELING: I fear it, I promise you.

BOTTOM: Masters, you ought to consider with your-selves: to bring in—God shield us!—a lion among ladies is a most dreadful thing; for there is not a more fearful wild-fowl than your lion living; and we ought to look to it.

SNOUT: Therefore another prologue must tell he is not a lion.

BOTTOM: Nay, you must name his name, and half his face must be seen through the lion's neck; and he himself must speak through, saying thus, or to the same defect,—"Ladies,"—or "Fair Ladies,—I would wish you,"—or "I would request you,"—or "I would entreat you,—not to fear, not to tremble: my life for yours. If you think I come hither as a lion, it were pity of my life: no, I am no such thing; I am a man as other men are"; and there indeed let him name his name, and tell them plainly he is Snug the joiner.

QUINCE: Well, it shall be so. But there is two hard things; that is, to bring the moonlight into a chamber; for, you know, Pyramus and Thisby meet by moonlight.

SNOUT: Doth the moon shine that night we play our play?

BOTTOM: A calendar, a calendar! Look in the almanac; find out moonshine, find out moonshine.

QUINCE: Yes, it doth shine that night.

BOTTOM: Why, then may you leave a casement of the great chamber window, where we play, open, and the moon may shine in at the casement.

QUINCE: Ay; or else one must come in with a bush of thorns and a lanthorn, and say he comes to disfigure, or to present, the person of moonshine. Then, there is another thing: we must have a wall in the great chamber; for Pyramus and Thisby, says the story, did talk through the chink of a wall.

SNOUT: You can never bring in a wall. What say you, Bottom?

BOTTOM: Some man or other must present Wall: and let him have some plaster, or some loam, or some rough-cast about him, to signify wall; and let him hold his fingers thus, and through that cranny shall Pyramus and Thisby whisper.

QUINCE: If that may be, then all is well. Come sit down, every mother's son, and rehearse your parts. Pyramus, you begin: when you have spoken your speech, enter into that brake; and so every one according to his cue.

Enter PUCK *behind.*
(PUCK is a mischief-working elf.)

PUCK: What hempen home-spuns have we swaggering here,
  So near the cradle of the Fairy Queen?
  What! a play toward! I'll be an auditor;
  And actor too, perhaps, if I see cause.

QUINCE: Speak. Pyramus, Thisby, stand forth.

BOTTOM: *Thisby, the flowers of odious savours sweet,—*

QUINCE: Odours, odours.

BOTTOM: *—odours savours sweet;*
  So doth thy breath, my dearest Thisby dear,
  But hark, a voice! stay thou but here a while,
   And by and by I will to thee appear. [*Exit.*

PUCK: A stranger Pyramus than e'er played here. [*Exit*

FLUTE: Must I speak now?

QUINCE: Ay, marry, must you; for you must understand he goes but to see a noise that he heard, and is to come again.

FLUTE: *Most radiant Pyramus, most lily-white of hue,*
  Of colour like the red rose on triumphant brier,
  Most brisky juvenal and eke most lovely Jew,
  As true as truest horse that yet would never tire,
  I'll meet thee, Pyramus, at Ninny's tomb.

QUINCE: "Ninus' tomb," man: why you must not speak

that yet; that you answer to Pyramus: you speak all your part at once, cues and all.—Pyramus, enter: your cue is past; it is, *never tire.*

FLUTE: O,—*As true as truest horse, that yet would never tire.*

Re-enter PUCK, *and* BOTTOM *with an ass's head.*

BOTTOM: *If I were fair, Thisby, I were only thine.*

QUINCE: O monstrous! O strange! we are haunted. Pray masters! fly, masters! Help!

[*Exeunt* QUINCE, SNUG, FLUTE, SNOUT, *and* STARVELING.

PUCK: I'll follow you, I'll lead you about around.

> Through bog, through bush, through brake, through brier:
> Sometimes a horse I'll be, sometimes a hound,
> A hog, a headless bear, sometimes a fire;
> And neigh, and bark, and grunt, and roar and burn,
> Like horse, hound, hog, bear, fire, at every turn.

[*Exit.*

BOTTOM: Why do they run away? this is knavery of them to make me afeard.

Re-enter SNOUT.

SNOUT: O Bottom, thou art changed! what do I see on thee?

BOTTOM: What do you see? you see an ass-head of your own, do you?

[*Exit* SNOUT.

Re-enter QUINCE.

QUINCE: Bless thee, Bottom. Bless thee! thou art translated.

[*Exit.*

BOTTOM: I see their knavery: this is to make an ass of me; to fright me if they could. But I will not stir from this place, do what they can: I will walk up and down here, and I will sing, that they shall hear that I am not afraid.

[*Sings.*

> *The ousel cock so black of hue,*
> *With orange-tawny bill,*
> *The throstle with his note so true,*
> *The wren with little quill.*

SCENE III.—*Athens.*   QUINCE'S *House*
Enter QUINCE, FLUTE, SNOUT, *and* STARVELING.

QUINCE: Have you sent to Bottom's house? is he come home yet?

STARVELING: He cannot be heard of.   Out of doubt he is transported.

FLUTE: If he come not, then the play is marred: it goes not forward, doth it?

QUINCE: It is not possible; you have not a man in all Athens able to discharge Pyramus but he.

FLUTE: No, he has simply the best wit in any handi-craft man in Athens.

QUINCE: Yea, and the best person too; and he is a very paramour for a sweet voice.

FLUTE: You must say "paragon": a paramour is, God bless us, a thing of naught.

Enter SNUG.

SNUG: Masters, the Duke is coming from the temple, and there is two or three lords and ladies more married: if our sport had gone forward, we had all been made men.

FLUTE: O sweet bully Bottom!   Thus hath he lost six-pence a day during his life; he could not have 'scaped sixpence a day: if the Duke had not given him sixpence a day for playing Pyramus, I'll be hanged; he would have deserved it: sixpence a day in Pyramus, or nothing.

Enter BOTTOM.

BOTTOM: Where are these lads? where are these hearts?

QUINCE: Bottom! O most courageous day! O most happy hour!

BOTTOM: Masters, I am to discourse wonders: but ask me not what; for if I tell you, I am no true Athenian. I will tell you everything, right as it fell out.

QUINCE: Let us hear, Bottom.

BOTTOM: Not a word of me. All that I will tell you is, that the Duke hath dined. Get your apparel together, good strings to your beards, new ribbons to your pumps; meet presently at the palace; every man look o'er his part; for the short and the long is, our play is preferred. In any case, let Thisby have clean linen; and let not him that plays the lion pare his nails, for they shall hang out for the lion's claws. And, most dear actors, eat no onions or garlic, for we are to utter sweet breath; and I do not doubt but to hear them say, it is a sweet comedy. No more words; away! go, away! *[Exeunt.*

SCENE IV.—*Athens. The palace of* THESEUS.
Enter THESEUS, HIPPOLYTA, LYSANDER, PHILOSTRATE,
DEMETRIUS, HERMIA, HELENA, *Lords and Attendants.*

PHILOSTRATE: So please Your Grace, the Prologue is address'd.

THESEUS: Let him approach. *[Flourish of trumpets.*
Enter QUINCE *for the Prologue.*

QUINCE: *If we offend, it is with our good will.*
   That you should think, we come not to offend,
   But with good will. To show our simple skill,
   That is the true beginning of our end.
   Consider then we come but in despite.
   We do not come as minding to content you,
   Our true intent is. All for your delight.
   We are not here. That you should here repent you,
   The actors are at hand and by their show
   You shall know all that you are like to know.

THESEUS: This fellow doth not stand upon points.

LYSANDER: He hath rid his prologue like a rough colt;
he knows not the stop.   A good moral, my lord; it is not
enough to speak, but to speak true.

THESEUS: Who is next?

Enter PYRAMUS, *and* THISBE, WALL, MOONSHINE, *and* LION.

QUINCE: *Gentles, perchance you wonder at this show;*
 But wonder on, till truth make all things plain.
 This man is Pyramus, if you would know;
  This beauteous lady Thisbe, is certain.
 This man, with lime and rough-cast, doth present
  Wall, that vile Wall which did these lovers sunder;
 And through Wall's chink, poor souls, they are content
  To whisper, at the which let no man wonder.
 This man, with lanthorn, dog and bush of thorn,
  Presenteth Moonshine; for, if you will know,
 By moonshine did these lovers think no scorn
  To meet at Ninus' tomb, there, there to woo.
 This grisly beast, which Lion hight by name,
 The trusty Thisby, coming first by night,
 Did scare away, or rather did affright;
 And, as she fled, her mantle she did fall,
  Which Lion vile with bloody mouth did stain.
 Anon comes Pyramus, sweet youth and tall,
  And finds his trusty Thisbe's mantle slain:
 Whereat, with blade, with bloody blameful blade,
  He bravely broached his boiling bloody breast;
 And Thisby, tarrying in mulberry shade,
 His dagger drew, and died.   For all the rest,
 Let Lion, Moonshine, Wall, and lovers twain
  At large discourse, while here do they remain.

  [*Exeunt* PROLOGUE, THISBE, LION *and* MOONSHINE.

THESEUS: I wonder if the lion be to speak.

DEMETRIUS: No wonder, my lord: one lion may when
many asses do.

WALL: *In this same interlude it doth befall.*
That I, one Snout by name, present a wall;
Through which the lovers, Pyramus and Thisby,
Did whisper very often secretly.
This loam, this rough-cast and this stone doth show
That I am that same wall; the truth is so:
And this the cranny is, right and sinister,
Through which the fearful lovers are to whisper.

THESEUS: Would you desire lime and hair to speak better?

DEMETRIUS: It is the wittiest partition that I ever heard discourse, my lord.

Enter PYRAMUS.

THESEUS: Pyramus draws near the wall: silence!

PYRAMUS: *O grim-look'd night! O night with hue so black!*
O night which ever art when day is not!
O night, O night! alack, alack, alack,
I fear my Thisby's promise is forgot!
And thou, O wall, O sweet, O lovely wall,
That stand'st between her father's ground and mine!
Thou wall, O wall, O sweet and lovely wall,
Show me thy chink, to blink through with mine eye.

[WALL *holds up his fingers.*

Thanks, courteous wall: Jove shield thee well for this.
But what see I? No Thisby do I see.
O wicked wall, through whom I see no bliss!
Cursed be thy stones for thus deceiving me!

THESEUS: The wall, methinks, being sensible, should curse again.

PYRAMUS: Yonder she comes.

Enter THISBE.

THISBE: *O wall, full often thou hast heard my moans,*
For parting my fair Pyramus and me!
My cherry lips have often kissed thy stones,
Thy stones with lime and hair knit up in thee.

PYRAMUS: *I see a voice; now will I to the chink,*
To spy, and I can hear my Thisby's face.
Thisby!

THISBE: *My love, thou art my love, I think.*

PYRAMUS: *Think what thou wilt, I am thy lover's grace;*
And, like Limander, am I trusty still.

THISBE: *And I like Helen, till the fates me kill.*

PYRAMUS: *O, kiss me through the hole of this vile wall!*

THISBE: *I kiss the wall's hole, not your lips at all.*

PYRAMUS: *Wilt thou at Ninny's tomb meet me straightway?*

THISBE: *'Tide life, 'tide death, I come without delay.*

[*Exeunt* PYRAMUS *and* THISBE.

WALL: *Thus have I, Wall, my part discharged so:*
And, being done, thus Wall away doth go. [*Exit.*

HIPPOLYTA: This is the silliest stuff that ever I heard.

THESEUS: The best in this kind are but shadows; and the worst are no worse, if imagination amend them.

HIPPOLYTA: It must be your imagination, then, and not theirs.

THESEUS: If we imagine no worse of them than they of themselves, they may pass for excellent men. Here come two noble beasts in, a man and a lion.

Enter LION *and* MOONSHINE.

LION: *You ladies, you, whose gentle hearts do fear*
The smallest monstrous mouse that creeps on floor,
Now may perchance both quake and tremble here,
When lion rough in wildest rage doth roar.
Then know that I, one Snug, the joiner, am
A lion fell, nor else no lion's dam;
For, if I should as lion come in strife
Into this place, 'twere pity on my life.

THESEUS: A very gentle beast, and good of conscience.

DEMETRIUS: The very best as a beast, my lord, that e'er I saw.

THESEUS: Let us listen to the Moon.

MOON: *This lanthorn doth the horned moon present;—*

DEMETRIUS: He should have worn the horns on his head.

MOON: *This lanthorn doth the horned moon present;—*
Myself the man in the moon do seem to be.

THESEUS: This is the greatest error of all the rest: the man should be put into the lanthorn. How is it else the man i' the moon?

DEMETRIUS: He dares not come there for the candle.

HIPPOLYTA: I am weary of this moon: would he would change!

LYSANDER: Proceed, Moon.

MOON: All that I have to say, is, to tell you that the lanthorn is the moon; I, the man in the moon; this thorn bush, my thorn-bush; this dog, my dog.

DEMETRIUS: Why, all these should be in the lanthorn; for all these are in the moon. But, silence! here comes Thisby.   *Enter* THISBE.

THISBE: *This is old Ninny's tomb.   Where is my love?*

LION (*roaring*): *Oh—*   [THISBE *runs off.*

DEMETRIUS: Well roared, Lion.

THESEUS: Well run, Thisby.

HIPPOLYTA: Well shone, Moon.   Truly the moon shines with a good grace. [*The* LION *shakes* THISBE's *mantle, and exit.*

THESEUS: Well moused, Lion.

LYSANDER: And so the lion vanished.

DEMETRIUS: And then came Pyramus.

Enter PYRAMUS.

PYRAMUS: *Sweet Moon, I thank thee for thy sunny beams;*
I thank thee, Moon, for shining now so bright;
For, by thy gracious, golden, glittering gleams,
I trust to take of truest Thisby sight.
   But stay, O spite!
   But mark, poor knight,
What dreadful dole is here!
Eyes, do you see?
   How can it be?
O dainty duck! O dear!
   Thy mantle good,
   What, stained with blood!
Approach, ye Furies fell!
   O Fates, come, come,
   Cut thread and thrum;
Quail, crush, conclude, and quell!

THESEUS: This passion, and the death of a dear friend,
would go near to make a man look sad.

PYRAMUS: *O wherefore, Nature, didst thou lions frame?*
Since lion vile hath here deflower'd my dear:
Which is—no, no—which was the fairest dame
That lived, that loved, that liked, that look'd with cheer.
   Come, tears, confound;
   Out, sword, and wound.
   Thus die I, thus, thus, thus.   [*Stabs himself.*
   Now am I dead,
   Now am I fled;
My soul is in the sky:
   Tongue, lose thy light;
   Moon, take thy flight;   [*Exit* MOONSHINE.
Now, die, die, die, die, die.   [*Dies.*

LYSANDER: He is dead; he is nothing.

THESEUS: With the help of a surgeon he might yet
recover, and prove an ass.

HIPPOLYTA: How chance Moonshine is gone before
Thisbe comes back and finds her lover?

THESEUS: She will find him by starlight. Here she comes, and her passion ends the play.

Re-enter THISBE.

HIPPOLYTA: Methinks she should not use a long one for such a Pyramus: I hope she will be brief.

DEMETRIUS: A mote will turn the balance, which Pyramus, which Thisbe, is the better; he for a man, God warrant us; she for a woman, Gold bless us.

LYSANDER: She hath spied him already with those sweet eyes.

THISBE: *Asleep, my love?*
    What, dead, my dove?
  O Pyramus, arise!
    Speak, speak.   Quite dumb?
    Dead, dead?   A tomb
Must cover thy sweet eyes.
    These lily lips,
    This cherry nose,
These yellow cowslip cheeks,
    Are gone, are gone:
    Lovers, make moan:
His eyes were green as leeks.
    O sisters, three,
    Come, come to me,
With hands as pale as milk;
    Lay them in gore,
    Since you have shore
With shears his thread of silk.
    Tongue, not a word:
    Come, trusty sword:
Come, blade, my breast imbrue:

      [*Stabs herself with the sword of* PYRAMUS.

    And farewell, friends;
    Thus, Thisby ends:
Adieu, adieu, adieu.

THESEUS: Moonshine and Lion are left to bury the dead.

DEMETRIUS: Ay, and Wall too.

BOTTOM (*starting up*): No, I assure you; the wall is down that parted their fathers. Will it please you to see the epilogue, or to hear a Bergomask dance between two of your company?

THESEUS: No epilogue, I pray you; for your play needs no excuse. Never excuse; for when the players are all dead, there need none to be blamed. Marry, if he that writ it had played Pyramus and hanged himself in Thisbe's garter, it would have been a fine tragedy; and so it is, truly; and very notably discharged. But come, your Bergomask: let your epilogue alone.

[*They dance the Bergomask, and then retire.*

The iron tongue of midnight hath told twelve:
Lovers, to bed: 'tis almost fairy time.
I fear we shall outsleep the coming morn
As much as we this night have overwatched.
This palpable-gross play hath well beguiled.
The heavy gait of night. Sweet friends, to bed.
A fortnight hold we this solemnity,
In nightly revels and new jollity.

[THESEUS *and* HIPPOLYTA *mount the staircase;* LYSANDER *and* HERMIA, DEMETRIUS *and* HELENA, *and all the rest follow them, leaving the great chamber deserted, except for the guttering candles.*

—*William Shakespeare*

STUDY AND ENJOYMENT

1. A play is not a play until it is acted before an audience. Even reading the parts aloud in front of the class is better than nothing. If you can act it, then the play will really come to life. Remember that the secret of the successful playing of Bottom and his friends is to show that they took themselves very seriously. The more seriously they do the "lamentable comedy" of Pyramus and Thisbe, the funnier it will be to the audience. Theseus and his friends are, of course, highly amused at the efforts of the workmen, but they are too truly gentlemen to hurt the actors' feelings by ridicule.

2. Bully Bottom is a striking picture of the stage-struck amateur, who wants to play all the principal parts, and boss everybody. Is he likeable in spite of his faults, or is he likeable because of these little weaknesses?

3. *Glossary: Marry*, indeed, in truth; *Ercles*, Hercules; *have a beard coming*, Flute knew that boys took women's parts in plays in those days, but he felt he was too old for such parts; *Phibbus*, Phoebus was the Sun; *tiring house*, dressing-room or "attiring" place; *by'r lakin*, "By our lady-kin!"; *Ninus*, Ninus founded Nineveh; *Limander and Helen*, Hero and Leander; *Furies*, three female demons who tormented men; *Fates*, three sisters—goddesses of destiny.

4. There may be other words and expressions in the play that may be strange to you. Make a list of them, and ask the teacher to help explain them. Don't worry too much about them, though. You can get the fun of the play without understanding every word. Bottom and his friends use a good many words that they plainly do not understand.

5. You will notice that this play does not give much information as to how the characters looked, and what they did. The action of players is called "business" by professional actors. When you act one of these parts, you should have a lot of fun thinking up business: how he stands, what he does with his hands, when and how he sits down, and so on.

6. There are a great many books on how to put on plays. Perhaps the two most useful to you would be: *Shakespeare for Community Players*, and *The School Theatre*, both by Mr. Roy Mitchell. They should be in the school library.

BOOKWORMS DON'T HAVE TO BITE

Characters

MARY, *who came because she was told to.*
BOOKWORM, *who decided to be a butterfly instead.*
JO MARCH, *who is very outspoken.*
HEIDI, *who is an illustrated edition.*
ALICE, *who followed a rabbit.*
CHORUS, *who are ready to give good advice at any time.*

COSTUMES:

All characters wear modern clothes. Bookworm wears a long flowing green gauze robe with butterfly wings. Book characters may be dressed in everyday clothes, with a cardboard tied back and front telling the name of the book represented.

Bookworms Don't Have to Bite may be produced by amateurs without payment of royalty. Music by Dorothy Anderson will be supplied for 50c. by writing Alberta W. Constant at 1404 North Liberty St., Independence, Mo.

THE PLAY:

The curtain opens on scene of a library reading room. Around one table is seated the CHORUS *with open books before them, reading busily. Enter* MARY. *She looks around, picks up a book, and glances at it. She puts the book down, picks up another, and then says aloud. . . .*

MARY: Well, I guess I've seen all there is to see. Teacher said for me to come to the library and here I am. Now I can go home and have some fun.

[*Starts to go but drops book with a bang and knocks over a chair.*

CHORUS (*looks up from reading*): Sh . . . Sh . . . Shshsh.

MARY: What's that?

CHORUS (*stands up and points at Mary*): Sh . . . Sh . . . Shshsh.

MARY: Oh, you said "Sh." What for?

CHORUS (*recites in a sing-song rhythm*):

> This is the Reading Room,
> So please be quiet as a mouse.
> This is the Reading Room,
> The best room in the house.
> If you will just turn a page,
> No matter what your job or age,
> We guarantee that we'll engage,
> Your interest to the last.
> For all these books are full of tales,
> Think of it, tales by the bales,
> You'll weep in quarts and laugh in gales,
> Before the day is past. For . . .
> This is the Reading Room,
> So please be quiet as a mouse.
> This is the Reading Room,
> The best room in the house.
> The Reading Room, the Reading Room
> Be quiet as a . . .

MARY (*screams*): Mouse! (*Jumps on a chair and points at the floor.*) Goodness gracious, they told me this was the library, not the zoo.

1ST CHORUS MEMBER: Oh, don't bother about him. He just jumped out of *Wind in the Willows* because *The Cat Who Went to Heaven* was put next to him by mistake. He'll go back when they arrange the shelves.

2ND CHORUS MEMBER: He's looking in the *Che* volume of the encyclopedia to find some cheese for a little lunch.

3RD CHORUS MEMBER: What are you looking so surprised about? Mice love cheese, you know.

MARY: It's just that I had no idea a library was such a lively place.

4TH CHORUS MEMBER: Lively? It's the liveliest place in the world.

5TH CHORUS MEMBER: Just think of all the people in it. And they come from every place you can think of. Why there must be a million people here . . . and all properly accessioned, too.

6TH CHORUS MEMBER: And catalogued and alphabetized; the very best people.

MARY: People? They're nothing but a pack of books and I hate books.

CHORUS (*turning to look at one another with astonishment. Recite*):

> She hates books,
> Why the poor little thing!
> She hates books,
> Put her head in a sling.
> There is one thing that will right her,
> We must let the Bookworm bite her,
> Then perhaps she'll be politer,
> And she'll change and sing . . .

"I love books,
I love the tales I read.
I love books,
I really do, indeed.
There is nothing that's more fun,
Than to open at page one,
And read until the tale is done." (*Point at* MARY.)
That is what you need.

MARY: I don't either and I can tell you I don't want any nasty old Bookworm biting me. (*Enter* BOOKWORM.) Well, who are you?

BOOKWORM: Why I'm the Bookworm. I thought I heard somebody mention my name.

MARY: You a Bookworm? You don't look a bit . . . uh . . . wormy. You look more like a butterfly.

BOOKWORM: Well, my dear, handsome is as handsome does in this world, and some worms do turn into butterflies, so I decided to sprout my wings while I could still enjoy them. (*Holds out wings.*) They are rather nice, aren't they?

MARY: Yes, they're very pretty, but tell me . . . do you bite? (*Points to* CHORUS.) They said you did.

BOOKWORM: Only when I get very hungry. I'm quite full just now for I've just been to the graduation exercises of a library school and I've bitten dozens of young librarians. I just couldn't eat another mouthful.

MARY: You sound pretty fierce to me.

BOOKWORM: Not at all. As a matter of fact, I'm just a figure of speech, anyway. If people would stop talking I would wither away. But, of course, they won't stop talking. They never do. I promise on my wings to do no biting here.

MARY: Then I guess you won't hurt me. You won't try to make me like any of those horrid old books, will you?

BOOKWORM: Oh, my, no. In fact, I'm not even sure that they would like you.

MARY: Not like me? Oh, my mother says I'm a very nice little girl and have lovely manners.

BOOKWORM: That doesn't mean you have good book manners.

MARY: Book manners? I never heard of them.

BOOKWORM: Well, it's time you did.

CHORUS (*recites with actions suggested by words*):

> Do you crack us open
> And put us down
> And break our backs
> Without even a frown?
> Do you mark our pages
> And dog our ears
> And never listen to our tears?
> Do you leave us out
> In the wind or rain
> To be reduced to
> Wood pulp again?
> Do you lend us out
> To the friend of a friend,
> That terrible circle
> That has no end?
> If all of these
> You are sure you *don't*
> And furthermore
> You will promise *won't*
> Then good book manners
> You may claim.
> And try to teach
> Your friends the same.

MARY: I never thought about having manners for books. Do they care?

BOOKWORM: Oh, books are very particular people. Library books go all sorts of places and most folks never hear a word out of them, but let me tell you, they have their own opinions.

[*Enter* JO MARCH *wearing cardboard marked* "*Little Women.*"

JO: I should say we do!

MARY: Oh, I didn't know some one had come in.

BOOKWORM: She just stepped out from behind her index for a minute. Mary, this is Jo March who lives in *Little Women.* I'm afraid you'll find her a little outspoken, but she's really a lovely character.

JO: Well, why shouldn't I be outspoken? The last child who took me out kept reading me at the table while she was eating bread and butter. Then she ended by setting a glass of milk on my cover. Just look at my nice brown dress. [*Points to a ring spot on cover.*

MARY: What an ugly mark! Won't it come out?

JO: No. I'll have to keep it till I'm rebound, and goodness knows when that will be with the repair fund what it is.

[*Enter* HEIDI.

HEIDI: Rebinding won't do this any good.

[*Shows torn page.*

BOOKWORM: This seems to be a regular indignation meeting. Mary, this is Heidi. She used to live up in the mountains but now she has gone all over the world she has so many friends.

HEIDI: Please add that I'm an illustrated edition . . . or was. Some child wanted my pictures for paper dolls. Now just look at me.

JO: That's bad, but did you hear about Lamb's *Tales?* Poor fellow, he had his appendix torn out.

HEIDI: Oh my, look at Alice. (*Enter* ALICE *limping*

and bent over.) What is the matter? You look as if you had been thrown through your own looking glass.

ALICE: I feel like it, too. The child who took me out wanted to keep a place to read after supper so she put me face down, mind you, on a chair and sat on me while she was eating. Of course my back was broken.

MARY: Why, this is dreadful! Don't you ever meet any nice children?

JO: Oh, my, yes.

HEIDI: Lots of them.

ALICE: More than the other kind.

JO: But the trouble is that the careless ones make it so hard on the nice ones.

HEIDI: Just think, no other child will get to look at my ·pretty pictures.

ALICE: And I'm not good for much more at all.

JO: And poor Tom Sawyer over there. Just a vacant space on the shelf since somebody left him on the street car.

BOOKWORM: Well, cheer up, all of you or we'll have this little girl in tears. I'm sure she wouldn't do any of these careless things for she wouldn't even take you out. She hates books.

BOOKS (*together*): Hates books? Hates us?

MARY: Oh, no, no, no. I don't hate you. I didn't know you were there. I mean I didn't know you were really in the books. I didn't know you were real people . . . like me.

JO: We're much more real than you and much more famous.

ALICE: And much older.

HEIDI: Let's turn our backs on her.

[BOOKS *all turn backs out towards* MARY.

MARY: Please, please, don't be mad at me. (*Turns to* BOOKWORM *as* BOOKS *refuse to answer and turn up their noses.*) Oh, what shall I do? I wanted to be nice and I've been hateful. What shall I do?

BOOKWORM: Well, in a way it's a trade secret but I suppose I can tell you. If you truly want to win friends and influence book people, just. . . . (*Whispers.*) Ask to look at their first page.

MARY: I'll try. But do you think they will let me? They look so very cross.

BOOKWORM: My dear, no book can resist a chance to be read. Go on, you'll find out.

MARY (*timidly, to* JO): Ah, excuse me, but may I see your first page?   [JO *turns around and so do the others.*

JO: My first page? Why the idea, I thought you didn't like books?

MARY: I guess I didn't know any of the nice ones. But if it's too much trouble never mind.   [*Starts away.*

JO: Here, here, come back a minute. You may not be so bad after all.

HEIDI: Little girl, if you want to see my first page. . . .

ALICE: Or mine. Mine has a rabbit on it.

JO: She asked me first. Just get in line, please. Now young lady, just look at this.

            [*Hands out page of paper.* MARY *reads . . .*

MARY: "Christmas won't be Christmas without any presents. . . ." Oh my, does it begin at Christmas? And didn't you get any presents at all?

JO: It wouldn't be fair to tell but there are lots of other things besides Christmas. Love affairs and trips abroad and plays we put on and even a pair of twins and . . .

HEIDI: All that's very well but about my goat. . . .

ALICE: And speaking of animals . . . my rabbit, cater-
pillar and dormouse and millions . . . well, anyway,
dozens more are very well known. Just look here.

[*Holds out a page.*

MARY (*reads*): ". . . picking daisies when suddenly a
white rabbit with pink eyes ran close by her." Did it
really, quite close?

ALICE: So close I could almost touch him . . . but read
on a way.

MARY (*reads*): "The rabbit actually took a watch out of
his waistcoat pocket." . . . Oh, my. I never heard of
rabbits wearing waistcoats.

ALICE: Neither had I. But that's only half the
story. . . . I followed him down the rabbit hole and there
I found . . .

HEIDI: Look here, Alice. I'm not having half a chance
when mine is much the best story. If you will come with
me I'll take you up instead of down. Who would run
down an old rabbit hole when she could go right up a
mountain.

MARY: A mountain? I've never seen a mountain.

HEIDI: Come with me and you'll see lots more than just
a mountain.

MARY: Oh, Bookworm, may I go with her? I do want
to. I want to go with them all. How in the world can I?

BOOKWORM: Very simple, my dear. Your library card
is your ticket. Your own chair is your seat in the pullman,
and your good book manners (you will remember them,
won't you?) are your welcome.

[*During this speech* HEIDI, JO, *and* ALICE *slip out.*

MARY: Then you mean they will go home with me?
Oh, they've gone, they've gone. And just when I was so
fond of them.

BOOKWORM: Now, now, they've just gone to the desk so that you can check them out in the proper way. You go find them.

MARY: I will! I will! (*Runs towards door. Turns.*) And thank you . . . all of you. Lots and lots.

CHORUS: SHHH . . . SHHH . . . SHHH . . .

> This is the Reading Room,
> So please be quiet as a mouse.
> This is the Reading Room,
> The best place in the house,
> The Reading Room, the Reading Room
> Be quiet as a mouse!
>
> [MARY *leaves on tip-toe, finger on lips during recitation.*

NOTE: *If you have a curtain, close it just as "mouse" is said. If no curtain, have* CHORUS *and* BOOKWORM *tiptoe from room with fingers on lips during the recitation of the* CHORUS.

—Alberta W. Constant

From *Twenty-five Non-royalty Plays for Children*
Compiled by M. Jagendorf. Greenberg, Publisher, Inc., New York

READ A BOOK

Master Skylark. By Burrill Edgar White. A dramatization of the old favourite story of Nicholas.

Toad of Toad Hall. By A. A. Milne. Scribner. Dramatization of *The Wind in the Willows.*

Tales of Shakespeare. By Charles and Mary Lamb. Dent. Many of Shakespeare's plays, retold for children.

Patchwork Plays. By Rachel Field. Doubleday. Five easily produced one-act plays.

Form Room Plays. By Evelyn Smith. Dent. Junior and Intermediate books have a good collection of scenes from well-known books.

Eight Modern Plays. Edited by John Hampden. Nelson. This includes "The Princess and the Woodcutter," by A. A. Milne, "Robin Hood" and "Slippers of Cinderella."

Cameo Plays. Edited by George Holroyd. Macmillan. Books I, II and VII are suitable for Grade VII.

Home is Best

HOMES

Short words may sometimes have long histories, and little words great traditions. Some words quickly grow thin and weak and mean and disappear. Other words there are that gather to themselves richer meanings every day, and are crowned with all the glory of the years. There is no place like home, no word quite so beautiful as *home*.

When the world was young, the savage crept into his dripping cave among the hills, that he might find shelter from the elements and protection from his foes. This burrow among the rocks, floored with moss and festooned with ivy, was home. As time passed, men contrived to take their homes nearer to their work, their hunting and fishing. They built huts of mud and the stocks of young trees, and thatched them with grass or bark. Gathered in the semi-darkness, seated on dank rush mats upon the ground, they shared their meagre meal together and fondly spoke of it as home.

Swarthy nomads, following their flocks and herds to fresh pastures among the eastern hills, raised their tents in the twilight, rested from their roving, and were at home. So, too, the Indian of the Plains set up his teepee. Its walls and roof were the tanned skins of bison, and on them he painted in gaudy colours tribal totems and signs pleasing to his gods. There the redman made his home, never far from the roving multitudes of buffalo which were his food and raiment, his shelter and fortune besides.

On the top of the world, in the land of the midnight sun, the Eskimo makes a habitation with blocks of ice and snow. Huddled together in the igloo, squatting upon fur rugs around the dim light and fitful heat of the oil lamp, they exchange stories of the hunt, keep alive the folk-tales of their race, and sing their primitive "Home, Sweet Home."

The warrior knight built his grim castle a-top a crag, and guarded his hearth with wall and draw-bridge. Rousing tales of tournaments, pious memories of holy pilgrimages, argument of scholar and song of troubadour echoed through the Great Hall. High and low, rich and poor, saint and scholar, knew what it meant, in an uneasy world, for a castle to be a home, and a man's home his castle.

The humble peasant reared his cottage among the sweet-scented fields, that love might sweeten his labour. He would pause a moment to rest his oxen, look toward the roof-tree that sheltered wife and brood, and then turn and till his fields again with fresh courage.

They all called it home.

First a shelter "out of the wind's and the rain's way," then a place of rest and refreshment, by and by a castle and a defence, and later still a sanctuary, and a school for love. So the word "home" has grown.

Look, and you will discern beauty in the word—loveliness gathered from all the happy homes since the world began. Listen, and you will hear music in the word—the laughter of children, the wonder speech of lovers, and the lullabies of all the years. Among all the words our lips can form there is none so radiant, for it has gathered to itself the golden sunlight of the immemorial years. There is no name so strong, for it means father, defence and security, provider and pride of name. And there is none so tender, for it means mother, and the soft, warm curve of her loving arms, unwavering trust, undying compassion, and "the glad sweet face of her."

—Lorne Pierce

STUDY AND ENJOYMENT

1. Words are beautiful to us chiefly on account of the ideas we link with them. What are some of the ideas that the author links with the happy home of today?
2. List six different kinds of homes mentioned in the selection. Which of the six do you think is pictured best? What details and describing words help to make the picture a good one?
3. Select one sentence that sums up how the word "home" has grown.
4. *Great traditions*, noble standards handed down from the past; *elements*, forces of nature, such as wind and rain; *dank*, unpleasantly damp; *meagre*,

poor, scanty; *swarthy*, dark in complexion; *nomads*, members of roving tribes who move from place to place in search of pasture; *bison*, buffalo; *gaudy*, showy; *totems*, images of animals used as emblems; *habitation*, place of abode, home; *sanctuary*, holy place, place of refuge; *discern*, see clearly; *immemorial*, very old, too far back to be remembered; *compassion*, sympathy.

5. The quotation "out of the wind's and the rain's way" is from the poem *An Old Woman of the Roads* by the Irish poet, Padraic Colum. Perhaps a pupil could find the poem and read it to the class. *Home, Sweet Home!* by the American poet John Howard Payne (1791-1852) is another poem worth reading, as most people know only the first of the four stanzas.

PRAYER FOR A LITTLE HOME

God send us a little home
To come back to when we roam.

Low walls and fluted tiles,
Wide windows, a view for miles.

Red firelight and deep chairs,
Small white beds upstairs.

Great talk in little nooks,
Dim colours, rows of books.

One picture on each wall,
Not many things at all.

God send us a little ground,
Tall trees standing round.

Homely flowers in brown sod.
Overhead, thy stars, O God!

—*Author Unknown*

STUDY AND ENJOYMENT

1. A home is a kind of mirror. It reflects the interests of the people who live in it. The mention of the fine view from the wide windows in the second stanza tells us of the author's delight in beauty of landscape. Can you find other interests in each of the other stanzas.

2. *Homely* flowers. What does the adjective "homely" mean here? How has this word come to have less kindly meaning? What are some of the homely flowers in your district?
3. *Fluted* means grooved.
4. The home pictured here is comfortable, it is attractive, but it is simple. How does the poet emphasize this simplicity by (i) the kind of words he uses, (ii) the details he describes, (iii) the colours he mentions?
5. How do the eyes travel in their search for beauty in the last stanza? Why is this stanza a fine conclusion for the poem?

THE HOUSE IN A BOAT

David Copperfield goes with his nurse Peggotty to visit at her brother's home in Yarmouth in the south of England. Ham, Peggotty's nephew, is waiting for them at the public-house. He is a huge strong fellow, who puts David on his back and sets out down lanes, past boat-builders' yards, until he comes out at last upon the sands of the seashore.

"Yon's our house, Master Davy!"

I looked in all directions, as far as I could stare over the wilderness, and away at the sea, and away at the river, but no house could *I* make out. There was a black barge, or some other kind of superannuated boat, not far off, high and dry on the ground, with an iron funnel sticking out of it for a chimney and smoking very cozily, but nothing else in the way of a habitation that was visible to me.

"That's not it?" said I, "that ship-looking thing?"

"That's it, Master Davy," returned Ham.

If it had been Aladdin's Palace, roc's egg and all, I suppose I could not have been more charmed with the romantic idea of living in it. There was a delightful door cut in the side, and it was roofed in, and there were little windows in it; but the wonderful charm of it was, that it was a real boat which had no doubt been upon the water hundreds of times, and which had never been intended to be lived in, on dry land. That was the captivation of it to me. If it had ever been meant to be lived in, I might have thought it small, or inconvenient, or lonely, but never having been designed for any such use, it became a perfect abode.

It was beautifully clean inside, and as tidy as possible. There was a table, and a Dutch clock, and a chest of drawers, and on the chest of drawers there was a tea tray with a painting on it of a lady with a parasol, taking a walk with a military-looking child who was trundling a hoop. The tray was kept from tumbling down by a Bible, and the tray, if it had tumbled down, would have smashed a quantity of cups and saucers and a teapot that were grouped around the book. On the walls there were some common coloured pictures, framed and glazed, of Scripture subjects, such as I have never seen since in the hands of peddlers, without seeing the whole interior of Peggotty's brother's house again, at one view. Abraham in red going to sacrifice Isaac in blue, and Daniel in yellow cast into a den of green lions, were the most prominent of these. Over the little mantel-shelf, was a picture of the *Sarah Jane* lugger, built at Sunderland, with a real little wooden stern stuck on to it; a work of art, combining composition with carpentry, which I considered to be one of the most enviable possessions that the world could afford. There were some hooks in the beams of the ceiling, the use of which I did not divine then; and some lockers and boxes and conveniences of that sort, which served for seats, and eked out the chairs.

All this I saw in the first glance after I crossed the threshold—childlike, according to my theory—and then Peggotty opened a little door and showed me my bedroom. It was the completest and most desirable bedroom ever seen; in the stern of the vessel; with a little window where the rudder used to go through; a little looking-glass, just the right height for me, nailed against the wall, and framed with oyster shells; a little bed which there was just room enough to get into; and a nosegay of seaweed in a blue mug on the table. The walls were whitewashed as white as milk, and the patchwork counterpane made my eyes quite ache with its brightness. One thing I particularly noticed in this delightful house was the smell of fish; which was so searching that when I took out my pocket handkerchief to wipe my nose, I found it smelt exactly as if it had wrapped up a lobster. On my imparting this discovery in confidence to Peggotty, she informed me that her brother dealt in lobsters, crabs, and crawfish; and I afterward found that a heap of these creatures, in a state of wonderful conglomeration with one another, and never leaving off pinching whatever they laid hold of, were usually to be found in a little wooden outhouse where the pots and kettles were kept.

We were welcomed by a very civil woman in a white apron, whom I had seen curtesying at the door when I was on Ham's back, about a quarter of a mile off. Likewise by a most beautiful little girl (or I thought her so) with a necklace of blue beads on, who wouldn't let me kiss her when I offered to, but ran away and hid herself. By and by, when we had dined in a sumptuous manner off boiled dabs, melted butter, and potatoes, with a chop for me, a hairy man with a very good-natured face came home. As he called Peggotty "Lass," and gave her a hearty smack on the cheek, I had no doubt, from the general propriety of her conduct, that he was her brother; and so he turned out: being presently introduced to me as Mr. Peggotty. "Glad to see you, sir," said Mr. Peggotty. "You'll find us rough, sir, but you'll find us ready."

I thanked him, and replied that I was sure I should be happy in such a delightful place.

"How's your ma, sir," said Mr. Peggotty. "Did you leave her pretty jolly?"

I gave Mr. Peggotty to understand that she was as jolly as I could wish, and that she desired her compliments— which was a polite fiction on my part.

"I'm much obleeged to her, I'm sure," said Mr. Peggotty. "Well, sir, if you can make out here, fur a fortnut, 'long wi' her," nodding at his sister, "and Ham, and little Em'ly, we shall be proud of your company."

Having done the honours of his house in this hospitable manner, Mr. Peggotty went out to wash himself in a kettleful of hot water, remarking that "cold would never get *his* muck off." He soon returned, greatly improved in appearance, but so rubicund that I couldn't help thinking his face had this in common with lobsters, crabs, and crawfish: that it went into the hot water very black, and came out very red.

After tea, when the door was shut, and all was made snug (the nights being cold and misty now) it seemed to me the most delicious retreat that the imagination of man could conceive. To hear the wind getting out at sea, to know that the fog was creeping over the desolate flat outside, and to look at the fire, and think that there was no house near but this one, and this one a boat, was like enchantment.

—*Charles Dickens*

STUDY AND ENJOYMENT

1. Why did David find the house so delightful?
2. What do you know, or can you find out, about Aladdin's Palace and the roc's egg?
3. What details in the description of the bedroom make you think of the sea?
4. How can you tell from this selection that David is an observant boy? Test his care in description by sketching the chest of drawers with the objects upon it. What details show us that he notices (i) colour, (ii) the appearance of people, (iii) the way that people act?
5. You will find another selection about David on page 325 of this Reader. The whole story is told in the novel *David Copperfield* by Charles Dickens.

HOW WE KEPT MOTHER'S DAY

When is Mother's Day? In this story it was on a week-day.

Of all the different ideas that have been started lately, I think that the very best is the notion of celebrating once a year "Mother's Day." I don't wonder that May the eleventh is becoming such a popular date all over America and I am sure the idea will spread to England too.

It is especially in a big family like ours that such an idea takes hold. So we decided to have a special celebration of Mother's Day. We thought it a fine idea. It made us all realize how much Mother had done for us for years, and all the efforts and sacrifice that she had made for our sake.

So we decided that we'd make it a great day, a holiday for all the family, and do everything we could to make Mother happy. Father decided to take a holiday from his office, so as to help in celebrating the day, and my sister Anne and I stayed home from college classes, and Mary and my brother Will stayed home from High School.

It was our plan to make it a day just like Christmas or any big holiday, and so we decided to decorate the house with flowers and with mottoes over the mantelpieces, and all that kind of thing. We got Mother to make mottoes and arrange the decorations, because she always does it at Christmas.

The two girls thought it would be a nice thing to dress in our very best for such a big occasion, and so they both got new hats. Mother trimmed both the hats, and they looked fine, and Father had bought four-in-hand silk ties for himself and us boys as a souvenir of the day to remember Mother by. We were going to get Mother a new hat too, but it turned out that she seemed to really like her old grey bonnet better than a new one, and both the girls said that it was awfully becoming to her.

Well, after breakfast we had it arranged as a surprise for Mother that we would hire a motor car and take her for a beautiful drive away into the country. Mother is hardly ever able to have a treat like that, because we can only afford to keep one maid, and so Mother is busy in the house nearly all the time. And of course the country is so lovely now that it would be just grand for her to have a lovely morning, driving for miles and miles.

But on the very morning of the day we changed the plan a little bit, because it occurred to Father that a thing it would be better to do even than to take Mother for a motor drive would be to take her fishing. Father said that as the car was hired and paid for, we might just as well use it for a drive up into hills where the streams are. As Father said, if you just go out driving without any object, you have a sense of aimlessness, but if you are going to fish, there is a definite purpose in front of you to heighten the enjoyment.

So we all felt that it would be nicer for Mother to have a definite purpose; and anyway, it turned out that Father had just got a new rod the day before, which made the idea of fishing all the more appropriate, and he said that Mother could use it if she wanted to; in fact, he said it was practically for her, only Mother said she would much rather watch him fish and not try to fish herself.

So we got everything arranged for the trip, and we got Mother to cut up some sandwiches and make up a sort of lunch in case we got hungry, though of course we were to come back home again to a big dinner in the middle of the day, just like Christmas or New Year's Day. Mother packed it all up in a basket for us ready to go in the motor.

Well, when the car came to the door, it turned out that there hardly seemed as much room in it as we had supposed, because we hadn't reckoned on Father's fishing basket and the rods and the lunch, and it was plain enough that we couldn't all get in.

Father said not to mind him, he said that he could just as well stay home, and that he was sure that he could put in the time working in the garden; he said that there was a lot of rough dirty work that he could do, like digging a trench for the garbage, that would save hiring a man, and so he said that he'd stay home; he said that we were not to let the fact of his not having had a real holiday for three years stand in our way; he wanted us to go right ahead and be happy and have a big day, and not to mind him. He said that he could plug away all day, and in fact he said he'd been a fool to think there'd be any holiday for him.

But of course we all felt that it would never do to let Father stay home, especially as we knew he would make trouble if he did. The two girls, Anne and Mary, would gladly have stayed and helped the maid get dinner, only it seemed such a pity to, on a lovely day like this, having their new hats. But they both said that Mother had only to say the word, and they'd gladly stay home and work. Will and I would have dropped out, but unfortunately we wouldn't have been any use in getting the dinner.

So in the end it was decided that Mother would stay home and just have a lovely restful day round the house, and get the dinner. It turned out anyway that Mother doesn't care for fishing, and also it was just a little bit cold and fresh out of doors, though it was lovely and sunny, and Father was rather afraid that Mother might take cold if she came.

He said he would never forgive himself if he dragged Mother round the country and let her take a severe cold at a time when she might be having a beautiful rest. He said it was our duty to try and let Mother get all the rest and quiet that she could, after all that she had done for all of us, and he said that that was principally why he had fallen in with this idea of a fishing trip, so as to give Mother a little quiet. He said that young people seldom realize how much quiet means to people who are getting old. As to himself, he could still stand the racket, but he was glad to shelter Mother from it.

So we all drove away with three cheers for Mother, and Mother stood and watched us from the veranda for as long as she could see us, and Father waved his hand back to her every few minutes till he hit his hand on the back edge of the car, and then said that he didn't think that Mother could see us any longer.

Well, we had the loveliest day up among the hills that you could possibly imagine, and Father caught such big specimens that he felt sure that Mother couldn't have landed them anyway, if she had been fishing for them, and Will and I fished too, though we didn't get so many as Father, and the two girls met quite a lot of people that they knew as we drove along, and there were some young men friends of theirs that they met along the stream and talked to, and so we all had a splendid time.

It was quite late when we got back, nearly seven o'clock in the evening, but Mother had guessed that we would be late, so she had kept back the dinner so as to have it just nicely ready and hot for us. Only first she had to get towels and soap for Father and clean things for him to put on, because he always gets so messed up with fishing, and that kept Mother busy for a little while, that and helping the girls get ready.

But at last everything was ready, and we sat down to the grandest kind of dinner—roast turkey and all sorts of things like on Christmas Day. Mother had to get up and down a good bit during the meal fetching things back and forward, but at the end Father noticed it and said she simply mustn't do it, that he wanted her to spare herself, and he got up and fetched the walnuts over from the sideboard himself.

The dinner lasted a long while, and was great fun, and when it was over all of us wanted to help clear the things up and wash the dishes, only Mother said that she would really much rather do it, and so we let her, because we wanted just for once to humour her.

It was quite late when it was all over, and when we all kissed Mother before going to bed, she said it had been the most wonderful day in her life, and I think there were tears in her eyes. So we all felt awfully repaid for all that we had done.

—Stephen Leacock
From *Laugh with Leacock*

STUDY AND ENJOYMENT

1. At what point in this story did you first realize that the author is poking fun at the family? What makes the account amusing? What is the most amusing incident?

2. Whom do you like best in the story? Who is the most selfish person? How can you tell that he doesn't know he is selfish? What were some of the tasks that Mother did to make "her day" a success?

3. Plan an informal play giving the conversation on the morning of Mother's Day, when it is decided: (i) to take Mother for a drive; (ii) to take her fishing instead; (iii) to have her pack a lunch; (iv) to leave her at home. How many people will be in the play? Who has the biggest part? After one group has acted the play, talk it over, and then have another group try the acting.

THE KING'S BREAKFAST

The King asked
The Queen, and
The Queen asked
The Dairymaid:
"Could we have some butter for
The Royal slice of bread?"
The Queen asked
The Dairymaid.

The Dairymaid
Said, "Certainly,
I'll go and tell
The cow
Now
Before she goes to bed."

The Dairymaid
She curtsied,
And went and told
The Alderney:
"Don't forget the butter for
The Royal slice of bread."
The Alderney
Said sleepily:
"You'd better tell
His Majesty
That many people nowadays
Like marmalade
Instead."
The Dairymaid
Said, "Fancy!"
And went to
Her Majesty.
She curtsied to the Queen, and
She turned a little red:
"Excuse me,
Your Majesty,
For taking of
The liberty,
But marmalade is tasty, if
It's very
Thickly
Spread."

The Queen said,
"Oh!"
And went to
His Majesty:
"Talking of the butter for
The Royal slice of bread,
Many people
Think that
Marmalade
Is nicer.
Would you like to try a little
Marmalade
Instead?"

The King said,
"Bother!"
And then he said,
"Oh, deary me!"
The King sobbed, "Oh, deary me!"
And went back to bed.
"Nobody,"
He whimpered,
"Could call me
A fussy man:
I *only* want
A little bit
Of butter for
My bread!"

The Queen said,
"There, there!"
And went to
The Dairymaid.
The Dairymaid
Said, "There, there!"
And went to the shed.

The cow said,
"There, there!
I didn't really
Mean it;
Here's milk for his porringer
And butter for his bread."

The Queen took
The butter
And brought it to
His Majesty;
The King said,
"Butter, eh?"
And bounced out of bed.
"Nobody," he said,
As he kissed her
Tenderly,
"Nobody," he said,
As he slid down
The banisters,
"Nobody,
My darling,
Could call me
A fussy man—
BUT
I do like a little bit of butter to my bread!"

—A. A. Milne

STUDY AND ENJOYMENT

1. In what way does Milne create humour in this poem?
2. Select three ridiculous situations from the poem.
3. This is a good poem to act. Choose a narrator and some one to read each part, even the Alderney cow's. Be sure to choose a jolly person to read that part.

IT NEEDS SOME PEOPLE LIVING INSIDE

THE HOUSE WITH NOBODY IN IT

Whenever I walk to Suffern along the Erie track
I go by a poor old farmhouse with its shingles broken and
   black.
I suppose I've passed it a hundred times, but I always stop
   for a minute
And look at the house, the tragic house, the house with
   nobody in it.

I never have seen a haunted house, but I hear there are such
   things;
That they hold the talk of spirits, their mirth and sorrowings.
I know this house isn't haunted, and I wish it were, I do;
For it wouldn't be so lonely if it had a ghost or two.

This house on the road to Suffern needs a dozen panes of
glass,
And somebody ought to weed the walk and take a scythe
to the grass.
It needs new paint and shingles, and the vines should be
trimmed and tied;
But what it needs the most of all is some people living inside.

If I had a lot of money and all my debts were paid
I'd put a gang of men to work with brush and saw and spade.
I'd buy that place and fix it up the way it used to be
And I'd find some people who wanted a home and give it
to them free.

Now, a new house standing empty, with staring window
and door,
Looks idle, perhaps, and foolish, like a hat on its block in
the store.
But there's nothing mournful about it; it cannot be sad
and lone
For the lack of something within it that it has never known.

But a house that has done what a house should do, a house
that has sheltered life,
That has put its loving wooden arms around a man and his
wife,
A house that has echoed a baby's laugh and held up his
stumbling feet,
Is the saddest sight, when it's left alone, that ever your
eyes could meet.

So whenever I go to Suffern along the Erie track
I never go by the empty house without stopping and
looking back,

Yet it hurts me to look at the crumbling roof and the
    shutters fallen apart,
For I can't help thinking the poor old house is a house with
    a broken heart.

—*Joyce Kilmer*

STUDY AND ENJOYMENT

1. What does the poet think that the old farmhouse misses?
2. If you were painting a picture of the old house, what are some of the details you would put in?
3. Why does the poet say that a new house standing empty can't be lonely?
4. Which stanza of this poem do you like best? Read it aloud.

THE CRATCHITS' CHRISTMAS DINNER

Scrooge, a hard-hearted old miser, is visited on Christmas Eve by three ghosts—the Spirits of Christmas Past, Christmas Present, and Christmas Yet to Come—who change him into a kindly, generous gentleman. Here the Spirit of Christmas Present lets Scrooge see the Christmas party at the home of Bob Cratchit, his poorly paid clerk.

Perhaps it was the pleasure the Good Spirit had in showing off this power of his, or else it was his own kind, generous, hearty nature, and his sympathy with all poor men, that led him straight to Scrooge's clerk's; for there he went, and took Scrooge with him; on the threshold of the door the Spirit smiled and stopped to bless Bob Cratchit's dwelling. Think of that!

Then up rose Mrs. Cratchit, Cratchit's wife, dressed out but poorly in a twice-turned gown, but brave in ribbons, which are cheap and made a goodly show for sixpence; and she laid the cloth, assisted by Belinda Cratchit, second of her daughters, also brave in ribbons; while Master Peter Cratchit plunged a fork into the saucepan of potatoes, and, getting the corners of his monstrous shirt collar (Bob's private property, conferred upon his son and heir in honour of the day) into his mouth, rejoiced to find himself so gallantly attired and yearned to show his linen in the fashionable parks.

THESE YOUNG CRATCHITS DANCED ABOUT THE TABLE

And now two smaller Cratchits, boy and girl, came tearing in, screaming that outside the baker's they had smelt the goose, and known it for their own; and, basking in luxurious thoughts of sage and onion, these young Cratchits danced about the table, and exalted Master Peter Cratchit to the skies, while he (not proud, although his collar nearly choked him) blew the fire, until the slow potatoes, bubbling up, knocked loudly at the saucepan-lid to be let out and peeled.

"Here's Martha, mother!" cried the two young Cratchits. "Hurrah! There's *such* a goose, Martha!"

"Why, bless your heart alive, my dear, how late you are!" said Mrs. Cratchit, kissing her a dozen times, and taking off her shawl and bonnet for her with officious zeal.

"We'd a deal of work to finish up last night," replied the girl, "and had to clear away this morning, mother!"

"Well! Never mind, so long as you are come," said Mrs. Cratchit. "Sit ye down before the fire, my dear!"

"No, no! There's father coming," cried the two young Cratchits, who were everywhere at once. "Hide, Martha, hide!"

So Martha hid herself, and in came little Bob, the father, with at least three feet of comforter,[1] exclusive of the fringe, hanging down before him; and his threadbare clothes darned up and brushed, to look seasonable; and Tiny Tim upon his shoulder. Alas for Tiny Tim, he bore a little crutch, and had his limbs supported by an iron frame!

"Why, where's our Martha?" cried Bob Cratchit, looking round. "Not coming upon Christmas Day!"

Martha didn't like to see him disappointed, if it were only in joke; so she came out prematurely from behind the closet door, and ran into his arms, while the two young Cratchits hustled Tiny Tim, and bore him off that he might hear the pudding singing in the copper.

"And how did little Tim behave?" asked Mrs. Cratchit.

"As good as gold," said Bob, "and better. Somehow he gets thoughtful, sitting by himself so much, and thinks the strangest things you ever heard. He told me, coming home, that he hoped the people saw him in the church, because he was a cripple, and it might be pleasant to them to remember upon Christmas Day who made lame beggars walk and blind men see."

Bob's voice was tremulous when he told them this, and trembled more when he said that Tiny Tim was growing strong and hearty.

His active little crutch was heard upon the floor, and back came Tiny Tim before another word was spoken, escorted by his brother and sister to his stool before the fire; and Master Peter, and the two young Cratchits went to fetch the goose, with which they soon returned in high procession.

Such a bustle ensued that you might have thought a

[1] Scarf or muffler.

goose the rarest of all birds; and in truth it was something
very like it in that house. Mrs. Cratchit made the gravy
(ready beforehand in a little saucepan) hissing hot; Master
Peter mashed the potatoes with incredible vigour; Miss
Belinda sweetened up the apple-sauce; Martha dusted the
hot plates; Bob took Tiny Tim beside him in a tiny corner
at the table; the two young Cratchits set chairs for everybody, not forgetting themselves, and mounting guard upon
their posts, crammed spoons into their mouths, lest they
should shriek for goose before their turn came to be helped.

At last the dishes were set on, and grace was said. It
was succeeded by a breathless pause, as Mrs. Cratchit,
looking slowly all along the carving-knife, prepared to
plunge it in the breast; but when she did, and when the
long-expected gush of stuffing issued forth, one murmur
of delight arose all round the board, and even Tiny Tim,
excited by the two young Cratchits, beat on the table
with the handle of his knife and feebly cried Hurrah!

There never was such a goose. Bob said he didn't
believe there ever was such a goose cooked. Its tenderness
and flavour, size and cheapness, were the themes of universal
admiration. Eked out by apple-sauce and mashed potatoes, it was a sufficient dinner for the whole family; indeed,
as Mrs. Cratchit said with great delight (surveying one
small atom of a bone upon the dish), they hadn't eaten it all
at last! Yet every one had had enough, and the youngest
Cratchits in particular were steeped in sage and onion to
the eyebrows! But now, the plates being changed by Miss
Belinda, Mrs. Cratchit left the room alone—too nervous
to bear witnesses—to take the pudding up and bring it in.

Suppose it should not be done enough! Suppose it
should break in turning out! Suppose somebody should
have got over the wall of the back-yard and stolen it, while
they were merry with the goose—a supposition at which
the two young Cratchits became livid! All sorts of horrors
were supposed.

Hallo! A great deal of steam! The pudding was out of the copper. A smell like a washing-day! That was the cloth. A smell like an eating-house and a pastrycook's next door to each other, with a laundress's next door to that! That was the pudding! In half a minute Mrs. Cratchit entered—flushed, but smiling proudly—with the pudding, like a speckled cannon-ball, so hard and firm, and bedight with Christmas holly stuck into the top.

Oh, a wonderful pudding! Bob Cratchit said, and calmly, too, that he regarded it as the greatest success achieved by Mrs. Cratchit since their marriage. Mrs. Cratchit said that now the weight was off her mind, she would confess she had had her doubts about the quantity of flour. Everybody had something to say about it, but nobody said or thought it was at all a small pudding for a large family. Any Cratchit would have blushed to hint at such a thing.

At last the dinner was all done, the cloth was cleared, the hearth swept, and the fire made up; apples and oranges were put upon the table, and a shovelful of chestnuts on the fire. Then all the Cratchit family drew round the hearth, in what Bob Cratchit called a circle, meaning half a one; and while the chestnuts on the fire sputtered and cracked noisily, Bob proposed:

"A Merry Christmas to us all, my dears. God bless us!" Which all the family re-echoed.

"God bless us every one!" said Tiny Tim, the last of all.

He sat very close to his father's side upon his little stool. Bob held his withered little hand in his, as if he loved the child, and wished to keep him by his side, and dreaded that he might be taken from him. Then he gave another toast.

"Mr. Scrooge!" said Bob; "I'll give you Mr. Scrooge, the Founder of the Feast!"

"The Founder of the Feast indeed!" cried Mrs. Cratchit, reddening. "I wish I had him here. I'd give him a piece of my mind to feast upon, and I hope he'd have a good appetite for it!"

"My dear," said Bob, "the children! Christmas Day."

"It should be Christmas Day, I am sure," said she, "on which one drinks the health of such a stingy, hard, unfeeling man as Mr. Scrooge. You know he is, Robert! Nobody knows it better than you do, poor fellow!"

"My dear," was Bob's mild answer, "Christmas Day."

"I'll drink his health for your sake and the Day's," said Mrs. Cratchit, "not for his. Long life to him! A merry Christmas and a happy New Year! He'll be very merry and very happy, I have no doubt!"

Bob Cratchit told them how he had a situation in his eye for Master Peter, which would bring in, if obtained, full five-and-sixpence weekly. The two young Cratchits laughed tremendously at the idea of Peter's being a man of business; and Peter himself looked thoughtfully at the fire from between his collar, as if he were deliberating what particular investments he should favour when he came into the receipt of that bewildering income. Martha, who was a poor apprentice at a milliner's, then told them what kind of work she had to do, and how many hours she worked at a stretch, and how she meant to lie abed tomorrow morning for a good long rest; tomorrow being a holiday she passed at home. Also how she had seen a countess and a lord some days before, and how the lord "was much about as tall as Peter"; at which Peter pulled up his collar so high that you couldn't have seen his head if you had been there. All this time the chestnuts went round and round; and by and by they had a song, about a lost child travelling in the snow, from Tiny Tim, who had a plaintive little voice, and sang it very well indeed.

There was nothing of high mark in this. They were not a handsome family; they were not well dressed; their shoes were far from being waterproof; their clothes were scanty; and Peter might have known, and very likely did, the inside of a pawnbroker's. But they were happy, grateful, pleased with one another, and contented with the time.

—*Charles Dickens*
From *The Christmas Carol*

STUDY AND ENJOYMENT

1. What signs of poverty are evident in the Cratchits' home?
2. How do you explain the family's happiness?
3. What item on the menu was Mrs. Cratchit most nervous about? How did it turn out?
4. You will always find humour in Dickens's stories. Here is one example: "The youngest Cratchits in particular were steeped in sage and onion to the eyebrows!" Find other examples.
5. If you would like to read how Scrooge befriends Bob and his family, especially Tiny Tim, read the book *A Christmas Carol* from beginning to end.

LOVE AMONG THE BIRDS

Jack Miner, Canada's famous birdman, was never happier than when studying the wild creatures of the woods, the pond, and the air. On his property near Kingsville, Ontario, on the north shore of Lake Erie, he established a bird sanctuary, where wild ducks, swans, and geese found shelter, food and protection. Since his death, in 1944, arrangements have been made to continue the sanctuary. You may read more of this great naturalist in his book, *Jack Miner and the Birds*.

In 1907, the third year I had my clipped Canada geese, one pair nested, and every season since I have had from one to three pairs raise young. This is the very time these old ganders especially expose their incomparable, clean, noble ways, which even we human beings might well envy them.

One spring I had a painter from town out here brightening things up a little, so one day I told him to paint the cornice of the bird house, which is about seven feet high. I paid no more attention to him, but went on with my work at the tile factory, about three hundred feet away. All at once I heard a scream that was joined with language

HE WAS NEARLY FRIGHTENED INTO FITS

too loud to look well in print. I got out just in time to see this scared man come rolling over the brick wall, his legs and arms sticking up like odd sections in a Ferris-wheel! To see and hear him wrinkled my red face into a broad grin; he came towards me with both torn shirt-sleeves fluttering in the wind and white paint dabbled on one leg of his trousers, without hat, paint, pail or pipe. He began to reel it off. Then it all came to me in a flash. I had forgotten to tell him about the goose-nest that was concealed in the weeds near that spot. And now it was too late to give him any explanation, for really he did not know whether he was bitten or stung. While he was not hurt a particle, he was nearly frightened into fits, and he could not, or would not, believe there were only two geese there. I finally went and found his pipe, Christy hat and paint pail, but he never would go back in that enclosure; and worse still, I doubt if he has ever forgiven me, as he thought I had put up a job on him.

One picture would do for all the pairs of Canada geese I ever saw nesting. While the gander takes no part in building the nest or setting, turn about, on the eggs, as some birds do, yet he is always guarding her and is never over two rods away, seeing all enemies before they do him. He will usually lie flat on the ground, his black neck and snake-like head straight out, and if any creature goes right on by, all is well; but should one note him and stop, then he will suddenly jump on it from an unexpected quarter. His looks and hissing honks will almost frighten any other creature into decline; and while frightening is his chief defence, yet I know from personal experience how he can bite, and hang on like a pup, while he deals unbelievably heavy blows with the first joint of his powerful wings. The worst blow I ever got in my life was from an old gander that I caught to tag; he struck me on the jaw with the first joint of his doubled-up wings and, believe me, I had the mumps for weeks!

While I have seen the goose run at a domestic fowl or so, yet she does not pretend to do much fighting. She usually leaves that strenuous exercise for him, and depends on his protection; and well she may, for he never fails her. He will even leave his family and fight for her.

A pair once nested near the tile kiln, and a collie dog attacked this gander. The goose won out, but the dog bit the end of his backbone right off. I saw the blood running down his legs and in a few days I noticed he was always in the one place, lying down by his sweetheart. I went over and found he was sick and so weak he let me pick him up. I saw what was wrong, so I went and got the turpentine bottle and poured some in this decaying cavity. I then brought the dear old fellow water and food, but it was fully a week before he could stand up. He finally got well, and I still have him, but he was dying at his post. His name is Tom Johnson.

I never saw the wild geese go near where one of these pairs was nesting. So one spring I took fully ten bushels of corn and scattered it around near a nest. And the thousands of geese that came here would not combine their forces and go near, after the corn, or interfere with his preserve, but would prefer flying all over the country to feed, where some of them are continually getting shot. This will explain to you how they respect each others' rights.

—Jack Miner

STUDY AND ENJOYMENT

1. Which incident showed the most intense love?
2. Find and read aloud some lines which show Jack Miner's sense of humour.

LEETLE BATEESE

You bad leetle boy, not moche you care
How busy you're kipin' your poor gran'pere
Tryin' to stop you ev'ry day
Chasin' de hen aroun' de hay—
W'y don't you geev' dem a chance to lay?
     Leetle Bateese!

Off on de fiel' you foller de plough
Den w'en you're tire you scare de cow
Sickin' de dog till dey jomp de wall
So de milk ain't good for not'ing at all—
An' you're only five an' a half dis fall,
     Leetle Bateese!

Too sleepy for sayin' de prayer tonight?
Never min' I s'pose it'll be all right
Say dem tomorrow—ah! dere he go!
Fas' asleep in a minute or so—
An' he'll stay lak dat till de rooster crow,
     Leetle Bateese!

Den wake us up right away toute suite
Lookin' for somet'ing more to eat,
Makin' me t'ink of dem long leg crane
Soon as dey swaller, dey start again,
I wonder your stomach don't get no pain,
                    Leetle Bateese!

But see heem now lyin' dere in bed,
Look at de arm onderneat' hees head;
If he grow lak dat till he's twenty year
I bet he'll be stronger dan Louis Cyr
An' beat all de voyageurs leevin' here,
                    Leetle Bateese!

Jus' feel de muscle along hees back,
Won't geev' heem moche bodder for carry pack
On de long portage, any size canoe,
Dere's not many t'ing dat boy won't do
For he's got double-joint on hees body too,
                    Leetle Bateese!

But leetle Bateese! please don't forget
We rader you're stayin' de small boy yet,
So chase de chicken an' mak' dem scare,
An' do w'at you lak wit' your ole gran'pere
For w'en you're beeg feller he won't be dere—
                    Leetle Bateese!

                                —*William Henry Drummond*

STUDY AND ENJOYMENT

William Henry Drummond (1854-1907) was a doctor who lived in the
Province of Quebec.   He loved the French Canadians, especially the *habitants*,
about whom he wrote many poems.   He wrote them in a dialect of broken
English mixed with French to represent the way that the *habitants* talked to
their English-speaking neighbours.

1. What mischief did the little boy in the poem get into?   How did the grandfather feel towards him?   Read the lines that show that the boy has a big
   appetite.
2. What did the grandfather think that the boy would become when he grew
   up?   What made him think this?

AT HOME WITH THE TULLIVERS

Tom and Maggie Tulliver are children of the owner of a flour mill on the Floss River, England. Tom, aged thirteen, has arrived home from boarding school, much to the delight of his nine-year-old sister, Maggie, who loves him with all her heart.

"What is it?" said Maggie, in a whisper. "I can see nothing but a bit of yellow."

"Why, it's—a—new—guess, Maggie!"

"Oh, I *can't* guess, Tom," said Maggie impatiently.

"Don't be a spitfire, else I won't tell you," said Tom, thrusting his hand back into his pocket, and looking determined.

"No, Tom," said Maggie, imploringly, laying hold of the arm that was held stiffly in the pocket. "I'm not cross, Tom; it was only because I can't bear guessing. *Please* be good to me."

Tom's arm slowly relaxed, and he said, "Well, then, it's a new fish-line—two new uns—one for you, Maggie, all to yourself. I wouldn't go halves in the taffy and ginger-bread on purpose to save the money; and Gibson and Spouncer fought with me because I wouldn't. And here's hooks; see here! I say, *won't* we go and fish tomorrow down by Round Pool? And you shall catch your own fish, Maggie, and put the worms on, and every-thing—won't it be fun?"

Maggie's answer was to throw her arms round Tom's neck and hug him, and hold her cheek against his without speaking, while he slowly unwound some of the line, saying, after a pause—"Wasn't I a good brother, now, to buy you a line all to yourself? You know, I needn't have bought it, if I hadn't liked."

"Yes, very, very good.—I *do* love you, Tom."

Tom had put the line back in his pocket, and was looking at the hooks one by one, before he spoke again. "And the fellows fought me, because I wouldn't give in about the taffy."

"Oh, dear! I wish they wouldn't fight at your school, Tom. Didn't it hurt you?"

"Hurt me? No," said Tom, putting up the hooks again.

"Oh, how brave you are, Tom! I think you're like Samson. If a lion came roaring at me, I think you'd fight him—wouldn't you, Tom?"

"How can a lion come roaring at you, you silly thing? There's no lions, only in the shows."

"No; but if we were in the lion countries—I mean in Africa, where it's very hot—the lions eat people there. I can show it to you in the book where I read it."

"Well, I should get a gun and shoot him."

"But if you hadn't got a gun—we might have gone out, you know, not thinking—just as we go fishing; then a great lion might run toward us roaring, and we couldn't get away from him. What should you do, Tom?"

Tom paused, and at last turned away contemptuously, saying, "But the lion *isn't* coming. What's the use of talking?"

"But I like to fancy how it would be," said Maggie, following him. "Just think what you would do, Tom."

"Oh, don't bother, Maggie! You're such a silly—I shall go and see my rabbits."

Maggie's heart began to flutter with fear.

She dared not tell the sad truth at once, but she walked after Tom in trembling silence as he went out, thinking how she could tell him the news so as to soften at once his sorrow and his anger; for Maggie dreaded Tom's anger of all things—it was quite a different anger from her own.

"Tom," she said timidly, when they were out-of-doors, "how much money did you give for your rabbits?"

"Two half-crowns and a sixpence," said Tom promptly.

"I think I've got a great deal more than that in my steel purse upstairs. I'll ask mother to give it to you."

"What for?" said Tom. "I don't want *your* money, you silly thing. I've got a great deal more money than you, because I'm a boy. I always have half-sovereigns and sovereigns for my Christmas boxes, because I shall be a man, and you only have five-shilling pieces, because you're only a girl."

"Well, but Tom—if mother would let me give you two half-crowns and a sixpence out of my purse to put into your pocket and spend, you know; and buy some more rabbits with it?"

"More rabbits? I don't want any more."

"Oh, but Tom, they're all dead."

Tom stopped immediately in his walk and turned round toward Maggie. "You forgot to feed 'em, then, and Harry forgot?" he said, his colour heightening for a moment, but soon subsiding. "I'll pitch into Harry—I'll have him turned away. And I don't love you, Maggie. You shan't go fishing with me tomorrow. I told you to go and see the rabbits every day." He walked on again.

"Yes, but I forgot—and I couldn't help it, indeed, Tom. I'm so very sorry," said Maggie, while the tears rushed fast.

"You're a naughty girl," said Tom severely, "and I'm sorry I bought you the fish-line. I don't love you."

"Oh, Tom, it's very cruel," sobbed Maggie. "I'd forgive you, if *you* forgot anything—I wouldn't mind what you did—I'd forgive you and love you."

"Yes, you're a silly—but I never *do* forget things—I don't."

"Oh, please forgive me, Tom; my heart will break," said Maggie, shaking with sobs, clinging to Tom's arm, and laying her wet cheek on his shoulder.

Tom shook her off, and stopped again, saying in a decisive tone, "Now, Maggie, you just listen. Aren't I a good brother to you?"

"Ye-ye-es," sobbed Maggie, her chin rising and falling convulsedly.

"Didn't I think about your fish-line all this quarter, and mean to buy it, and saved my money o' purpose, and wouldn't go halves in the taffy, and Spouncer fought me because I wouldn't?"

"Ye-ye-es—and I—lo-lo-love you so, Tom."

"But you're a naughty girl. Last holidays you licked the paint off my lozenge-box, and the holidays before that you let the boat drag my fish-line down when I'd set you to watch it, and you pushed your head through my kite, all for nothing."

"But I didn't mean," said Maggie; "I couldn't help it."

"Yes, you could," said Tom, "if you'd minded what you were doing. And you're a naughty girl, and you shan't go fishing with me tomorrow."

With this terrible conclusion, Tom ran away from Maggie toward the mill.

Maggie stood motionless, except for her sobs, for a minute or two; then she turned and ran into the house, and up to her attic, where she sat on the floor, and laid her head against the worm-eaten shelf, with a crushing sense of misery. Tom was come home, and she had thought how happy she should be—and now he was cruel to her. What use was anything, if Tom didn't love her? Oh, he was very cruel! Hadn't she wanted to give him the money, and said how very sorry she was? She knew she was naughty to her mother, but she had never been naughty to Tom—had never *meant* to be naughty to him.

"Oh, he is cruel!" Maggie sobbed aloud, finding a wretched pleasure in the hollow echo that came through the long, empty space of the attic.

Maggie soon thought she had been hours in the attic, and it must be tea-time, and they were all having their tea, and not thinking of her. Well, then, she would stay up there and starve herself—hide herself behind the tub, and stay there all night; then they would all be frightened, and Tom would be sorry. Thus Maggie thought in the pride of her heart, as she crept behind the tub; but presently she began to cry again at the idea that they didn't mind her being there.

If she went down again to Tom now—would he forgive
her?—Perhaps her father would be there, and he would
take her part.   But then she wanted Tom to forgive her
because he loved her, not because his father told him.
No, she would never go down if Tom didn't come to fetch
her.   This resolution lasted in great intensity for five dark
minutes behind the tub; but then the need of being loved,
the strongest need in poor Maggie's nature, began to wrestle
with her pride, and soon threw it.   She crept from behind
her tub into the twilight of the long attic, but just then she
heard a quick footstep on the stairs.

Tom had been too much interested in going the round
of the premises, walking in and out where he pleased, and
whittling sticks without any particular reason, except that
he didn't whittle sticks at school, to think of Maggie and
the effect his anger had produced on her.   He meant to
punish her, and that business having been performed, he
occupied himself with other matters, like a practical person.

But when he had been called in to tea, his father said,
"Why, where's the little wench?" and Mrs. Tulliver,
almost at the same moment, said, "Where's your little
sister?"—both of them having supposed that Maggie and
Tom had been together all the afternoon.

"I don't know," said Tom.   He didn't want to "tell"
on Maggie, though he was angry with her; for Tom
Tulliver was a lad of honour.

"What! hasn't she been playing with you all this
while?" said the father.   "She'd been thinking o' nothing
but your coming home."

"I haven't seen her this two hours," said Tom, com-
mencing on the plumcake.

"Goodness heart! she's got drownded!" exclaimed Mrs.
Tulliver, rising from her seat and running to the window.
"How could you let her do so?" she added, as became a
fearful woman, accusing she didn't know whom of she
didn't know what.

"Nay, nay, she's none drownded!" said Mr. Tulliver. "You've been naughty to her, I doubt, Tom?"

"I'm sure I haven't, father," said Tom indignantly. "I think she's in the house."

"Perhaps up in that attic," said Mrs. Tulliver, "a-singing and talking to herself, and forgetting all about meal-times."

"You go and fetch her down, Tom," said Mr. Tulliver, rather sharply, his fatherly fondness for Maggie making him suspect that the lad had been hard upon "the little un," else she would never have left his side. "And be good to her, do you hear? Else I'll let you know better."

Tom never disobeyed his father, for Mr. Tulliver was a decisive man, and, as he said, would never let anybody get hold of his whip-hand; but he went out rather sullenly, carrying his piece of plumcake, and not intending to reprieve Maggie's punishment, which was no more than she deserved. It was Tom's step, then, that Maggie heard on the stairs, when her need of love had triumphed over her pride, and she was going down with her swollen eyes and dishevelled hair to beg for pity.

But she knew Tom's step, and her heart began to beat violently with the sudden shock of hope. He only stood still at the top of the stairs and said, "Maggie, you're to come down." But she rushed to him and clung round his neck, sobbing, "Oh, Tom, please forgive me—I can't bear it—I will always be good—always remember things—do love me—please, dear Tom!"

Maggie and Tom were still very much like young animals, and so she could rub her cheek against his, and kiss his ear in a random, sobbing way; and there were tender fibres in the lad that had been used to answer to Maggie's fondling; so that he behaved with a weakness quite inconsistent with his resolution to punish her as much as she deserved: he actually began to kiss her in return, and say—

"Don't cry, then, Magsie—here, eat a bit o' cake."

Maggie's sobs began to subside, and she put out her mouth for the cake and bit a piece; and then Tom bit a piece, just for company, and they ate together and rubbed each other's cheeks and brows and noses together, while they ate, like two friendly ponies.

So ended the sorrows of the day, and the next morning Maggie was trotting with her own fishing-rod in one hand and a handle of the basket in the other, stepping always, by a peculiar gift, in the muddiest places, and looking darkly radiant from under her beaver-bonnet because Tom was good to her. She had told Tom, however, that she should like him to put the worms on the hook for her, although she accepted his word when he assured her that worms couldn't feel (it was Tom's private opinion that it didn't much matter if they did). He knew all about worms, and fish, and those things; and what birds were mischievous, and how padlocks opened, and which way the handles of the gates were to be lifted. Maggie thought this sort of knowledge was very wonderful—much more difficult than remembering what was in the books; and she was rather in awe of Tom's superiority, for he was the only person who called her knowledge "stuff," and did not feel surprised at her cleverness. Tom, indeed, was of opinion that Maggie was a silly little thing; all girls were silly—they couldn't throw a stone so as to hit anything, couldn't do anything with a pocket-knife, and were frightened at frogs. Still he was very fond of his sister, and meant always to take care of her, make her his housekeeper, and punish her when she did wrong.

They were on their way to the Round Pool—that wonderful pool which the floods had made a long while ago: no one knew how deep it was; and it was mysterious, too, that it should be almost a perfect round, framed in with willows and tall reeds, so that the water was only to be seen when one got close to the brink. The sight of the old favourite spot always heightened Tom's good-humour, and he spoke to Maggie in the most amicable whispers, as he opened the precious basket, and prepared their tackle. He threw her line for her, and put the rod into her hand. Maggie thought it probable that the small fish would come to her hook, and the large ones to Tom's. But she had forgotten all about the fish, and was looking dreamily at the glassy water, when Tom said, in a loud whisper, "Look, look, Maggie!" and came running to prevent her from snatching her line away.

Maggie was frightened lest she had been doing something wrong, as usual, but presently Tom drew out her line and brought a large fish bouncing on the grass.

Tom was excited.

"Oh, Magsie! you little duck! Empty the basket."

Maggie was not conscious of unusual merit, but it was enough that Tom called her Magsie, and was pleased with her. There was nothing to mar her delight in the whispers and the dreamy silences, when she listened to the light dipping sounds of the rising fish, and the gentle rustlings, as if the willows and the reeds and the water had their happy whisperings also. Maggie thought it would make a very nice heaven to sit by the pool in that way, and never be scolded. She never knew she had a bite till Tom told her; but she liked fishing very much.

—George Eliot
From *The Mill on the Floss*

STUDY AND ENJOYMENT

This story is taken from a famous book, *The Mill on the Floss*, written by Mary Ann Evans (1819-1880) under the male pen-name of George Eliot. Miss Evans wrote under a man's name because, in her day, woman's place was supposed to be in the home, and women were not expected to express, or even to have, strong views of their own. Most of her novels are based on English country life, and her characters are drawn from people whom she knew. Tom and Maggie Tulliver may be taken to represent her brother and herself.

1. Maggie is the more likeable of the two Tulliver children, is she not? Give some reasons why you think so.

2. Where in the story do you like Tom best? In what place in the story do you find that boys were considered superior to girls?

3. Tom and Maggie were both clever, but in different ways. In what way was Maggie clever? In what way was Tom clever?

A PIONEER HOME

Mrs. Traill, the author of this selection, was the wife of a Scottish army officer who came out to settle in Upper Canada in the early 1830's, on Rice Lake, near Peterborough, Ontario. Her letters written home to her mother and old friends in England were later put in a book, under the title *The Backwoods of Canada*. Here she tells of her first log house.

But it is time that I should give you some account of our log-house, into which we moved a few days before Christmas. Many unlooked-for delays having hindered its completion before that time, I began to think it would never be habitable.

The first misfortune that happened was the loss of a fine yoke of oxen that were purchased to draw in the house-logs, that is, the logs for raising the walls of the house. Not regarding the bush as pleasant as their former master's cleared pastures, or perhaps foreseeing some hard work to come, early one morning they took into their heads to ford the lake at the head of the rapids, and march off, leaving no trace of their route excepting their footing at the water's edge. After many days spent in vain search for them, the work was at a stand, and for one month they were gone, and we began to give up all expectation of hearing any news of them. At last we learned they were some twenty miles off, in a distant township, having made their way through bush and swamp, creek and lake, back to their former owner, with an instinct that supplied to them the want of roads and compass.

It was the latter end of October before even the walls of our house were up. To effect this we called "a bee." Sixteen of our neighbours cheerfully obeyed our summons; and though the day was far from favourable, so faithfully did our hive perform their tasks, that by night the outer walls were raised.

The work went merrily on with the help of plenty of Canadian nectar (whiskey), the honey that our bees are solaced with. Some huge joints of salt pork, a peck of

potatoes, with a rice-pudding, and a loaf as big as an
enormous Cheshire cheese, formed the feast that was to
regale them during the raising. This was spread out in the
shanty in a very rural style. In short, we laughed, and
called it a picnic in the backwoods; and rude as was the
fare, I can assure you, great was the satisfaction expressed
by all the guests of every degree, our "bee" being considered as very well conducted. In spite of the difference
of rank among those that assisted at the bee, the greatest
possible harmony prevailed, and the party separated well
pleased with the day's work and entertainment.

The following day I went to survey the newly-raised
edifice, but was sorely puzzled, as it presented very little
appearance of a house. It was merely an oblong square of
logs raised one above the other, with open spaces between
every row of logs. The spaces for the doors and windows
were not then chopped out, and the rafters were not up.
In short, it looked a very queer sort of a place, and I
returned home a little disappointed, and wondering that
my husband should be so well pleased with the progress
that had been made. A day or two after this I again visited
it. The sleepers were laid to support the floors, and the
places for the doors and windows cut out of the solid
timbers, so that it had not quite so much the look of a
bird-cage as before.

After the roof was shingled, we were again at a stand,
as no boards could be procured nearer than Peterborough,
a long day's journey through horrible roads. At that time
no sawmill was in progress; now there is a fine one building
within a little distance of us. Our flooring-boards were all
to be sawn by hand, and it was some time before any one
could be found to perform this necessary work, and that at
high wages—six-and-sixpence per day. Well, the boards
were at length down, but of course of unseasoned timber;
this was unavoidable; so, as they could not be planed, we
were obliged to put up with their rough, unsightly appearance, for no better were to be had. We console ourselves

with the prospect that by next summer the boards will all be
seasoned, and then the house is to be turned topsy-turvy,
by having the floors all relaid, jointed, and smoothed.

—*Catharine Parr Traill*

STUDY AND ENJOYMENT

1. People living in the country sometimes have "bees," even today, for raising
barns or similar work. Why were "bees" much more important in
pioneer days?
2. Mrs. Traill keeps up the "bee" metaphor by calling the neighbours "our
hive." In what other way does she keep up the comparison?
3. The author, before coming to Canada, had lived in a comfortable and
refined home in England. What comments in the selection show (i)
that she has people divided into "classes," and (ii) that she is accustomed
to well-built houses? What remarks show that she appreciates the
kindness of her neighbours? What does she say that shows she is
cheerfully trying to "fit in" with new ways in a new land?
4. Mrs. Traill's sister, Mrs. Moodie, was also a pioneer in Upper Canada, and
she also wrote a book. Its title is *Roughing It in the Bush*. You will
find it in most libraries.

THE EVENING HOUR AT KINGSCROFT

Do you remember "The Children's Hour," the poem in which Longfellow gives a picture of the children in a poet's home in the hour "between
the dark and the daylight"? Evidently this hour is a favourite one for
author's children, for in this essay Lloyd Roberts gives us a delightful
picture of the evening hour in his boyhood home. "Papa" is Charles
G. D. Roberts (1860-1943), who was Sir Charles Roberts in his last years.
At the time described in this selection he was a professor at King's College,
Windsor, Nova Scotia. Bliss Carman was the children's cousin.

My father was the strongest man in the world, there
was no doubt about it. He was also a professor, one
having authority, without the house as well as within.
His word, not repeated, was law, and even Lizzie obeyed
it. I suppose a considerable amount of discipline was
required at Kingscroft, seeing that there were four of us
children, besides a Boston bull terrier and Lizzie, who was
Irish. My mother wasn't much of a hand at this line of
work. The mailed glove, however, incased a warm and

very human hand. After implicit obedience had been
demanded and rendered, we were given almost unlimited
freedom for the purpose of happiness, out-of-doors. There
we could romp and row at our own sweet will, provided
our hands were clean, and our feet on time for meals.
"No romping in the house," I can hear my father say,
and straightway we'd subside, no matter how exploding
we were inside. So we would seat ourselves demurely
around the dining-table and put our heads in our plates,
while Papa pronounced a rapid-fire grace in a dead language.
We would accompany him, buzzing in unison like a swarm
of bees. We hadn't been taught this trick, any more than
Hecate, our Maltese cat, had been taught to beg, but we
had always performed it as an inevitable part of the table
ritualism.

Eggs were a luxury then as now, it seems. Whenever
Papa would indulge in one, he would most carefully decapi-
tate the shell, giving the top to each of us in turn. We
children ate porridge, if it were breakfast. During the
dinner, if there were two courses and no Lizzie, who was
rather intermittent, we would rise after the first course
and scrape our plates out of the dining-room window to a
large and expectant assembly of fowls. This brilliant
scheme saved both waste and dish-washing, though my
mother never quite approved, especially if there were
guests. After each meal, unless college classes were on,
the study door would be closed on Papa and the Major,
and the rest of the house became silent as a church. One
knew instinctively that mighty things were brewing in the
book-lined room on the other side of the door, and it
behooved us not to meddle therein. Now when I glance at
my own study shelves, I can see the reason why.

During the summer evenings, we would play out of the
house up to the last pre-bed second, but in winter time,
being indoors, we were granted the freedom of the study
from seven to eight. Three sides of this room supported

books; a huge flat desk filled one corner; there was a black-and-green-veined marble fireplace. The mantel contained a clock, two terra-cotta busts of mid-Victorian poets, a miniature oil or two, and a Venus. These objects might seem a mere trifle to you, but they were as unique to seven-year me as they would have been to the Congo dwarfs. Immediately on entering you were required to possess yourself of a book and chair and become "still as a mouse." The book was usually "The Hairbreadth Escapes of Major Mendax," profusely and appropriately illustrated. The dancing firelight glinted magically on the gilt-lined back and cover. It also did things, comfortable things, to your limbs and imagination, fusing the slow tick-tock of the clock, the scratch of pen, the wavering shadows, the tropical pictures, and your wide-eyed dreams into one delicious whole. After a while it would do things to your eyes, too, if you weren't careful. Suddenly your father's voice would break the spell with "Time for bed old chicks," and you'd stumble around, kissing any one who happened to be in the room, and climb heavily up the stairs. Papa would follow a little later, after Mama had got us well tucked in, for a farewell hug and kiss. Papa wore a Louis Quinze moustache in those days, not his skimpy tooth-brush affair of the Great War, and he would stroke it back with his thumb and finger before leaning over the bed.

We not only loved our Papa tremendously, but we also respected him, a rarer emotion. We were sure that he possessed no frailties; he never lost his temper, or grumped, or nagged, or talked loud, or swore, or did any other of the things that lesser mortals did. If a lion had attacked us he would have dispatched it with bare hands. We had seen him lift Professor Bauber on a chair, with one hand, and we heard one morning how he had descended to the yard in pyjamas in the wee small hours and propelled Lizzie's swain from beneath her window down to the Red Gate, using his bedroom-slippered feet in more ways than one.

Then there was a moth-eaten, scarlet tunic in the attic that told you that your father had once been a soldier in the brave militia. But that was long, long ago and people didn't go to war any more, you were happily certain.

Most pay days Papa would start off for town right after dinner, "before the banks closed," whatever that meant, with a majestic swing, a bump-covered cane and Major. We would see him returning through the woods, while yet a long way off, and a wild stampede for his open arms would ensue. He had great difficulty in keeping us from all talking at once.

On Sundays everything was changed. A suppressing gloom seemed to pervade the house, accentuated about 10 a.m. by preparations for church. "Best clothes" were an abomination, like iron bars to a prisoner. Your hair must surrender its snarls, your shoes be shined, your finger-nails cut, your ribbons tied, all in a rush, the very last moment, and the prayer-books were always difficult to find. Papa kept aloof during these goings-on. He took his religion conscientiously, but not seriously. That is, he conformed to the conventions as all good professors must, but scarcely believed that man was made for the Sabbath or children were, either.

Of all cosy memories perhaps the cosiest was of snuggling up on the study sofa after tea, before the lamps were lit. Papa reclines on one elbow while we four stow ourselves in vacant nooks and corners about him like the chicks he calls us. The fire-flames fill the room with dancing goblins. Then Papa begins to sing the most glorious songs ever written: college songs with heaps of zest and jest, and we even join with Mama in the choruses, all on the same flat. "A Grasshopper Sat on the Railroad Track" is followed by "Bingo," "I Wish I Were a Butter-cup," "Rolling Home," "Clementina," and a lot more, always including "A Capital Ship for an Ocean Trip," until the clock begins to strike something it shouldn't, and breaks up the party. I fear that we loved our Papa as children are supposed to love God. Is it any wonder?

—Lloyd Roberts
From *The Book of Roberts*

STUDY AND ENJOYMENT

1. Describe the children's hour in the Roberts' home.
2. Who was Lizzie? Who was Major?
3. What did the children especially admire in their father?
4. You will find one story by Sir Charles Roberts in this Reader, *The Bear that Thought He Was a Dog.* What else did he write?

THE TRAMP

Open wide the door—
What does it matter
That his dusty clothes
Are all a-tatter?
He carries moonlight
On his shoulder—
Open wide the door,
The night grows colder.

Heap the hearth fire,
Seat the stranger near.
Do not cringe, children,
There's naught to fear—
Though he comes and goes
With an alien tongue,
On his ragged sleeve
A thrush has sung.

—Martha Ostenso

STUDY AND ENJOYMENT

Martha Ostenso was born in Norway, but moved with her family to America when she was two years old. Receiving her early education in the schools of Minnesota and of Brandon, Canada, she later attended the University of Manitoba. She is the author of several novels. This little poem-picture appears in her book of verse, *A Far Land*.

1. Some tramps are dangerous vagabonds. Others, like the stranger in this poem, are only poor. Why would some people not make this tramp welcome? Why does the author open the door wide for him?

2. "He carries moonlight on his shoulder." This might mean that the moon is shining on his shoulder as he stands in the doorway. Has it some other meaning?

3. What two things do you learn about the stranger in the last four lines?

THE CARRIP

Barbara's interests are almost entirely agricultural these days. She spends every moment she can at the farm across the way, and venerates the lightest words of the old farmer and his wife. I am afraid Barbara is beginning to regard her father and mother as contemptible triflers. She is probably right. After all, our conversation is not about real and exciting things, such as turkeys and pigs and Tiny the cart-horse, all the time. Whereas everything the farmer says is part of a tremendous game. There are several toy farmers in the nursery cupboard, but there are no toy authors and editors and publishers. I hope there never will be.

We have our place, however, as I discovered the other day. Barbara announced to her mother that she was going to be a farmer as soon as ever she grew up. "But," she added, "I shall keep a man with a typewriter in a little house in the garden, and he'll go on writing books all the time on his typewriter and earn a lot of money for me." I suspect that this is the real feminine view of authorship, and I am not sure that it is not the soundest view. It has done me good to see myself as a man kept in a little house (my study) in the garden, a man presented with a typewriter and requested, very firmly, to make some money with it.

Such is Barbara in her eighth year. It is like having a mad farmer in the house. This afternoon she insisted upon talking to me about vegetables, just as if I were a constant reader of "The Smallholder." My own interest in vegetables only appears when they have reached the tureen stage, but I considered it high time I had my own share of the conversation.

"And then," I remarked, "there are carrips."

"Yes," said Barbara dubiously.

"Now don't confuse them with turnots. Carrips are quite different from turnots, though I have met people who never knew the difference. They aren't the same now, are they?"

"No." Still dubious, she was silent for a moment. Then—"What sort of leaves have carri-carrips?" she asked.

To this I returned the laugh of a triumphant pedant. "They haven't any leaves."

"No leaves at all?"

"Not a leaf."

This was puzzling. I could see her brooding, with enormous hollow eyes, over these leafless vegetables. "Well, what are they then?" she asked—"just roots?"

"Not a bit of it," I replied with great emphasis. "A carrip has no roots. A carrip has neither leaves nor roots, nor, truthfully speaking, can it be said to have stems or flowers. A carrip has none of these things."

"It must be funny."

"I don't know whether you can rightly call it funny. But there it is. That's why a carrip is so rare."

To this she made no reply whatever, she was biding her time.

"That's why you never see a carrip about nowadays. It's the rarest vegetable there is. That's another difference between the carrip and the turnot. People haven't actually found a turnot for years, but several times lately they've nearly found one. But they've never even nearly found a carrip. When they go to look for it, it simply isn't there. And most of them don't even know what to look for, which is stupid of them, I think."

"Where do they go?"

"Why, to the carrip fields, of course. And they are always next to the turnot fields, so it's not hard to find them."

Barbara turned wide, innocent eyes upon me. "Have you ever eaten one?"

"One what?"

"What you said. A carrip."

"No, I must confess," I said very heavily, "I have never eaten a carrip."

"Well, I have. And"—here she rattled away breathlessly and triumphantly—"it was a whole one—a whole carrip, and it was long and round and cooked in a pan, and very nice indeed to eat, not too sweet or sour, but just enough of everything. I loved it."

I pointed out that I was very busy. Apparently there is such a thing as being hoist with one's own canard.

—*J. B. Priestley*

STUDY AND ENJOYMENT

1. The humour in this story is almost all just nonsense, but there is one bit near the first that is different. Can you find it?
2. How does Priestley begin the nonsense part?
3. *The Smallholder* is an English magazine for market gardeners.
4. *Canard* is another word for hoax; the phrase should be, of course, "hoist with one's own petard," which means "blown up by one's own explosive," or getting the worst of something you intended for somebody else. How does Barbara hoax or fool her father with his own foolery?

A LETTER TO A CLOCKMAKER

If you knew nothing of Dickens what would you guess about his character from this letter?

Higham by Rochester, Kent,

My dear Sir:

Since my hall clock was sent to your establishment to be cleaned it has gone (as indeed it always has) perfectly, but has struck with great reluctance, and after enduring internal agonies of a most distressing nature it has now ceased striking altogether. Though a happy release for the clock, this is not a convenience for the household. If you can send down any confidential person with whom the clock can confer, I think it may have something on its works that it would be glad to make a clean breast of.

Faithfully yours,

Monday night,
Sep. 14, 1863.

Charles Dickens

JOHNNIE COURTEAU

Here is another poem by Dr. Drummond, who also wrote "Leetle Bateese." Because this poet loved the *habitants* he has made us love them, too. This rollicking poem should be read aloud with gusto.

Johnnie Courteau of de mountain,
Johnnie Courteau of de hill,
Dat was de boy can shoot de gun,
Dat was de boy can jomp an' run,
An' it's not very offen you ketch heem still,
Johnnie Courteau!

Ax dem along de reever,
Ax dem along de shore,
Who was de mos' bes' fightin' man
From Managance to Shaw-in-i-gan?
De place w'ere de great beeg rapide roar,
Johnnie Courteau!

Sam' t'ing on ev'ry shaintee
Up on de Mekinac,
Who was de man can walk de log,
W'en w'ole of de reever she's black wit' fog,
An' carry de beeges' load on hees back?
Johnnie Courteau!

JOHNNIE'S MAKIN' DAT RAF' GO FLYIN' DOWN

On de rapide you want to see heem
If de raf' she's swingin' roun'
An' he's yellin' "Hooraw, Bateese! good man!"
W'y de oar come double on hees han'
W'en he's makin' dat raf' go flyin' down,
                         Johnnie Courteau!

An' Tête de Boule chief can tole you
De feller w'at save hees life
W'en beeg moose ketch heem up a tree,
Who's shootin' dat moose on de head, sapree!
An' den run off wit' hees Injun wife,
                         Johnnie Courteau!

An' he only have pike pole wit' heem
On Lac à la Tortue
W'en he meet de bear comin' down de hill,
But de bear very soon is get hees fill!
An' he sole dat skin for ten dollar too,
                         Johnnie Courteau!

Oh, he never was scare for not'ing
Lak' de ole coureurs de bois,
But w'en he's gettin' hees winter pay
De bes' t'ing sure is kip out de way
For he's goin' right off on de Hip Hooraw!
                         Johnnie Courteau!

Den pullin' hees sash aroun' heem
He dance on hees botte sauvage
An' shout "All aboar' if you want to fight!"
Wall! you never can see de finer sight
W'en he go lak' dat on de w'ole village!
                         Johnnie Courteau!

But Johnnie Courteau get marry
On Philomene Beaurepaire,
She's nice leetle girl was run de school
On w'at you call parish of Sainte Ursule
An' he see her off on de pique-nique dere,
                    Johnnie Courteau!

Den somet'ing come over Johnnie
W'en he marry on Philomene
For he stay on de farm de w'ole year roun'
He chop de wood an' he plough de groun'
An' he's quieter feller was never seen,
                    Johnnie Courteau!

An' ev'ry wan feel astonish
From La Tuque to Shaw-in-i-gan
W'en dey hear de news was goin' aroun',
Along on de reever up an' down,
How wan leetle woman boss dat beeg man,
                    Johnnie Courteau!

He never come out on de evening
No matter de hard we try
'Cos he stay on de kitchen an' sing hees song,
    "A la claire fontaine,
      M'en allant promener,
      J'ai trouvé l'eau si belle
      Que je m'y suis baigner!
      Lui y'a longtemps que je t'aime
      Jamais je ne t'oublierai."
Rockin' de cradle de w'ole night long
Till baby's asleep on de sweet bimeby,
                    Johnnie Courteau!

An' de house, wall!   I wish you see it,
De place she's so nice an' clean,
Mus' wipe your foot on de outside door,
You're dead man sure if you spit on de floor,
An' he never say not'ing on Philomene,
                              Johnnie Courteau!

An' Philomene watch de monee
An' put it all safe away
On very good place; I dunno w'ere,
But anyhow nobody see it dere
So she's buyin' new farm de 'noder day,
                              Madame Courteau!

—William Henry Drummond

STUDY AND ENJOYMENT

1. How did Johnnie Courteau earn a living before his marriage?   What did he do in winter? in the spring?   What incidents show his strength, skill, and daring?   Show that Johnnie was a little wild, too, before he met Philomene.

2. How did Johnnie's ways change after his marriage?   Why do you think the last stanza ends with "Madame Courteau!" when all the other stanzas ended with "Johnnie Courteau!"?

3. "A la claire fontaine," is one of the loveliest of French Canadian folk-songs.   Mr. John Murray Gibbon, in his *Canadian Folk-Songs Old and New* (Dent) translates the first stanza and refrain as follows:

   "At the clear-running fountain,
   Sauntering on my way,
   I found such lovely water,
   Therein I had to play.
      Your love long since overcame me,
      Ever in my heart you'll stay."

   Both French and English words and music are to be found in the book mentioned, and also in Sir Ernest MacMillan's *A Canadian Song Book* (Dent).   Someone might learn it and sing it to the group.   The class could join in the chorus.

4. Glossary: *ax*, ask; *great beeg rapide*, Shawinigan, now the site of extensive hydro-electric developments; *shaintee*, shanty, winter camp of lumber-men; *come double on hees han'*, moves his oar so rapidly that he seems to have two of them in his hand at once; *Tête de Boule*, a place name; *sapree*, a mild oath; *pike pole*, a long pole tipped with steel for handling logs; *Lac à la Tortue*, Turtle Lake; *coureurs de bois*, trappers, explorers, and adventurers of the French régime in Canada; *on de Hip Hooraw*, on a spree; *botte sauvage*, moccasin.

THE HOUSE AND THE ROAD

A song for those who leave home.

The little Road says Go,
The little House says Stay:
And O, it's bonnie here at home,
But I must go away.

The little Road, like me,
Would seek and turn and know;
And forth I must, to learn the things
The little Road would show!

And go I must, my dears,
And journey while I may,
Though heart be sore for the little House
That had no word but Stay.

Maybe, no other way
Your child could ever know
Why a little House would have you stay,
When the little Road says, Go.

—Josephine Preston Peabody

STUDY AND ENJOYMENT

1. What urges young people to leave home? What tugs them back?
2. Which stanza expresses the idea that a person never knows the value of home until he leaves it?

READ A BOOK

Anne of Green Gables. By L. M. Montgomery. Ryerson. Anne's life on a farm in Prince Edward Island.

A Christmas Carol. By Charles Dickens. Macmillan. Old Scrooge, the miser, learns all about Christmas.

The Adventures of Billy Topsail. By Norman Duncan. Revell. A story of the fisher folk living on the shores of Newfoundland.

Little Women. By Louisa M. Alcott. Grosset. Delightful adventures of the March sisters—Jo, Beth, Meg and Amy.

Jan of the Windmill. By Juliana Ewing. Bell. An orphan, raised in an English mill, becomes a famous painter.

VII

School Days

THE SCHOOL-HOUSE BY THE ROAD

Still sits the school-house by the road,
  A ragged beggar sunning;
Around it still the sumachs grow,
  And blackberry vines are running.

Within, the master's desk is seen,
  Deep scarred by raps official:
The warping floor, the battered seats,
  The jack-knife's carved initial;

The charcoal frescoes on its wall;
  Its door's worn sill, betraying
The feet that, creeping slow to school,
  Went storming out to playing!

—*John Greenleaf Whittier*

STUDY AND ENJOYMENT

John Greenleaf Whittier (1807-1892), an American poet, was past fifty when he did his best literary work. He was a Quaker farmer, largely self-educated, who strove to abolish slavery. He loved beauty and goodness. It has been said, "Whittier, during his whole life, rarely lost a friend."

1. Which presents the pleasanter picture—the exterior or the interior of the old school-house?

2. *Raps official*, blows on the desk from the teacher's ruler, calling for attention; *frescoes*, wall paintings; here, drawings done by boys with bits of charred wood from the stove.

3. Although no people are pictured in the poem, Whittier tells us something of what the masters and children were like. Quote lines in which he does so.

PAUL BUNYAN AS A BOY

Just as folk tales sprang up in Europe so yarns about Paul Bunyan have flourished among lumberjacks on this continent. Paul was a legendary hero of tremendous size—tall as a Douglas fir. His Big Blue Ox, Babe, was as wide as twenty-four axe-handles and a plug of tobacco. It is said that Paul Bunyan dug out the St. Lawrence River to help you tell whether you were in Canada or in the United States, and that he made the Grand Canyon of Colorado by dragging his pick. He is even said to have built a hotel with the last seven storeys on hinges so that they could be swung back to let the moon go by. Now that you know the kind of tall tales spun about Paul, you will be ready for these stories.

I

Paul's fond father thought that something ought to be done to give his son an education. He wrote to the Canadian government asking help. All that he received in reply was an autographed photograph of the Governor General and some agricultural pamphlets of small value. He was advised to carry the matter higher up to Queen Victoria but he felt no hope of success and did not carry out the idea. He finally decided to send him to the parish school, but, luckily perhaps for the boy, he contracted a bad case of mumps. He was sick for eleven years, and it took three doctors, an osteopath, twelve chiropractors and a mind-reader to pull him through.

After his recovery he started school in the eighth grade. He carried a tin bucket which his indulgent mother filled with bread, meat and other food. One day he sat down on it, and that, authorities say, is the way the hamburger sandwich was invented.

His teachers were always complaining about Paul, and the school Board began protesting also. Every time he wrote his name he wore out a lead pencil. As he could not get more than one letter on each page of his copybook his teacher would not let him spell words of more than four letters, except on his birthday. It took a strong ox team to bring his geography to school. He could only study one subject a day in order to keep the schoolyard from being jammed with teams.   He was too big to be thrashed when he was unruly.

Paul never did get very much satisfaction out of his schooling.   All of the pretty girls were afraid of him, and he seldom got a chance to carry home their books.   The boys would not fight him unless he tied his feet at the ankles and his hands behind his back.

II

Paul was very big for his age, of course, but he was never clumsy as many big boys are.   Once—the first time he ever went hunting—he sneaked his father's old shotgun out of the house and set forth to see what he could find. He kept his sharp eyes wide open, and at last he saw a deer stick its head around a tree four or five miles away.   He blazed away at the animal with the old gun, and then was so anxious to see if he had killed it that he started for the spot, lippity-cut.   He ran so fast that he outran the load he had fired from the gun, with the result that he got the full charge of buckshot in the seat of his breeches.

So, as one can readily see, his size did not in the least interfere with his spryness.   Even when he was an old man, or what would be old for most men, he was so quick on his feet that he could blow out the light in the bunkhouse at night, and be in bed and asleep before the room got dark.

As the years of his boyhood went on he continued to get bigger and stronger and quicker of action, as well as becoming better versed in everything that pertained to the woods.   He was learning that he seldom dared to exert his full strength, so powerful was he in every way, for fear of the damage he might do.   He was only about fourteen or fifteen years old when he found out that he could kill a pond full of bullfrogs just with one yell, and as his voice was getting stronger all the time, he had to watch closely and always speak softly, or else the tremendous sound would stun every one within hearing or perhaps flatten out a few houses.

—*Charles E. Brown and Wallace Wadsworth*

From *Legends of Paul Bunyan*

THE SPELLING MATCH

You may have read "The Bear Hunt" in an earlier part of this Reader. The following selection is from the same book, *Glengarry School Days*, but here Hughie is younger than when he went bear hunting. The scene of this story is laid in a rural school in Eastern Ontario about the middle of the nineteenth century.

The "Twentieth" school was built of logs hewn on two sides. The cracks were chinked and filled with plaster, which had a curious habit of falling out during the summer months, no one knew how; but somehow the holes always appeared on the boys' side and, being there, were found to be most useful. As looking out of the window was forbidden, through these holes the boys could catch glimpses of the outer world—glimpses worth catching, too, for all around stood the great forest, the playground of boys and girls during noon-hour recesses; an enchanted land, peopled, not by fairies, elves, and other shadowy beings of fancy, but with living things, squirrels, and chipmunks, and weasels, chattering ground-hogs, thumping rabbits, and stealthy foxes, not to speak of a host of flying things, from the little grey-bird that twittered its happy nonsense all day to the big-eyed owl that hooted solemnly when the moon came out. A wonderful place this forest for children to live in, to know, and to love, and in after days to long for.

One Friday afternoon, the long, hot July day was drawing to a weary close. Mischief was in the air, and the master, Archibald Munro, or "Archie Murro," as the boys called him, was holding himself in with a very firm hand, the lines about his mouth showing that he was fighting back the pain which had never quite left him from the day he had twisted his knee out of joint five years ago, in a wrestling match, and which, in his weary moments, gnawed into his vitals. He hated to lose his grip of himself, for then he knew he should have to grow stern and terrifying, and rule these imps at the desks in front of him by "sheer brute force," and that he always counted a defeat.

Munro was a born commander. His pale, intellectual face, with its square chin and firm mouth, its noble forehead and deep-set grey eyes, carried a look of such strength and indomitable courage that no boy, however big, ever thought of anything but obedience when the word of command came. He was the only master who had ever been able to control, without at least one appeal to the trustees, the stormy tempers of the young giants that used to come to school in the winter months.

The school never forgot the day when big Bob Fraser "answered back" in class. Before the words were well out of his lips, the master, with a single stride, was in front of him, and laying two swift, stinging cuts from the rawhide over big Bob's back, commanded, "Hold out your hand!" in a voice so terrible, and with eyes of such blazing light, that before Bob was aware, he shot out his hand and stood waiting the blow. Never, in all its history, did the school receive such a thrill as the next few moments brought; for while Bob stood waiting, the master's words fell clear-cut upon the dead silence: "No, Robert, you are too big to thrash. You are a man. No man should strike you— and I apologize." And then big Bob forgot his wonted sheepishness and spoke out with a man's voice, "I am sorry I spoke back, sir." And then all the girls began to cry and wipe their eyes with their aprons, while the master and Bob shook hands silently. From that day and hour Bob Fraser would have slain any one offering to make trouble for the master. Archibald Munro's rule was firmly established.

He was just and impartial in all his decisions, and absolute in his control; besides, he had the rare faculty of awakening in his pupils an enthusiasm for work inside the school and for sports outside.

But now he was holding himself in, and with set teeth keeping back the pain. The week had been long and hot and trying, and this day had been the worst of all. Through the little dirty panes of the uncurtained windows the hot sun had poured itself in a flood of quivering light all the long day. Only an hour remained of the day, but that hour was to the master the hardest of all the week. The big boys were droning lazily over their books; the little boys, at the desks just below the master's desk, were bubbling over with spirits—spirits of which origin there was no reasonable ground for doubt.

Suddenly Hughie Murray, the minister's boy, a very special imp, held up his hand.

"Well, Hughie," said the master, for the tenth time within the hour replying to the signal.

"Spelling-match!"

The master hesitated. It would be a vast relief but it was a little like shirking. On all sides, however, hands went up in support of Hughie's proposal, and, having hesitated, he felt he must surrender or become terrifying at once.

"Very well," he said. "Margaret Aird and Thomas Finch will act as captains." At once there was a gleeful hubbub. Slates and books were slung into desks.

"Order! or no spelling-match." The alternative was awful enough to quiet even the impish Hughie, who knew the tone carried no idle threat, and who loved a spelling-match with all the ardour of his little fighting soul.

The captains took their places on each side of the school, and, with careful deliberation, began the selection of their teams, scanning anxiously the rows of faces looking at the maps or out of the windows and bravely trying to seem unconcerned. Chivalry demanded that Margaret should have first choice. "Hughie Murray!" called out Margaret;

for Hughie, though only eight years old, had preternatural gifts in spelling; his mother's training had done that for him. At four he knew every Bible story by heart, and would tolerate no liberties with the text; at six he could read the third reader; at eight he was the best reader in the fifth; and, to do him justice, he thought no better of himself for that. It was no trick to read. If he could only run, and climb, and swim, and dive, like the big boys, then he would indeed feel uplifted; but mere spelling and reading, "Huh! that was nothing."

"Ranald Macdonald!" called Thomas Finch, and a big, lanky boy of fifteen or sixteen rose and marched to his place. He was a boy one would look at twice. He was far from handsome. His face was long, and thin, and dark, with a straight nose, large mouth, and high cheek-bones; but he had fine black eyes, though they were fierce and had a look in them that suggested the woods and the wild things that live there. But Ranald, though his attendance at school was spasmodic and dependent upon the suitability or otherwise of the weather for hunting, was the best speller in the school.

For that reason Margaret would have chosen him, and for another which she would not for worlds have confessed, even to herself. But do you think she would have called Ranald Macdonald to come and stand up beside her before all these boys? Not for the glory of winning the match and carrying the medal for a week. But how gladly would she have given up glory and medal for the joy of it—if she had dared.

At length the choosing was over, and the school ranged in two opposing lines, with Margaret and Thomas at the head of their respective forces, and little Jessie MacRae and Johnnie Aird, with a single big curl on the top of his head, at the foot. It was a point of honour that no blood should be drawn at the first round. To Thomas, who had second choice, fell the right of giving the first word. So to little Jessie, at the foot, he gave "Ox."

"O-x, ox," whispered Jessie, shyly dodging behind her neighbour.

"In!" said Margaret to Johnnie Aird.

"I-s, in," said Johnnie, stoutly.

"Right!" said the master, silencing the shout of laughter. "Next word."

With like gentle courtesies the battle began; but in the second round the little A, B, C's were ruthlessly swept off the field with second-book words, and retired to their seats in supreme exultation, amid the applause of their fellows still left in the fight. After that there was no mercy shown. It was a give-and-take battle, the successful speller having the right to give the word to the opposite side. The master was umpire, and after his "Next!" had fallen there was no appeal. But if a mistake were made, it was the opponent's part and privilege to correct with all speed, lest a second attempt should succeed.

Steadily, and amid growing excitement, the lines grew less, till there were left on one side Thomas, with Ranald supporting him, and on the other, Margaret, with Hughie beside her, his face pale, and his dark eyes blazing with the light of battle.

Without varying fortune the fight went on. Margaret, still serene, and with only a touch of colour in her face, gave out her words with even voice, and spelled her opponent's with calm deliberation. Opposite her Thomas stood, stolid, slow, and wary. He had no nerves to speak of, and the only chance of catching him lay in lulling him off to sleep.

They were now among the deadly words.

"Parallelopiped!" challenged Hughie to Ranald, who met it easily, giving Margaret "hyphen" in return.

"H-y-p-h-e-n," spelled Margaret, and then, with cunning carelessness, gave Thomas "heifer." ("Hypher," she called it.)

Thomas took it lightly.

"H-e-i-p-h-e-r."

Like lightning Hughie was upon him.   "H-e-i-f-e-r."

"F-e-r," shouted Thomas.   The two yells came almost together.

There was a deep silence.   All eyes were turned upon the master.

"I think Hughie was first," he said slowly.   A great sigh swept over the school; then a wave of applause.

The master held up his hand.

"But it was so very nearly a tie, that if Hughie is willing—"

"All right, sir?" cried Hughie, eager for more fight.

But Thomas, in sullen rage, strode to his seat muttering, "I was just as soon, anyway."   Every one heard and waited, looking at the master.

"The match is over," said the master, quietly.   Great disappointment showed in every face.

"There is just one thing better than winning, and that is, taking defeat like a man."   His voice was grave, and with just a touch of sadness.   The children, sensitive to moods, as is characteristic of children, felt the touch and sat subdued and silent.

There was no improving of the occasion, but with the same sad gravity the school was dismissed; and the children learned that day one of life's golden lessons, that the man who remains master of himself never knows defeat.

—Ralph Connor

STUDY AND ENJOYMENT

Ralph Connor was the pen-name of the Reverend Charles William Gordon (1860-1937), who wrote many books with scenes laid in Canada.   Born in Glengarry County in Ontario, this author spent the greater part of his life as a minister in Winnipeg.

1. In what respects does the school described here differ from country schools of today?
2. There are several instances of sportsmanship in this story; tell what they are.   Who "played the game" best?   Give reasons for your answer.
3. When Johnnie Aird spelled *in* "i-s," why did the schoolmaster say, "Right"?
4. How do you account for the "curious habit" the plaster had of falling out of the chinks during the summer months?
5. Explain exactly how this spelling match was conducted.   How does it differ from the rules you follow?

THE EDUCATION OF HELEN KELLER

When Helen Keller, who lives in the United States, was two years old she lost her sight and hearing through a serious illness. A few years later, her parents were fortunate in getting a teacher, Anne Sullivan, to teach her to read and to write in Braille, and finally to speak. With Miss Sullivan's help, and by her own great efforts, Miss Keller overcame her handicaps, and has lived a most useful life. She has given lectures, written books, and worked faithfully to secure better care for the blind.

HELEN KELLER WRITES TO THE EDITOR OF *St. Nicholas*

Dear *St. Nicholas:*

It gives me very great pleasure to send you my autograph because I want the boys and girls who read *St. Nicholas* to know how blind children write. I suppose some of them wonder how we keep the lines so straight, so I will try to tell them how it is done. We have a grooved board which we put between the pages when we wish to write. The parallel grooves correspond to lines, and when we have pressed the paper into them by means of the blunt end of the pencil, it is very easy to keep the words even. The small letters are all made in the grooves, while the long ones extend above and below them. We guide the pencil with the right hand, and feel carefully with the forefinger of the left hand to see that we shape and space the letters correctly. It is very difficult at first to form them plainly, but if we keep on trying, it gradually becomes easier, and after a great deal of practice we can write legible letters to our friends. Then we are very, very happy. Some time they may visit a school for the blind.

Very sincerely, your little friend,

HELEN KELLER

THE SEEING HAND

I have just touched my dog. He was rolling on the grass, with pleasure in every muscle and limb. I wanted to catch a picture of him in my fingers, and I touched him as lightly as I would cobwebs; but lo, his fat body revolved, stiffened and solidified into an upright position, and his tongue gave my hand a lick! He pressed close to me, as if he were fain to crowd himself into my hand. He loved it with his tail, with his hair, with his tongue. If he could speak, I believe he would say with me that paradise is attained by touch; for in touch is all love and intelligence.

This small incident started me on a chat about hands, and if my chat is fortunate I have to thank my dog-star. . . . My hand is to me what your hearing and sight together are to you. In large measure we travel the same highways, read the same books, speak the same language, yet our experiences are different. All my comings and goings turn on the hand as on a pivot. It is the hand that binds me to the world of men and women. . . . The delicate tremble of a butterfly's wings in my hand, the soft petals of violets curling in the cool folds of their leaves or lifting sweetly out of the meadow grass, the clear, firm outline of face and limb, the smooth arch of a horse's neck and the velvety touch of his nose—all these, and a thousand resultant combinations, which take shape in my mind, constitute my world.

My world is built of touch-sensations, devoid of physical colour and sound; but without colour and sound it breathes and throbs with life. . . . All palpable things are mobile or rigid, solid or liquid, big or small, warm or cold, and these qualities are variously modified. The coolness of a water lily rounding into bloom is different from the coolness of an evening wind in summer, and different again from the coolness of the rain that soaks into the hearts of growing things and gives them life and body. The velvet of a rose is not that of a ripe peach or of a baby's dimpled cheek.

The hardness of the rock is to the hardness of the wood what a man's deep bass is to a woman's voice when it is low. What I call beauty I find in certain combinations of all these qualities, and is largely derived from the flow of curved and straight lines which is over all things. . . .

When I think of hills, I think of the upward strength I tread upon. When water is the object of my thought, I feel the cool shock of the plunge and the quick yielding of the waves that crisp and curl and ripple about my body. The pleasing changes of rough and smooth, pliant and rigid, curved and straight, in the bark and branches of a tree give the truth to my hand. The immovable rock, with all its juts and warped surface, bends beneath my fingers into a manner of grooves and hollows. The bulge of a water-melon and the puffed-up rotundities of squashes that sprout, bud, and ripen in that strange garden planted somewhere behind my fingertips are the ludicrous in my tactual (touch) memory and imagination. My fingers are tickled to delight by the soft ripple of a baby's laugh, and find amusement in the lusty crow of the barnyard autocrat.

My fingers cannot, of course, get the impression of a large whole at a glance; but I feel the parts and my mind puts them together. I move around my house, touching object after object in order, before I can form an idea of the entire house. The process reminds me of the building of Solomon's Temple, where was neither saw, nor hammer, nor any tool heard while the stones were being laid one upon another. The silent worker is imagination which decrees reality out of chaos.

—*Helen Keller*

STUDY AND ENJOYMENT

1. "My hand is to me what your hearing and sight together are to you." Give examples to show that this statement is true.

2. How does Miss Keller get the impression of large things like her house? How can you tell from this selection that she is happy and very clever?

3. What school for teaching blind children in Canada is nearest to your community? Where is the nearest school for deaf children? Such schools are listed in *The Canadian Almanac* (Copp Clark). Find out what is meant by "Braille."

DOTHEBOYS HALL

In Dickens's day there were many bad private schools in England. It is hard to believe that teachers were as cruel and ignorant as Mr. Squeers, but the conditions described were scarcely exaggerated. In fact, several Yorkshire schoolmasters were very angry with Dickens because each believed he was the original of Squeers.

I. INTRODUCING NICHOLAS NICKLEBY

The story opens with the Nicklebys (Mrs. Nickleby, her son Nicholas and her daughter Kate) in London, seeking help from Ralph Nickleby, the rich but miserly uncle of Nicholas.

"Well, Ma'am," said Ralph impatiently, "the creditors have administered, you tell me, and there's nothing left for you?"

"Nothing," replied Mrs. Nickleby.

"And you spent what little money you had in coming all the way to London, to see what I could do for you?" pursued Ralph.

"I hoped," faltered Mrs. Nickleby, "that you might have an opportunity of doing something for your brother's children. It was his dying wish that I should appeal to you in their behalf."

"Are you willing to work, sir?" he inquired, frowning on his nephew.

"Of course I am," replied Nicholas haughtily.

"Then see here, sir," said his uncle. "This caught my eye this morning, and you may thank your stars for it."

With this exordium, Mr. Ralph Nickleby took a newspaper from his pocket, and after unfolding it, and looking for a short time among the advertisements, read as follows:

"EDUCATION.—At Mr. Wackford Squeers's Academy, Dotheboys Hall, at the delightful village of Dotheboys, near Greta Bridge, in Yorkshire, youth are boarded, clothed, booked, furnished with pocket-money, provided with all necessaries, instructed in all languages living and dead, mathematics, orthography, geometry, astronomy, trigonometry, the use of the globes, algebra, writing, arithmetic, fortification and every other branch of classical literature. Terms, twenty guineas per annum. No extras, no vacations, and diet unparalleled. Mr. Squeers is in town, and attends daily, from one till four, at the Saracen's Head, Snow Hill. N.B. An able assistant wanted. Annual salary £5. A Master of Arts would be preferred." . . . Nicholas starting gaily up, and wringing his uncle's hand, said, "I am ready to do anything you wish me. Let us try our fortune with Mr. Squeers at once; he can but refuse."

"He won't do that," said Ralph. "He will be glad to have you on my recommendation. Make yourself of use to him, and you'll rise to be a partner in the establishment in no time. Bless me! only think, if he were to die, why your fortune's made at once."

II. Introducing Mr. Squeers

Mr. Squeers' appearance was not prepossessing. He had but one eye, and popular prejudice runs in favour of two. The eye he had was unquestionably useful, but decidedly not ornamental: being of a greenish grey, and in shape resembling the fan-light of a street door. The blank side of his face was much wrinkled and puckered up, which gave him a very sinister appearance, especially when he smiled, at which times his expression bordered closely on the villainous. His hair was very flat and shiny, save at the ends where it was brushed stiffly up from a low protruding forehead, which assorted well with his harsh voice and coarse manner. He was about two or three and fifty, and a trifle below the middle size; he wore a white neckerchief with long ends, and a suit of scholastic black; but his coatsleeves being a great deal too long, and his trousers a great deal too short, he appeared ill at ease in his clothes, and as if he were in perpetual state of astonishment at finding himself so respectable.

Mr. Squeers was standing in a box by one of the coffee-room fireplaces, fitted with one such table as is usually seen in coffee-rooms, and two of extraordinary shapes and dimensions made to suit the angles of the partition. In a corner of the seat was a very small deal trunk, tied round with a scanty piece of cord; and on the trunk was perched —his lace-up half-boots and corduroy trousers dangling in the air—a diminutive boy, with his shoulders drawn up to his ears, and his hands planted on his knees, who glanced timidly at the schoolmaster, from time to time, with evident dread and apprehension.

"Half-past three," muttered Mr. Squeers, turning from the window, and looking sulkily at the coffee-room clock. "There will be nobody here today."

Here the little boy on the top of the trunk gave a violent sneeze.

"Halloa, sir!" growled the schoolmaster, turning round. "What's that, sir?"

"Nothing, please, sir," said the little boy.

"Nothing, sir!" exclaimed Mr. Squeers.

"Please, sir, I sneezed," rejoined the boy, trembling till the little trunk shook under him.

"Oh! sneezed, did you?" retorted Mr. Squeers. "Then what did you say 'nothing' for, sir?"

In default of a better answer to this question, the little boy screwed a couple of knuckles into each of his eyes and began to cry, wherefore, Mr. Squeers knocked him off the trunk with a blow on one side of his face, and knocked him on again with a blow on the other.

"Wait till I get you down into Yorkshire, my young gentleman," said Mr. Squeers, "and then I'll give you the rest. Will you hold that noise, sir?"

"Ye-ye-yes," sobbed the little boy.

"Then do so at once, sir," said Squeers. "Do you hear?"

"Mr. Squeers," said the waiter, looking in at this juncture; "here's two gentlemen asking for you at the bar."

"Show the gentlemen in, Richard," replied Mr. Squeers, in a soft voice. "Put your handkerchief in your pocket, you little scoundrel or I'll murder you when the gentlemen go."

The schoolmaster had scarcely uttered these words in a fierce whisper, when Nicholas and his uncle entered. Affecting not to see him, Mr. Squeers feigned to be intent upon mending a pen, and offering benevolent advice to his youthful pupil.

"My dear child," said Mr. Squeers, "all people have their trials. This early trial of yours that is fit to make your little heart burst, and your very eyes come out of your head with crying, what is it? Nothing; less than nothing. You are leaving your friends, but you will have a father in me, my dear, and a mother in Mrs. Squeers."

III. At Breakfast with Mr. Squeers Prior to Leaving London

Nicholas found that learned gentleman sitting at breakfast with the three little boys before noticed, and two others who had turned up by some lucky chance since the interview of the previous day, ranged in a row on the opposite seat. Mr. Squeers had before him a small measure of coffee, a plate of hot toast, and a cold round of beef; but he was at that moment intent on preparing breakfast for the little boys.

"This is twopenn'orth of milk, is it, waiter?" said Mr. Squeers, looking down into a large blue mug and slanting it gently, so as to get an accurate view of the quantity of liquid contained in it.

"That's twopenn'orth," replied the waiter.

"What a rare article milk is to be sure, in London," said Mr. Squeers with a sigh. "Just fill up that mug with lukewarm water, William, will you?"

"To the very top, sir?" inquired the waiter. "Why, the milk will be drownded."

"Never you mind that," replied Mr. Squeers. "Serve it right for being so dear. You ordered that thick bread and butter for three, did you?"

"Coming directly, sir."

"You needn't hurry yourself," said Squeers; "there's plenty of time. Conquer your passions, boys, and don't be eager after vittles." As he uttered this moral precept, Mr. Squeers took a large bite out of the cold beef, and recognized Nicholas.

"Sit down, Mr. Nickleby," said Squeers. "Here we are a-breakfasting, you see!"

Nicholas did not see that anybody was breakfasting, except Mr. Squeers; but he bowed with all becoming deference, and looked as cheerful as he could.

"Oh! that's the milk and water, is it, William?" said Squeers. "Very good; don't forget the bread and butter presently."

At this fresh mention of the bread and butter, the five little boys looked very eager, and followed the waiter out, with their eyes; meanwhile Mr. Squeers tasted the milk and water.

"Ah!" said that gentleman, smacking his lips, "here's richness! Think of the many beggars and orphans in the streets that would be glad of this, little boys. A shocking thing hunger is, isn't it, Mr. Nickleby?"

"Very shocking, sir," said Nicholas.

"When I say Number One," pursued Mr. Squeers, putting the mug before the children, "the boy on the left hand nearest the window may take a drink; and when I say Number Two, the boy next him will go in, and so till we come to Number Five, which is the last boy. Are you ready?"

"Yes, sir," cried all the little boys with great eagerness.

"That's right," said Squeers, calmly getting on with his breakfast; "keep ready till I tell you to begin. Subdue your appetites, my dears, and you've conquered human nature. This is the way we inculcate strength of mind,

Mr. Nickleby," said the schoolmaster, turning to Nicholas, and speaking with his mouth full of beef and toast.

Nicholas murmured something—he knew not what—in reply; and the little boys dividing their gaze between the mug, the bread and butter (which had by this time arrived), and every morsel which Mr. Squeers took into his mouth, remained with strained eyes in torments of expectation.

"Thank God for a good breakfast," said Squeers when he had finished.

"Number One may take a drink."

Number One seized the mug ravenously, and had just drunk enough to make him wish for more, when Mr. Squeers gave the signal for Number Two, who gave up at the same interesting moment to Number Three; and the process was repeated until the milk and water terminated with Number Five.

"And now," said the schoolmaster, dividing the bread and butter for three into as many portions as there were children, "You had better look sharp with your breakfast, for the horn will blow in a minute or two, and then every boy leaves off."

Permission being thus given to fall to, the boys began to eat voraciously, and in desperate haste: while the schoolmaster (who was in high good humour after his meal) picked his teeth with a fork, and looked smilingly on.

IV. Nicholas Is Introduced to the "Shop"

"There," said the schoolmaster, as they stepped in together; "this is our shop, Nickleby!"

It was such a crowded scene, and there were so many objects to attract attention, that, at first, Nicholas stared about him, really without seeing anything at all. By degrees, however, the place resolved itself into a bare and dirty room, with a couple of windows, whereof a tenth part might be of glass, the remainder being stopped up with old

"THIS IS OUR SHOP, NICKLEBY!"

copybooks and paper. There were a couple of long, old, rickety desks, cut and notched, and inked, and damaged, in every possible way; two or three forms; a detached desk for Squeers; and another for his assistant. The ceiling was supported, like that of a barn, by cross-beams and rafters; and the walls were so stained and discoloured that it was impossible to tell whether they had ever been touched with paint or whitewash.

Pale and haggard faces, lank and bony figures, children with the countenances of old men, boys of stunted growth, and others whose long, meagre legs would hardly bear their stooping bodies, all crowded on the view together. There were little faces that should have been handsome, darkened with scowls of sullen, dogged suffering; there was childhood with the light of its eye quenched, its beauty gone, and its helplessness alone remaining; there were vicious-faced boys, with leaden eyes, like malefactors in a jail.

And yet, this scene, painful as it was, had its grotesque features, which, in a less interested observer than Nicholas, might have provoked a smile. Mrs. Squeers stood at one of the desks, presiding over an immense basin of brimstone and treacle, of which delicious compound she administered a large instalment to each boy in succession; using for the purpose a common wooden spoon, which might have been originally manufactured for some gigantic top, and which widened every young gentleman's mouth considerably; they being all obliged under heavy corporal penalties to take in the whole of the bowl at a gasp. In another corner, huddled together for companionship, were the little boys who had arrived on the preceding night, three of them in very large leather breeches, and two in old trousers, a something tighter fit than drawers are usually worn; at no great distance from these was seated the juvenile son and heir of Mr. Squeers—a striking likeness of his father—kicking, with great vigour, under the hands of Smike, who was fitting upon him a new pair of boots that bore a most suspicious resemblance to those which the least of the little boys had worn on the journey down. Besides these, there was a long row of boys waiting, with countenances of no pleasant anticipation, to be treacled; and another file, who had just escaped from the infliction, making a variety of wry mouths indicative of anything but satisfaction. The whole were attired in such motley, ill-sorted, extraordinary garments, as would have been irresistibly ridiculous, but for the foul appearance of dirt, disorder and disease with which they were associated.

"Now," said Squeers, giving the desk a great rap with his cane, which made half the little boys nearly jump out of their boots, "is that physicking over?"

"Just over," said Mrs. Squeers.

For breakfast Mrs. Squeers poured into some bowls a brown composition, which looked like diluted pincushions without the covers, and was called porridge. A minute wedge of brown bread was inserted in each bowl, and when they had eaten their porridge by means of the bread, the boys ate the bread itself, and had finished their breakfast; whereupon Mr. Squeers said in a solemn voice, "For what we have received, may the Lord make us truly thankful!" and went away to his own.

After some half-hour's delay, Mr. Squeers reappeared, and the boys took their places and their books, of which latter commodity the average might be about one to eight learners. A few minutes having elapsed, during which Mr. Squeers looked very profound, as if he had a perfect apprehension of what was inside all the books, and could say every word of their contents by heart, if he only chose to take the trouble, that gentleman called up the first class.

Obedient to his summons there ranged themselves in front of the schoolmaster's desk, half-a-dozen scarecrows, out at knees and elbows, one of whom placed a torn and filthy book beneath his learned eye.

"This is the first class in English spelling and phi-losophy, Nickleby," said Squeers, beckoning Nicholas to stand beside him. "We'll get up a Latin one, and hand that over to you. Now, then, where's the first boy?"

"Please, sir, he's cleaning the back parlour windows," said the temporary head of the philosophical class.

"So he is, to be sure," rejoined Squeers. "We go upon the practical mode of teaching, Nickleby; the regular education system. C-l-e-a-n, clean, verb, active, to make bright, to scour. W-i-n, win, d-e-r, der, winder, a casement. When the boy knows this out of book, he goes and does it. It's just the same principle as the use of globes. Where's the second boy!"

"Please, sir, he's weeding the garden," replied a small voice.

"To be sure," said Squeers, by no means disconcerted. "So he is. B-o-t, bot, t-i-n, tin, bottin, n-e-y, ney, bot-tiney, means a knowledge of plants, he goes and knows 'em. That's our system, Nickleby; what do you think of it?"

"It's a very useful one, at any rate," answered Nickleby.

"I believe you," said Squeers, not remarking the emphasis of his usher. "Third boy, what's a horse?"

"A beast, sir," replied the boy.

"So it is," said Squeers. "Ain't it, Nickleby?"

"I believe there is no doubt of that, sir," answered Nicholas.

"Of course there isn't," said Squeers. "A horse is a quadruped, and quadruped's Latin for beast, as everybody that's gone through the grammar knows, or else where's the use of having grammars at all?"

"Where, indeed!" said Nicholas abstractedly.

"As you're perfect in that," resumed Squeers, turning to the boy, "go and look after *my* horse, and rub him down well, or I'll rub you down. The rest of the class go and draw water up, till somebody tells you to leave off, for it's washing-day tomorrow and they want the coppers filled." So saying, he dismissed the first class to their experiments in practical philosophy and eyed Nicholas with a look, half cunning and half doubtful, as if he were not altogether certain what he might think of him by this time.

"That's the way we do it, Nickleby," he said after a pause.

Nicholas shrugged his shoulders in a manner that was scarcely perceptible and said he saw how it was.

—*Charles Dickens*
From *Nicholas Nickleby*

STUDY AND ENJOYMENT

1. How does Dickens lead you to despise Squeers? How does he make you sympathize with Nicholas Nickleby?

2. What does the name "Dotheboys Hall" tell you about the school run by Squeers? (Separate the syllables into words.) Make a list of the cruelties and abuses in Dotheboys Hall.

3. *Exordium*, the beginning; *orthography*, spelling; *sinister*, forbidding, frightening, wicked; *protruding*, sticking out; *malefactors*, evil-doers; *grotesque*, distorted in a comical way.

CUFF'S FIGHT WITH DOBBIN

This story tells about a boys' school in England early in the nineteenth century. Since then the world has moved forward in its thinking, and boys no longer look down on other boys whose fathers are, for example, grocers. But human nature hasn't changed entirely, and the lads in this story from Vanity Fair *still seem real and very much alive.*

Cuff's fight with Dobbin, and the unexpected issue of that contest, will long be remembered by every man who was educated at Dr. Swishtail's famous school. The latter youth (who used to be called Heigh-ho Dobbin, Gee-ho Dobbin, and by many other names indicative of puerile contempt) was the quietest, the clumsiest, and, as it seemed, the dullest of all Dr. Swishtail's young gentlemen. His parent was a grocer in the city, and it was bruited abroad that he was admitted into Dr. Swishtail's academy upon what are called "mutual principles"—that is to say, the expenses of his board and schooling were defrayed by his father in goods, not money; and he stood there—almost at the bottom of the school—in his scraggy corduroys and jacket, through the seams of which his great big bones were bursting—as the representative of so many pounds of tea, candles, sugar, mottled-soap, plums (of which a very mild proportion was supplied for the puddings of the establishment), and other commodities. A dreadful day it was for young Dobbin when one of the youngsters of the school, having run into the town, espied the cart of Dobbin & Rudge, Grocers and Oilmen, Thames Street, London, at the Doctor's door, discharging a cargo of the wares in which the firm dealt.

Young Dobbin had no peace after that. The jokes were frightful, and merciless against him. "Hullo, Dobbin," one wag would say, "here's good news in the paper. Sugar is ris', my boy." Another would set a sum—"If a pound of mutton-candles cost sevenpence-halfpenny, how much must Dobbin cost?" and a roar would follow from all the circle of young knaves, who rightly considered that the selling of goods by retail is a shameful and infamous practice, meriting the contempt and scorn of all real gentlemen.

"Your father's only a merchant, Osborne," Dobbin said in private to the little boy who had brought down the storm upon him. At which the latter replied haughtily, "My father's a gentleman, and keeps his carriage"; and Mr. William Dobbin retreated to a remote out-house in the playground, where he passed a half-holiday in the bitterest sadness and woe. Who feels injustice; who shrinks before a slight; who has a sense of wrong so acute, and so glowing a gratitude for kindness, as a generous boy?

High and low, all made fun of him. They sewed up those corduroys, tight as they were. They upset buckets and benches, so that he might break his shins over them, which he never failed to do. They sent him parcels, which, when opened, were found to contain the paternal soap and candles. There was no little fellow but had his jeer and joke at Dobbin; and he bore everything quite patiently, and was entirely dumb and miserable.

Cuff, on the contrary, was the great chief and dandy of the Swishtail Seminary. He fought the town-boys. Ponies used to come for him to ride home on Saturdays. He had his top-boots in his room, in which he used to hunt in the holidays. He had been to the Opera, and knew the merits of the principal actors. He could knock you off forty Latin verses in an hour. He could make French poetry. What else didn't he know, or couldn't he do? They said even the Doctor himself was afraid of him.

Cuff, the unquestioned king of the school, ruled over his subjects, and bullied them, with splendid superiority. This one blacked his shoes; that toasted his bread; others would fag out, and give him balls at cricket during whole summer afternoons. "Figs" was the fellow whom he despised most, and with whom, though always abusing him, and sneering at him, he scarcely ever condescended to hold personal communication.

It happened that Mr. Cuff, on a sunshiny afternoon, was in the neighbourhood of poor William Dobbin, who was lying under a tree in the playground, spelling over a favourite copy of the *Arabian Nights* which he had— apart from the rest of the school, who were pursuing their various sports—quite lonely, and almost happy.

Well, William Dobbin had for once forgotten the world, and was away with Sindbad the Sailor in the Valley of Diamonds; when shrill cries, as of a little fellow weeping, woke up his pleasant reverie; and, looking up, he saw Cuff before him, belabouring a little boy.

It was the lad who had peached upon him about the grocer's art; but he bore little malice, not at least towards the young and small. "How dare you, sir, break the bottle?" says Cuff to the little urchin, swinging a yellow cricket-stump over him.

Down came the stump with a great heavy thump on the child's hand. A moan followed. Dobbin looked up: and there was everyday life before honest William; and a big boy beating a little one without cause.

"Hold out your other hand, sir," roars Cuff to his little schoolfellow, whose face was distorted with pain. Dobbin quivered, and gathered himself up in his narrow old clothes. Down came the wicket again; and Dobbin started up. Whatever may have been his incentive, up he sprang, and screamed out, "Hold off, Cuff; don't bully that child any more; or I'll—"

"Or you'll what?" Cuff asked, in amazement at this interruption. "Hold out your hand, you little beast."

"I'll give you the worst thrashing you ever had in your life," Dobbin said, in reply to the first part of Cuff's sentence; and little Osborne, gasping and in tears, looked up with wonder and incredulity at seeing this amazing champion put up suddenly to defend him; while Cuff's astonishment was scarcely less.

"After school," says he, of course; after a pause and a look, as much as to say, "Make your will, and communicate your last wishes to your friends between this time and that."

"As you please," Dobbin said. "You must be my bottle-holder, Osborne."

"Well, if you like," little Osborne replied; for, you see, his papa kept a carriage, and he was rather ashamed of his champion.

Yes, when the hour of battle came, he was almost ashamed to say "Go it, Figs"; and not a single other boy in the place uttered that cry for the first two or three rounds of this famous combat; at the commencement of which the scientific Cuff, with a contemptuous smile on his face, and as light and as gay as if he was at a ball, planted his blows upon his adversary, and floored that unlucky champion three times running. At each fall there was a cheer; and everybody was anxious to have the honour of offering the conqueror a knee.

"What a licking I shall get when it's over," young Osborne thought, picking up his man. "You'd best give in," he said to Dobbin; "it's only a thrashing, Figs, and you know I'm used to it." But Figs, all whose limbs were in a quiver, and whose nostrils were breathing rage, put his little bottle-holder aside, and went in for a fourth time.

As he did not in the least know how to parry the blows that were aimed at himself, and Cuff had begun the attack on the three preceding occasions, without ever allowing his enemy to strike, Figs now determined that he would commence the engagement by a charge on his own part; and, accordingly, being a left-handed man, brought that arm into action, and hit out a couple of times with all his might—once at Mr. Cuff's left eye, and once upon his beautiful Roman nose.

Cuff went down this time, to the astonishment of the

assembly. "Well hit, by Jove," says little Osborne, clapping his man on the back. "Give it him with the left, Figs, my boy."

Figs' left made terrific play during all the rest of the combat. Cuff went down every time. At the sixth round there were almost as many fellows shouting out, "Go it, Figs," as there were youths exclaiming, "Go it, Cuff." At the twelfth round the latter champion was all abroad, as the saying is, and had lost all presence of mind and power of attack or defence. Figs, on the contrary, was as calm as a Quaker. His face being quite pale, his eyes shining open, and a great cut on his underlip bleeding profusely, gave this young fellow a fierce and ghastly air, which perhaps struck terror into many spectators. Nevertheless, his intrepid adversary prepared to close for the thirteenth time.

Cuff coming up full of pluck, but quite reeling and groggy, the Fig-merchant put in his left as usual on his adversary's nose, and sent him down for the last time.

"I think *that* will do for him," Figs said.

And now all the boys set up such a shout for Figs as would make you think he had been their darling champion through the whole battle; and as absolutely brought Dr. Swishtail out of his study, curious to know the cause of the uproar. He threatened to flog Figs violently, of course; but Cuff, who had come to himself by this time, and was washing his wounds, stood up and said, "It's my fault, sir—not Figs'—not Dobbin's. I was bullying a little boy; and he served me right." By which magnanimous speech he not only saved his conqueror a whipping, but got back all his ascendancy over the boys which his defeat had nearly cost him.

Young Osborne wrote home to his parents an account of the transaction.

In consequence of Dobbin's victory, his character rose prodigiously in the estimation of all his schoolfellows, and the name of Figs, which had been a byword of reproach, became as respectable and popular a nickname as any other in use in the school.

—*William Makepeace Thackeray*
From *Vanity Fair*

STUDY AND ENJOYMENT

1. Why do you like Dobbin? How did he get the nickname, "Figs"? What effect did the fight have on his popularity with the other boys?
2. What details in the story cause you to dislike Cuff? Did he have any good quality?
3. What is your opinion of young Osborne?
4. *Puerile*, childish; *bruited* (pronounced "brooted") noised, or told, far and wide; *condescended to hold personal communication*, stooped to talk; *incentive*, a reason that stirs one to act; *contemptuous*, sneering; *magnanimous*, generous, big-hearted; *ascendancy*, influence or power over others; *prodigiously*, greatly.

NOW A LONG GOOD-BYE TO YOU, MY DEAR

In Britain, in olden times, not every boy or girl went to school, but children grew up in a world of song. While mothers spun, weaved, milked, or churned, while fathers reaped, fished, herded, or hunted, they sang songs about their work. Here is a sea-shanty, or chanty, sung as men toiled aboard ship. You can picture sailors hauling on ropes in time to the song.

Now a long good-bye to you, my dear,
　With a heave-oh haul,　[*Chorus*]
And a last farewell and a long farewell,
　And good-morning, ladies all.　[*Chorus*]

For we're outward bound to New York town;
　With a heave-oh haul,
And you'll wave to us till the sun goes down,
　And good-morning, ladies all.

And when we get to New York town,
　With a heave-oh haul,
Oh, it's there we'll drink, and sorrows drown,
　And good-morning, ladies all.

When we're back once more in London Docks,
  With a heave-oh haul,
All the pretty girls will come in flocks,
  And good-morning, ladies all.

And Poll, and Bet, and Sue will say:
  With a heave-oh haul,
"Oh it's here comes Jack with his three years' pay,"
  And good-morning, ladies all.

So a long good-bye to you, my dear,
  With a heave-oh haul,
And a last farewell and a long farewell,
  And good-morning, ladies all.

—*Traditional*

STUDY AND ENJOYMENT

1. One boy or girl might read the lines aloud, with other members of the class joining in the chorus, and miming the rope pulling.
2. Why not learn to sing some sea-shanties such as *Blow the Man Down*, *Shenandoah*, and *Billy Boy?*

OLD GREY SQUIRREL

A great while ago, there was a school-boy.
  He lived in a cottage by the sea;
And the very first thing he could remember
  Was the rigging of the schooners by the quay.

He could watch them, when he woke, from his window,
  With the tall cranes hoisting out the freight;
And he used to think of shipping as a sea-cook,
  And sailing to the Golden Gate.

For he used to buy the yellow penny dreadfuls,
  And read them where he fished for conger-eels,
And listened to the lapping of the water,
  The green and oily water round the keels.

SAILOR-MEN A-DANCING IN THE MOONLIGHT

There were trawlers with their shark-mouthed flat-fish,
    And red nets hanging out to dry,
And the skate the skipper kept because he liked 'em,
    And landsmen never knew the fish to fry.

There were brigantines with timber out of Norway,
    Oozing with the syrups of the pine,
There were rusty dusty schooners out of Sunderland,
    And ships of the Blue Cross line.

And to tumble down a hatch into the cabin
    Was better than the best of broken rules;
For the smell of 'em was like a Christmas dinner,
    And the feel of 'em was like a box of tools.

And before he went to sleep in the evening,
    The very last thing that he could see
Was the sailor-men a-dancing in the moonlight
    By the capstan that stood upon the quay.

He is perched upon a high stool in London,
   The Golden Gate is very far away.
For they caught him, and they caged him like a squirrel.
   He is totting up accounts, and going grey.

He will never, never, never sail to 'Frisco.
   But the very last thing that he will see
Will be sailor-men a-dancing in the sunrise
   By the capstan that stood upon the quay. . . .

To the tune of an old concertina,
   By the capstan that stood upon the quay.

—Alfred Noyes

STUDY AND ENJOYMENT

1. How did the boy learn so much about ships? How did he learn about foreign lands? What did he dream of doing when he grew up?
2. What stanzas tell of his life as a man? How was he disappointed? How did he earn his living? Suggest reasons that might have kept him at home. What sight will he see in his mind's eye as he dies?
3. *Quay* (pronounced "kee") dock; *Golden Gate*, entrance to the harbour of San Francisco, California; *Sunderland*, port on east coast of England; *capstan*, revolving barrel for winding cable; *totting*, totalling.
4. "They caught him and they caged him like a squirrel." One kind of cage for a small animal was a wire cylinder mounted in a frame in such a way that the cage spun around when the animal ran. Why was the accountant like an "old grey squirrel"?

DAVID AND THE WAITER

You may have read "A House in a Boat" earlier in this Reader. If so, you have met David Copperfield, who again appears in this selection. David's father having died, his mother marries for a second time. Mr. Murdstone, her second husband, does not like David and sends him away to boarding school. David is now on his way to the school, having been driven by a carrier, Barkis, to an inn, where he is to have dinner and take the stage-coach to London.

The coach was in the yard, shining very much all over, but without any horses to it as yet; and it looked, in that state, as if nothing was more unlikely than its ever going to

London. I was thinking this, and wondering what would ultimately become of my box, which Mr. Barkis had put down on the yard pavement by the pole (he having driven up the yard to turn his cart), and also what would ultimately become of me, when a lady looked out of a bow window where some fowls and joints of meat were hanging up, and said.

"Is that the little gentleman from Blunderstone?"

"Yes, ma'am," I said.

"What name?" inquired the lady.

"Copperfield, ma'am," I said.

"That won't do," returned the lady. "Nobody's dinner is paid for here, in that name."

"Is it Murdstone, ma'am?" I said.

"If you're Master Murdstone," said the lady, "why do you go and give another name first?"

I explained to the lady how it was, who then rang a bell, and called out, "William! show the coffee room!" Upon which a waiter came running out of a kitchen on the opposite side of the yard, to show it, and seemed a great deal surprised when he found he was only to show it to me

It was a large, long room with some large maps in it. I doubt if I could have felt much stranger if the maps had been real foreign countries, and I cast away in the middle of them. I felt it was taking a liberty to sit down, with my cap in my hand, on the corner of the chair nearest the door; and when the waiter laid a cloth on purpose for me, and put a set of casters on it, I think I must have turned red all over with modesty.

He brought me some chops and vegetables, and took the covers off in such a bouncing manner that I was afraid I must have given him some offense. But he greatly relieved my mind by putting a chair for me at the table, and saying very affably, "Now, six-foot, come on!"

I thanked him, and took my seat at the board; but found it extremely difficult to handle my knife and fork with anything like dexterity, or to avoid splashing myself with the gravy, while he was standing opposite, staring so hard, and making me blush in the most dreadful manner every time I caught his eye. After watching me into the second chop, he said:

"There's half a pint of ale for you. Will you have it now?"

I thanked him, and said yes. Upon which he poured it out of a jug into a large tumbler, and held it up against the light, and made it look beautiful.

"My eye!" he said. "It seems a good deal, don't it?"

"It does seem a good deal," I answered, with a smile. For it was quite delightful to me to find him so pleasant. He was a twinkle-eyed, pimple-faced man, with his hair standing upright all over his head; and as he stood with one arm akimbo, holding up the glass to the light with the other hand, he looked quite friendly.

"There was a gentleman here yesterday," he said, "a stout gentleman, by the name of Topsawyer—perhaps you know him!"

"No," I said, "I don't think—"

"In breeches and gaiters, broad-brimmed hat, grey coat, speckled choker," said the waiter.

"No," I said bashfully, "I haven't the pleasure—"

"He came in here," said the waiter, looking at the light through the tumbler, "ordered a glass of this ale—*would* order it—I told him not—drank it, and fell dead. It was too old for him. It oughtn't to be drawn; that's the fact."

I was very much shocked to hear of this melancholy accident, and said I thought I had better have some water.

"Why, you see," said the waiter, still looking at the light through the tumbler, with one of his eyes shut up, "our people don't like things being ordered and left. It offends 'em. But *I'll* drink it, if you like. I'm used to it, and use is everything. I don't think it'll hurt me if I throw my head back, and take it off quick. Shall I?"

I replied that he would much oblige me by drinking it, if he thought he could do it safely, but by no means otherwise. When he did throw his head back and take it off quick, I had a horrible fear, I confess, of seeing him meet the fate of the lamented Mr. Topsawyer, and fall lifeless on the carpet. But it didn't hurt him. On the contrary, I thought he seemed the fresher for it.

"What have we got here?" he said, putting a fork into my dish. "Not chops!"

"Chops," I said.

"Lord bless my soul!" he exclaimed, "I didn't know they were chops. Why, a chop's the very thing to take off the bad effects of that beer! Ain't it lucky?"

So he took a chop by the bone in one hand, and a potato in the other, and ate away with a very good appetite, to my extreme satisfaction. He afterward took another chop and another potato; and after that, another chop and another potato. When we had done, he brought me a pudding, and having set it before me, seemed to ruminate, and to become absent in his mind for some moments.

"How's the pie?" he said, rousing himself.

"It's a pudding," I made answer.

"Pudding?" he exclaimed. "Why, bless me, so it is! What!" looking at it nearer. "You don't mean to say it's a batter pudding!"

"Yes, it is indeed."

"Why, a batter pudding," he said, taking up a table-spoon, "is my favourite pudding! Ain't that lucky? Come on, little 'un, and see who'll get most."

The waiter certainly got most. He entreated me more than once to come in and win, but what with his tablespoon to my teaspoon, his dispatch to my dispatch, and his appetite to my appetite, I was left far behind at the first mouthful, and had no chance with him. I never saw anyone enjoy a pudding so much, I think; and he laughed, when it was all gone, as if his enjoyment of it lasted still.

Finding him so very friendly and companionable, it was then that I asked for the pen and ink and paper, to write to Peggotty. He not only brought it immediately, but was good enough to look over me while I wrote the letter. When I had finished it, he asked me where I was going to school.

I said, "near London," which was all I knew.

"Oh, my eye!" he said, looking very low-spirited, "I am sorry for that."

"Why?" I asked him.

"O Lord!" he said, shaking his head, "that's the school where they broke the boy's ribs—two ribs—a little boy he was. I should say he was—let me see—how old are you, about?"

I told him between eight and nine—almost nine.

"That's just his age," he said. "He was eight years and six months old when they broke his first rib; eight years and eight months old when they broke his second, and did for him."

I could not disguise from myself, or from the waiter, that this was an uncomfortable coincidence, and inquired how it was done. His answer was not cheering to my spirits, for it consisted of two dismal words, "With whopping."

The blowing of the coach horn in the yard was a seasonable diversion, which made me get up and hesitatingly inquire, in the mingled pride and diffidence of having a purse (which I took out of my pocket), if there were anything to pay.

"There's a sheet of letter paper," he returned. "Did you ever buy a sheet of letter paper?"

I could not remember that I ever had.

"It's dear," he said, "on account of the duty. Three pence. That's the way we're taxed in this country. There's nothing else, except the waiter. Never mind the ink. *I* lose by that."

"What should you—what should I—how much ought I to—what would it be right to pay the waiter, if you please?" I stammered, blushing.

"If I hadn't a family, and that family hadn't the cowpox," said the waiter, "I wouldn't take a sixpence. If I didn't support a aged pairint, and a lovely sister"—here the waiter was greatly agitated—"I wouldn't take a farthing. If I had a good place, and was treated well here, I should beg acceptance of a trifle, instead of taking of it. But I live on broken wittles—and I sleep on the coals"—here the waiter burst into tears.

I was very much concerned for his misfortunes, and felt that any recognition short of ninepence would be mere brutality and hardness of heart. Therefore I gave him one of my three bright shillings, which he received with much humility and veneration, and spun up with his thumb, directly afterward, to try the goodness of.

It was a little disconcerting to me, to find, when I was being helped up behind the coach, that I was supposed to have eaten all the dinner without any assistance. I discovered this from overhearing the lady in the bow window say to the guard: "Take care of that child, George, or he'll burst!" and observing that the woman-servants who were about the place came out to look and giggle at me as a young phenomenon. My unfortunate friend the waiter, who had quite recovered his spirits, did not appear to be disturbed by this, but joined in the general admiration without being at all confused. If I had any doubt of him, I suppose this half awakened it; but I am inclined to believe that with the simple confidence of a child, and the natural reliance of a child upon superior years (qualities I am very sorry any children should prematurely change for worldly wisdom), I had no serious mistrust of him on the whole, even then.

—*Charles Dickens*
From *David Copperfield*

STUDY AND ENJOYMENT

1. How did the waiter manage to get most of David's dinner?
2. Read sentences in the story to show that David was (i) lonely, (ii) shy, (iii) frightened.
3. Select four phrases which help us to form a clear picture of the waiter.
4. Which part of the story is most amusing?
5. What made David half suspect the waiter of deceiving him?
6. *Ultimately*, at last; *dexterity*, skill; *veneration*, respect; *disconcerting*, upsetting to one's self-possession.

AFTER SCHOOL

When Bliss Carman, in 1904, gathered all his poems into two large volumes, he wanted this lyric placed last—a place of honour in a book.

When all my lessons have been learned,
    And the last year at school is done,
I shall put up my books and games;
"Good-bye, my fellows, every one!"

The dusty road will not seem long,
    Nor twilight lonely, nor forlorn
The everlasting whippoorwills
    That lead me back where I was born.

And there beside the open door,
    In a large country dim and cool,
Her waiting smile shall hear at last,
"Mother, I am come home from school."

—Bliss Carman

STUDY AND ENJOYMENT

1. "After school" has many meanings. To some of you it may suggest games and fun; to some it may mean going home; to others it may mean the time when schooldays are over, and earning a living has begun. In this poem Bliss Carman thinks of life as a "school," and of his passing from this life to the great beyond as going "home."
2. What experiences in life might be meant by "my books"? by "games"?
3. One great influence upon Carman was his mother. When she died, he missed her to the end of his life. How does this explain the last stanza?

READ A BOOK

Glengarry School Days. By Ralph Connor. McClelland.

Tom Brown's Schooldays. By Thomas Hughes. Ginn. The classic story of life at Rugby, the English public school.

Otto of the Silver Hand. By Howard Pyle. Scribners. How the little son of a robber baron is brought up in a monastery, and later becomes a man of peace and good will.

Stalky and Co. By Rudyard Kipling. Macmillan. The deeds and misdeeds of three English boys at school.

The One-Eyed Trapper. By J. M. Gray. Macmillan. A yarn for boys, set in a Canadian boarding school that goes in more for sports and wood-lore than for bookish activities.

VIII

Skyways of Freedom

EAGLES OF FREEDOM

To the R.A.F.

Never since English ships went out
  To singe the beard of Spain,
Or English sea-dogs diced with death
  Along the Spanish Main;
Never since Drake and Raleigh won
  Our freedom of the seas,
Have sons of Britain dared and done
  More valiantly than these.

Whether at midnight or at noon,
  Through mist or open sky,
Eagles of freedom, all our hearts
  Are up with you on high;
While Britain's mighty ghosts look down
  From realms beyond the sun,
And whisper, as their record pales,
  Their breathless, deep, "Well done!"

—Alfred Noyes

STUDY AND ENJOYMENT

1. During the summer of 1940, the Nazis resolved to secure undisputed command of the air over Britain. Raid after raid swept over England, but each time the Royal Air Force answered blow for blow. Winston Churchill's great tribute to British airmen, "Never before in the field of human conflict has so much been owed by so many to so few," is echoed in this poem.
2. What two "mighty ghosts" of Britain's history are named in the poem? Name several others who might have been mentioned.
3. Why do you think each of the following expressions is well put?: (i) "singe the beard of Spain"; (ii) "diced with death"; (iii) "eagles of freedom"; (iv) "their record pales."
4. In what lines does the greatness of the R.A.F. receive the highest praise?

LIE IN THE DARK AND LISTEN

As the Second Great War went on, the battle of the skies shifted from Britain to the continent. This poem, also in praise of the R.A.F., is addressed to civilians.

Lie in the dark and listen.
It's clear tonight, so they're flying high,
Hundreds of them, thousands perhaps,
Riding the icy, moonlit sky,
Men, machinery, bombs, and maps,
Altimeters and guns and charts,
Coffee, sandwiches, fleece-lined boots,
Bones and muscles and minds and hearts,
English saplings with English roots
Deep in the earth they've left below.
Lie in the dark and let them go;
Lie in the dark and listen.

Lie in the dark and listen.
They're going over in waves and waves
High above villages, hills and streams
Country churches and little graves
And little citizens' worried dreams;
Very soon they'll have reached the sea
And far below them will lie the bays
And cliffs and sands where they used to be
Taken for summer holidays.
Lie in the dark and let them go;
Theirs is a world we'll never know.
Lie in the dark and listen.

—Noel Coward

STUDY AND ENJOYMENT

1. What lines express the poet's feeling that civilians like himself seem unimportant when faced with the shining courage of the airmen?
2. The first stanza gives you a glimpse inside the planes. What things connected with flying and fighting can you see? What everyday things are there?
3. What lines tell about the aviators as boys? as men?
4. What additional meaning has the phrase "in the dark" beyond simply the darkness of night time?

OTHER LIGHTS KEEP BURNING
London under Bombardment

I, who am known as London, have faced stern times before,
Having fought and ruled and traded for a thousand years
and more;
I knew the Roman legions and the harsh-voiced Danish
hordes;
I heard the Saxon revels, saw blood on the Norman swords.
But, though I am scarred by battle, my grim defenders vow
Never was I so stately nor so well-beloved as now.
The lights that burn and glitter in the exile's lonely dream,
The lights of Piccadilly, and those that used to gleam
Down Regent Street and Kingsway may now no longer
shine,
But other lights keep burning, and their splendour, too, is
mine,
Seen in the work-worn faces and glimpsed in the steadfast
eyes
When little homes lie broken and death descends from the
skies.
The bombs have shattered my churches, have torn my
streets apart,
But they have not bent my spirit and they shall not break
my heart.
For my people's faith and courage are the lights of London
town
Which still would shine in legends though my last broad
bridge were down.
                                                    —*Greta Briggs*

STUDY AND ENJOYMENT

1. It is good to read this selection after "Lie in the Dark and Listen," for this poem tells of the courage of the ordinary men and women under the blitz. Who is represented as speaker in this poem? What incidents in past history are mentioned?

2. Piccadilly, Regent Street and Kingsway are well known streets in London. Why were their lights not burning? What splendid "lights" can the poet still see?

3. When Lord Wavell was returning to Cyrenaica in April, 1941, to deal with
the counter attack of Rommel, the brilliant German general, he was
not feeling very comfortable.   He knew that he had insufficient strength
for the task.   In the bomber in which he was flying, he read this poem in
a newspaper, and committed it to memory.   It brought him much
encouragement.   Do you understand why it would do so?

THE ADVENTURE OF THE *ALTMARK*

On December 17, 1939, the German raider *Graf Spee* ingloriously
scuttled herself in the harbour of Montevideo, to which she had fled to
escape the British destroyers *Exeter*, *Ajax*, and *Achilles*.   Before destroy-
ing herself, the vessel landed her prisoners—naval officers captured during
her autumn raids.   Most of these officers had been transferred, after
capture, to a German tanker named the *Altmark*, a floating prison camp
that was crowded and uncomfortable in the extreme.   So crowded had
it become, as further raids furnished further prisoners, that these officers
had been returned to the *Graf Spee*.   Upon reaching land, their first step
was to give the British Embassy a description of the *Altmark*.

Seamen's memories do not make many errors in
recording the appearance of a ship that has harboured them
and their mates in captivity.   The description was detailed
and accurate.   It was immediately communicated to the
British Admiralty.   The hunt was up.

The seas are wide, however, and it was not until the
morning of February 16 that three reconnaissance machines
of the Royal Air Force sighted the *Altmark*.

"A beautiful day," wrote one of the pilots, "with
gorgeous sunshine and a Mediterranean sky.   Visibility
increased to more than 40 miles.   The coast of Norway
with its snow-covered mountains was visible more than 30
miles away.   Fifteen miles ahead I spotted a smudge of
smoke, and fifteen seconds later a grey ship with funnel aft,
the distinctive feature of the *Altmark*.   We flew up to her at
1000 feet and inspected her through glasses at a mile range.
Then we turned in on top of her for a close inspection.

"As we dived my eyes were riveted on the stern, searching for a name.   I saw letters about a foot high.   Because of
the speed at which we were diving the letters seemed to

dance in a jumble. I expected that when they could be read they would spell a Norwegian name. I could not suppress a whoop of joy when I saw that they read *Altmark*."

That afternoon the *Altmark* was sighted by a force of destroyers sent to intercept her. She was then steaming south, hugging the Norwegian coast and escorted by two Norwegian gunboats. At a point where the southern end of Norway curves a little to the east, in latitude 58° 18′ N., there is a little fiord called Josing fiord. The entrance is only two hundred yards wide; at its widest this inlet is barely a quarter of a mile across, and extends inland a little over a mile. The *Altmark* turned into this fiord accompanied by her Norwegian escort.

It seemed incredible to the senior officer of the destroyer flotilla in the *Cossack* that the *Altmark* should be ceremoniously conducted on her voyage to Germany by Norwegian men-of-war if she really had three hundred prisoners on board. *Cossack* accordingly followed the Norwegian gunboats into Josing fiord to ask for enlightenment.

The cliffs rose sheer from the water for hundreds of feet, streaked with snow and reflected in the glassy surface of the fiord. From a little settlement of fishermen's houses on the starboard hand all the inhabitants came crowding to watch the development of this incredible drama. The *Altmark* had proceeded some distance up the fiord, and the two gunboats turned to meet the *Cossack*. The Norwegian officer stated emphatically that the *Altmark* had been examined the previous day, that she was authorized to travel through territorial waters with a Norwegian pilot on board, that she carried no armament, and that he was ignorant of the presence of any British prisoners on board.

Rather astonished by these statements but accepting them without question, *Cossack* immediately withdrew outside territorial waters and asked for Admiralty instructions.

She got them. They were the kind of orders naval officers pray for in times of crisis. They were curt and perfectly clear. If the British prisoners were not on board *Altmark*, where were they? Only one person could answer that question, and that was the captain of the *Altmark*. The *Cossack* again entered Josing fiord to solve the mystery.

It was now dark, a brilliant moonlit night. The little houses ashore were all brilliantly illuminated. The beam of the *Cossack's* searchlight immediately located the *Altmark* in the pack ice at the far end of the fiord. The *Altmark* also switched on a searchlight and directed it onto the *Cossack's* bridge, trying to impede her navigation, and began signalling with a Morse lamp the rather redundant information that she was in Norway.

One of the Norwegian gunboats closed the *Cossack*, and the latter asked permission to send a joint British and Norwegian search party on board *Altmark* in the Norwegian gunboat.

The Norwegian captain replied that his ship was not able to reach *Altmark* through the ice, but he finally consented to go in *Cossack* and personally accompany the boarding party.

The *Altmark* was now manœuvring stern first out of the ice, towards the *Cossack*, in an endeavour to ram her. By the most dexterous handling of his ship the captain of the *Cossack* laid his bows alongside the stern of the *Altmark* and the first lieutenant jumped onto the *Altmark's* poop, caught a rope flung to him, and secured the two ships together. A boarding party of thirty men and two officers were in readiness. The officers were armed with revolvers and the men with rifles and bayonets. As a precaution against impulsive shooting the cutouts of the rifles were closed and only the magazines loaded. Immediately the ships were secured, the boarding party leaped on board.

The upper deck of the *Altmark* was brightly illuminated and there was not a soul visible. Followed by a party of his men, the first lieutenant ran forward along a plank

THEY WERE CONFRONTED BY AN OFFICER WITH A PISTOL

bridge spanning the after well deck and came to a steel door leading to the bridge and superstructure. Bursting through this they were confronted by a German officer with a pistol levelled at them, but realizing the futility of it he shrugged his shoulders and threw it on the deck.

The captain and officers were found on the bridge working the engine-room telegraphs and sullenly admitted they had British prisoners on board. The telegraphs were promptly stopped, but by this time the *Altmark* had so much sternway that she grounded stern first on some rocks on the opposite side of the fiord, on the only shelving beach there was.

In the meanwhile the Norwegian officer had decided after all not to accompany the boarding party and returned to his ship. The *Cossack* cast off and slipped clear of the *Altmark* to avoid sharing her fate on the rocks.

While the first lieutenant was getting control of the bridge, a lieutenant and a gunner were rounding up the German crew between decks. Suddenly a shot rang out in one of the alleyways and the gunner fell, seriously wounded. He was taken to the sick bay where the German doctor attended to him. Little melees were going on all over the ship as the Germans were overpowered and placed under guard. A boat full of Germans had been lowered and dropped through the ice, smashing it. These men stayed where they were, clinging to the life lines. Another party escaped with rifles across the ice to the shore. They were presumably the armed guard from the *Graf Spee*, put on board to guard the prisoners. They kept up an intermittent fire from the land, but hit nobody.

Once the officers were under guard the first lieutenant took the captain down to show where the prisoners were. The sentries had fled with the keys. The British boarders smashed locks with rifle butts and pried off the heavy hatches to the hold

"The Navy's here!" they shouted. "Come up out of it!"

They came, two hundred and ninety-nine of them, like men in a dream. And then they saw the familiar British uniforms and faces grinning at them under shrapnel helmets and they knew it was over. They mustered on the forecastle under their officers, cheering wildly.

The *Cossack* then came alongside bow to bow and the prisoners were transferred with their belongings. She was delayed by the rescue from the water of a German seaman who had jumped overboard.

The German officers and crew were brought onto the *Altmark's* forecastle, and the boarding party, carrying the wounded officer with them, re-embarked in *Cossack*. Once more the *Cossack* turned her bows towards the entrance and threaded her way through the navigational risks outside, which, in the words of the Norway pilot, "can only be taken by small vessels with local knowledge." The *Cossack's* navigating officer had never set eyes on the place till that afternoon.

And then she steamed full speed for home.

The following afternoon, after weary months of captivity, the *Altmark* prisoners found themselves once more on British soil. Once more free. Free as the winds of heaven.

—"Bartimeus"

STUDY AND ENJOYMENT

1. What distinctive features of the *Altmark* enabled the Royal Air Force reconnaissance machines to spot her?
2. Why did the *Cossack* follow the Norwegian gunboats into the fiord? Why did she withdraw? What orders did the Admiralty give her then?
3. In what ways did the *Altmark* try to prevent the approach of the *Cossack*?
4. What details show the skilful seamanship of the *Cossack's* officers?
5. This is what Winston Churchill said about the rescue of the prisoners aboard the *Altmark*: "And to Nelson's signal of one hundred and thirty-five years ago 'England expects that every man will do his duty,' there may now be added the not less proud reply, 'The Navy is here'."

THE FIGHTING *TÉMÉRAIRE*

The *Téméraire* (pronounced Tā-mā-rār) was the second ship in Nelson's line of battle at Trafalgar, October 21, 1805. Some thirty years later, unfit for further service, the ship was sold and towed down the Thames River to be broken up.

It was eight bells ringing,
    For the morning watch was done,
And the gunner's lads were singing,
    As they polished every gun.
It was eight bells ringing,
And the gunner's lads were singing,
For the ship she rode a-swinging,
    As they polished every gun.

Oh! to see the linstock lighting,
   Téméraire! Téméraire!
Oh! to hear the round shot biting,
   Téméraire! Téméraire!
Oh! to see the linstock lighting,
And to hear the round shot biting,
For we're all in love with fighting
   On the Fighting *Téméraire.*

It was noontide ringing,
   And the battle just begun,
When the ship her way was winging,
   As they loaded every gun.
It was noontide ringing
When the ship her way was winging,
And the gunner's lads were singing
   As they loaded every gun.

There'll be many grim and gory,
   Téméraire! Téméraire!
There'll be few to tell the story,
   Téméraire! Téméraire!
There'll be many grim and gory,
There'll be few to tell the story,
But we'll all be one in glory
   With the Fighting *Téméraire.*

There's a far bell ringing
   At the setting of the sun,
And a phantom voice is singing
   Of the great days done.
There's a far bell ringing,
And a phantom voice is singing
Of renown for ever clinging
   To the great days done.

Now the sunset breezes shiver,
Téméraire! Téméraire!
And she's fading down the river,
Téméraire! Téméraire!
Now the sunset breezes shiver,
And she's fading down the river,
But in England's song for ever
She's the Fighting *Téméraire.*

—*Sir Henry Newbolt*

STUDY AND ENJOYMENT

1. Each stanza, with the chorus that follows it, gives one picture in the life of the ship. The first might be entitled, "Before the Battle." What titles do you suggest for the other two pictures?

2. *Eight Bells.* At sea the day is divided into watches of four hours each, and each watch is marked off in half hours by the strokes of a bell. Eight bells indicates the end of a watch. *Linstock*, a cleft stick which held the rope-match with which the old-fashioned cannon was fired.

3. This poem has been set to stirring music. If you read it aloud you will know why. There is music just in its rhythm and in the sound of its words. Dwell a little on the "n" and "m" sounds in the last stanza and chorus, to bring out the full beauty of the verse.

4. Turner, the great English artist, painted a picture of the *Téméraire* being towed down the Thames to Deptford. In the background of the picture, a red sun is setting. Try to see a copy of this picture, as it will help you to catch the mood of the last stanza and chorus.

SUBMARINE EPIC

Since the surrendered German Fleet disappeared beneath the waters of Scapa Flow, theatrically scuttled by its own officers, there have been many mists over the North Sea.

One of these mists cleared recently to reveal a British submarine proceeding on patrol. Her log notes laconically that a full gale was blowing.

This made observations through the periscope difficult, because at one minute it was in the depths of a valley of grey water and the next in the spray of the crest.

She observed a neutral fishing fleet riding out the gale at its nets and dived beneath them to avoid unnecessary publicity. Neutral merchantmen, wallowing through the scud, sent her down like a coot.

At night she rose to the surface and her navigator, a Royal Naval Reserve Canadian Pacific man, observed the stars in their courses and fixed her position.

These uneventful happenings brought her, early one morning, to her allotted patrol area in enemy waters, and at the first hint of dawn she dived.

Shortly before breakfast the detonation of a depth charge quite close to her suggested emphatically that she was in the vicinity of enemy forces. Her captain decided to have a look at them through his periscope, and put his ballast pump in action.

Another depth charge promptly exploded much closer, blowing some of his fuses. It was unpleasantly obvious that he was being hunted. He stopped all his machinery, holding his breath, as it were, to listen.

The crew lay down to conserve valuable oxygen consumed by movement. During the next hour they counted the detonations of six explosions as the enemy groped about in search of them with sweep wires, electrically-operated bombs, and depth charges.

The submarine could do nothing except remain silent on the bottom, motionless.

To relieve the monotony, it seemed good to the crew to start a 6d. sweepstake on the time at which the next explosion would shake the hull.

An able seaman moved softly down the narrow alleyway among the motionless men, booking their bets against next pay day.

The bombardment intensified. For the next hour the explosions averaged one every two minutes. They grew gradually more distant. Then there was a lull.

About tea-time the strained, weary men in the submarine heard a wire scraping over the after jumping-stay. This was the bony fingers of death clawing at them with a vengeance. They listened tense, expectant.

A series of bumps thudded along the hull as if a giant were stamping along it in hob-nailed boots.

Then what they awaited happened. A shattering explosion seemed to contract the hull of the submarine as their own hearts contracted.

All lights were extinguished, there was everywhere the crash of broken glass, and in the silence that followed the sound of water spurting and the hiss of air escaping from the high-pressure air-system.

Portable electric lights revealed enough of the catastrophe. One motor and both engines were out of action. From half a dozen leaks in the air system, air hissed as from a punctured tire.

Working as noiselessly as possible, they contrived to restore the lighting and stop the air leaks as best they could.

Then, the air gradually growing fouler because they had been a long time submerged, they sat or lay about waiting.

The First Lieutenant bethought him of a bottle of boiled sweets and passed them round as a solace. It reminded someone else of a bag of peppermint-drops he possessed. He crept round the dripping spaces offering them to his shipmates, who sucked them appreciatively. The air was making breathing more difficult every minute.

Meanwhile, the Lieutenant in command was deciding on his course of action. As soon as he knew by the clock that darkness had fallen on the face of the sea, he mustered his little band of officers and men and told them of his decision.

To stay where they were meant to die the death of rats in a trap.

If the ballast tanks still held—and in his heart he doubted it—he intended to blow the water out of them and rise to the surface. Once there, although his ship was helpless as a log, he intended to fight to the death.

The crew accepted the alternative joyfully, exchanging gasping jokes among themselves. They turned-to, loaded the torpedo tubes, Lewis gun and rifles, and stacked ammunition ready for the gun.

As a last grim measure they prepared a demolition charge to blow their ship to pieces rather than let her fall into the hands of the enemy.

Finally, when all was ready for what they believed would be their last fight, they blew the tanks and, like the achievement of a miracle, the submarine rose floundering to the surface.

In a narrative of this description it is well for several reasons to avoid names. But one name must be mentioned —that of the firm of Cammell Laird, who built the submarine.

Had one riveter shirked or botched his job neither she nor her crew could have survived even thus far. Only the best steel and the best workmanship could have held the hull together through the ordeal of that day.

In spite of their efforts to stop the leaks, enough air had escaped inside the submarine from the air cylinders to raise the pressure to a dangerous point.

Mindful of this, her captain, who is lightly built, had to guard against the danger of being blown through the hatch when it was opened. He selected a 14-stone signalman to cling to his legs and, thus "anchored," threw open the hatch.

So great was the rush of air that it blew his heavy binoculars, which hung by a strap, vertically above his head.

He climbed out and looked anxiously about him. It was a clear night with a moderate swell. There was nothing in sight.

With periscope gone, wireless smashed, communication pipes crushed as if squeezed by the fist of a giant, and engines disabled, unable to dive again and with only one motor in action, even now the prospect was grim enough.

He crawled away from the scene on his remaining motor, while the warrant engineer below, with all the wizardry at his command, began a desperate attempt to put life into his distorted and damaged machinery.

Three hours after they had surfaced he reported the starboard engine ready and two hours later the port.

They had now, thanks to this man and his devoted little staff, a fighting chance of life. With water still pouring in from the leaks, trusting to the good providence of God, his own resources, the devotion and skill of his officers and men, and perhaps luck—the captain gallantly made his way on the surface all night.

In the dawn his wireless operator modestly reported another feat of magic. He had repaired the wireless.

Their first thought was to send a warning to sister submarines on patrol in the vicinity to avoid temporarily the area where trouble could be had for less than the asking.

After that, another to their base, asking for a helping hand.

Lying on the surface like a wounded duck, they saw in the afternoon a flight of enemy bombers approaching them. Wearily they again made preparations for the fight that must finish them.

The 'planes passed a couple of miles to seaward and disappeared. An hour later they returned. Once more the gun was manned, rifles distributed. The enemy disappeared again without seeing them.

The call for help brought destroyers racing across the North Sea to a rendezvous they reached at midnight. Cruisers and an aircraft carrier appeared with the daylight, and a few hours later the Fleet, terrible in its might, arrived to the support of its wounded cub.

An air attack by the enemy bombing 'planes crumpled under the anti-aircraft fire of the cruisers and the attacks of the fighters sent up by the carrier.

In due course the submarine returned to her base without further molestation.

The lieutenant in command found a letter awaiting him. It was from a relative in the country. "We hardly realize there is a war on," read the opening sentence.

He folded it reflectively and put it in his pocket to answer a little later.

—The Daily Telegraph

STUDY AND ENJOYMENT

1. Why did the lieutenant in command decide to go to the surface after dark? Explain: "As a last grim measure they prepared a demolition charge."
2. Scapa Flow is a channel in the Orkney Islands. It was at Scapa Flow, in June, 1919, that the German commander sank most of his fleet which had surrendered to the British in 1918.
3. Explain the meaning of the following terms: periscope, depth charge, aircraft carrier, ballast, torpedo, binoculars, riveters. You may need to consult reference books as well as your dictionary.
4. Why is the letter mentioned at the end of the account? How did it make the lieutenant feel?
5. An epic, strictly speaking, is a long heroic poem written in lofty style, but, in modern use, the word is applied to any tale of heroic deeds told in a vivid way.

THE BROWNS

There was a Brown at Stamford, nine hundred years ago,
When Harold fought Hardrada with the Saxon bill and bow;
A poor rough churl with heavy hand and fingers blunt from
    toil—
But not the least he was of those that fought for English soil.

A hind who could not read or write, in hardened leather
    clad,
No mail to turn the levelled spear, no shining blade he had;
But dearly did he sell his life, pierced through with many
    a shaft,
And died beside his battleaxe, his hand upon its haft.

THERE WAS A BROWN ...

There was a Brown at Crecy, when Edward routed France,
First in the rank that knelt to break the cavalry's advance;
A peasant from the plough he was, a rude unlettered thing,
But he had a heart for England, and an arm for England's
    King.

One skill he had, and nothing more; one art alone he knew—
To string and draw with dying hands the bow of tautened
    yew;
All that he had to give—his life—a thousand others gave;
But not the least he was of those that filled a Flemish grave.

There was a Brown of Devon, who sailed from Plymouth
    Hoe
With Francis Drake his admiral, four hundred years ago;
A yeoman born he was, a man of scanty speech and plain—
But well he loved the English fields he never saw again.

Nombre de Dios' bells rang sweet on incense-laden air,
The hour the Spaniards led him forth with chanted praise
    and prayer;
They touched the fagots with the fire.   Unflinching at the
    stake
He showed them how the man can die that dies for
    England's sake.

There was a Brown with Nelson, when on a day of fame,
The Nile ran red with Gallic blood and burned with English
    flame;
No pacer of the quarter-deck—a common sailor he;
They found him stark beside his gun, and buried him at sea.

And there were candles lit at night, and London rang with
    cheers;
Triumphant pealed a thousand bells, their merriest chime
    for years;
Who was there looked for him in vain among the crowds
    ashore?
Who missed him, save the Gloucester home to which he
    came no more?

There was a Brown in Flanders, whose blue Canadian eyes
Beheld but once the gallant cliffs, the gates of England, rise;
Once, only once, he heard the lark above the shimmering
    wheat,
And once he saw the mellow spires adown an Oxford street.

Ah, youth is sweet upon the lips!—the wine of life is good;
He poured that wine with steadfast hands one day in
    Ypres wood.
Let it forget him if it may, the land that gave him birth—
There is a glory where he lies in green though alien earth.

One with the nameless are they all; there never was a Brown
Who rose above the rank and file to gain the world's renown;
One with a common host they are, by dale and copse and
    fen—
But England's made and moulded by the lives of common
    men.

And while a loyal heart is left to beat for God and King,
Long as above an English field the English throstles sing—
When the bugles call at morning, and the brave old flag's
    unfurled,
There'll be Browns to die for England till the judgment of
    the world!

                    —*Audrey Alexandra Brown*

STUDY AND ENJOYMENT

1. Some families must be very large, for so many people have the same sur-
name—Brown, Smith, or Jones, for example. When Audrey Alexandra
Brown, the Canadian poet, thought of all the Browns, she liked to think
that men of that name had helped to build and protect England and the
Empire all down through the years.
2. Make a list of the five conflicts mentioned in which a Brown took his part.
Note the leader in each struggle, and any weapon mentioned. Organize
your answer as follows:

	Conflict	Leader	Weapon mentioned
1.	. . . .	. . . .	. . . .
2.	. . . .	. . . .	. . . .
3.	. . . .	. . . .	. . . .
4.	. . . .	. . . .	. . . .
5.	. . . .	. . . .	. . . .

You might add a column for the year of the event, but you would need
to consult your history text-book if you did so.
3. Why were the Browns in the first two battles "unlettered"? Which
Brown was born in Canada?
4. This poem was written after the First Great War. Miss Brown had a
brother who was a Naval Officer in the Second Great War. He died
because of his wounds. Try to write two more stanzas about him.
If you don't wish to write verse, write a paragraph in prose about him.
5. One line in the second last stanza tells that the poem is meant not only for
the Browns but for common men of any name. Read that line. Do you
believe that our country's greatness does depend on ordinary people like
the Browns in the poem, and like us, if our hearts are loyal like theirs?

THIS WAS MY BROTHER

This was my brother
At Dieppe,
Quietly a hero
Who gave his life
Like a gift,
Withholding nothing.

His youth . . . his love
His enjoyment of being alive
His future, like a book
With half the pages still uncut—

This was my brother
At Dieppe—
The one who built me a doll house
When I was seven,
Complete to the last small picture frame,—
Nothing forgotten.

He was awfully good at fixing things,
At stepping into the breach when he was needed.

That's what he did at Dieppe;
He was needed.
And even Death must have been a little shamed
At his eagerness.

—Mona Gould

STUDY AND ENJOYMENT

1. Mona Gould, a Canadian poet, wrote this poem about her dearly loved brother who was killed at Dieppe. What do you find in the poem to show that he was young? that he was generous?
2. In the early hours of August 19, 1942, a striking force made up chiefly of Canadians, landed at Dieppe, a point on the German-occupied coast of France. Many casualties resulted from fierce fighting on the heavily defended beaches.

IN FLANDERS FIELDS

In Flanders fields the poppies blow
Between the crosses, row on row,
   That mark our place; and in the sky
   The larks, still bravely singing, fly,
Scarce heard amid the guns below.

We are the Dead.   Short days ago
We lived, felt dawn, saw sunset glow,
   Loved and were loved, and now we lie
   In Flanders fields.

Take up our quarrel with the foe:
To you from failing hands we throw
   The torch; be yours to hold it high.
   If ye break faith with us who die
We shall not sleep, though poppies grow
   In Flanders fields.

—John McCrae

STUDY AND ENJOYMENT

1. In France and Belgium, field poppies grow even among the wheat. John McCrae, a Canadian doctor serving in the First Great War, had often seen them. He saw them, too, among the rows and rows of little white crosses that marked the graves of Canadian soldiers. "In Flanders Fields" is the greatest poem to come out of that war. All the world knows it. It was written in twenty minutes, as Dr. McCrae sat on the back of an ambulance, mourning for a friend whose grave lay near at hand.

2. Who is represented as speaking in this poem? What are they telling the living, for whose freedom they died?

3. In the old days in Greece, the torch was passed from hand to hand in relay races. The winner carried it still lighted to the goal. Now explain in your own words the challenge of the last stanza.

IX

High Ways of Peace

THE HIGH WAY

To every man there openeth
A Way, and Ways, and a Way.

And the High Soul climbs the High Way,
And the Low Soul gropes the Low,
And in between, on the misty flats,
The rest drift to and fro.

But to every man there openeth
A High Way and a Low,
And every man decideth
The Way his Soul shall go.

—*John Oxenham*

STUDY AND ENJOYMENT

1. What three Ways are mentioned by the poet? Who is said to follow each? Why are the verbs "climbs," "gropes," and "drift" particularly well chosen?
2. "A Way and Ways and a Way." Perhaps this means that a man first sees a way ahead of him, and then sees a parting of two ways, and has to choose. He cannot travel both, and once he has chosen, there is only one road for him.
3. More than 2,600 years ago, Hesiod, a Greek poet, wrote: "Before the gates of excellence the high gods have placed sweat. Long is the road thereto and rough and steep at the first. But when the height is achieved then there is ease—though grievously hard in the winning." Express this description of a "high way" in your own words.
4. Proverbs 4: 14-19 is a Bible passage that speaks of two kinds of paths.

THE GREAT PHYSICIAN

William Osler was the youngest son in a family of nine. He was born in the little village of Bond Head, Ontario, about fifty miles north of Toronto, on July 12, 1849. His father, who was an Englishman, after having served fourteen years in the British Navy, decided to abandon that calling and enter the ministry of the Church of England. He was sent to Bond Head which, at that time, was on the edge of a wilderness. The surrounding country was settled largely by immigrants from Britain whose courage, love of adventure and willingness to face pioneer hardships had led them to seek new homes overseas.

Here is a description of the district shortly before William Osler was born: "The nearest post-office was twelve miles away; the nearest doctor fifteen miles away; the nearest blacksmith six miles away and the roads in every direction were well-nigh impassable, much of the time." There were still more Indians than white settlers in the countryside, and a dozen nationalities were represented.

When William Osler was born, Bond Head had become a village of about two hundred. There was a girl born after William but she died, so he was the youngest of the eight living children in that backwoods rectory. In order to secure better education for his large family, Rev. F. L. Osler moved to the town of Dundas. To William, who was nine years of age and who had always lived in the backwoods, this town seemed very large indeed. There was in the town what was termed a common school, with a grammar school above it.

The first morning that William Osler and his brothers went to the Dundas school they were dubbed "Tecumseh Cabbages," as they had been born in Tecumseh township. It did not take the Osler boys long to settle down, and it must be confessed that young William was the biggest imp of them all. As a result of some prank—which seems to have been one of many—William left Dundas school and was sent to the grammar school in Barrie. That he was a very likeable boy, with high spirits and a rollicking sense of humour, seems certain. A relative from England, who visited the family about this time, wrote, "William is a light-hearted boy, full of fun, and with many of the tastes and much of the dependableness of a man."

When he was eighteen years of age he was sent to Trinity College in Toronto. His parents wished him to become a clergyman, but William announced his decision to study medicine. After three years in Trinity College he went to McGill Medical College in Montreal. Here he worked with wonderful devotion to his studies. In his second year he was awarded a medal by the faculty for a thesis, because it showed "so much originality and painstaking research." After leaving McGill he took postgraduate work in London, Berlin and Vienna and, in 1874, returned to Montreal to take a position as Professor of the Institute of Medicine.

The "Tecumseh Cabbage" was now a professor at the age of twenty-five. Furthermore, he had started on a career which was destined to become one of the most distinguished of his generation. But the years of study were packed with many hours of hard toil and conscientious effort: Here is what he himself said, thirty years afterwards:

"I started in life—I may as well own up and admit—with just an ordinary, everyday stock of brains. In my schooldays I was much more bent on mischief than upon books—I say it with regret now—but as soon as I got interested in medicine I had only a single idea, and I do believe that if I have had any measure of success at all, it has been solely because of doing the day's work that was before me just as faithfully and honestly and energetically as was in my power."

When he went to McGill, in 1874, the young professor had empty pockets, but he had an eagerness to investigate that soon made him one of the leading lecturers in the college. For ten years he remained there, exercising a profound influence over the lives of young medical students, and always having such a thirst for knowledge himself that he was the keenest student of them all. These ten years of his life were important ones for Dr. Osler. He was popular with the students, with his fellow physicians and with the general public, and when, in 1884, he decided to accept an important position as a professor in the University of Pennsylvania at Philadelphia, he took with him the good wishes and the affection of a vast number of people.

Doctor Osler was quite different from most of the professors in the University of Pennsylvania, and at first the students, who had heard of the distinguished new professor, were somewhat disappointed. Many really great men had served the university, but they had generally been conscious of their importance. Doctor Osler lived very simply. Instead of arriving each day in a carriage, he generally jumped off a street-car with a small black bag which contained his lunch. Frequently he slipped in by a back door instead of the main entrance, and when he lectured, instead of orating eloquently from the desk, he generally sat on the edge of a table, swinging his foot and talking in a quiet, simple but intense way.

What happened at McGill was repeated at Philadelphia. Osler's amazing thoroughness, his whole-hearted devotion to his work and the utter absence of personal vanity, soon caused him to be both honoured and loved. While at Philadelphia he was elected President of the Canadian Medical Association, and, although he never returned to live in Canada, every visit he paid to his native land was an occasion for demonstrations of his popularity. Canadians were justly proud of their boy from the backwoods who was now regarded as one of the world's greatest physicians.

In 1888 the great Johns Hopkins University was built at Baltimore and the hospital authorities looked round for a man, big enough in brain and personality, to become head of the Department of Medicine in the university. Their choice fell upon the young Canadian, Doctor William Osler, and so at the age of thirty-nine he left Philadelphia and took up his duties at Baltimore.

His appointment created a great stir, for it was one of the most important positions in the entire medical world. He was comparatively a newcomer in the United States and a young man for such a position, but there was no criticism; his appointment was extremely popular. His mother, now far advanced in years, wrote from Canada: "How proud I ought to be of you. I do know that my heart is full of love and thankfulness to God who has showered so many blessings on my life in the matter of dear precious sons and daughters."

Doctor Osler now entered upon the most important work of his lifetime. He tackled the difficult problem of organization, and in a short time he had created in the Medical Department of Johns Hopkins University an institution for the care of patients and for the instruction of students which undoubtedly ranked among the best in the English-speaking world. Here he remained for sixteen eventful years. It is not too much to say about Doctor Osler, that for more than thirty years he remained the foremost physician in the world.

Literally thousands of young medical men listened to Doctor Osler's lectures, and what lectures they were! Although he talked in a quiet, conversational manner, he had amazing ability to arouse enthusiasm in his hearers. He believed, with all his heart and soul, that the work of doctors and nurses afforded great opportunities for serving humanity; he devoutly thanked God for the privileges of his profession, and as students listened they caught his spirit and began to feel as he did. Osler pleaded with students to think of their profession in the highest way. It must never become, he insisted, simply a means of livelihood but a call from God to serve others, to relieve suffering and to bring health and healing to men and women everywhere.

Here are some of the delightful things that he said to medical students:

"After ten years of hard work in Montreal I left the city a rich man—rich, not in this world's goods, for these things I lightly esteem—but rich in the goods which neither moth nor rust doth corrupt—rich in treasures of friendship and good fellowship, and in those treasures of widened experience and fuller knowledge of men and manners which comes from contact with the brightest minds."

When pressing home to students the truth that they must deny themselves many things in order diligently to serve their fellows, he said: "Chief among the hard sayings of Jesus is the declaration, He that loveth father or mother or son or daughter more than Me is not worthy of Me. Yet this spirit is the same which, in all ages, has compelled men to follow ideals, even at the sacrifice of the near and dear ones at home. In varied tones to all, at one time or another, the call comes to serve . . . it is a call to scorn delights and live the laborious days of a student. You must live for your calling. This is the essence of what Jesus said: He that findeth his life shall lose it, and he that loseth his life for My sake shall find it. Remember the practice of medicine is not a trade or an art or a business. It is a *calling* into which you must carry both heart and head."

These quotations from his lectures will suffice to show that Osler, in addition to being one of the greatest physicians in the world, was also a man of noble character; devoutly religious and a true Christian gentleman. In 1905, at the request of King Edward VII, he accepted the position of Regius Professor of Medicine at Oxford University in England. He entered upon his work there with the same zeal that had marked his whole career. Honours came to him from many quarters. In 1911 he was created a baronet of the United Kingdom of Great Britain, and thus became Sir William Osler.

When the Great War of 1914-1918 broke out he was sixty-five years of age, but he did all that failing strength would permit to alleviate suffering. His only son was killed in France and while he bore up bravely, the blow saddened his closing years. In 1919 he was stricken by pneumonia and after a short illness he died. Thus came to an end the earthly life of one of earth's noblest gentlemen. Several years before his death, in speaking to a group of distinguished physicians, he had used these words which so fittingly express his aim in life:

"I have made mistakes, but they have been mistakes of the head, not of the heart. I can truly say, and I take upon myself to witness that—

> *I have loved no darkness,*
> *Evaded no truth,*
> *Nursed no delusion,*
> *Allowed no fear."*

—*Archer Wallace*
From *Men Who Played the Game*

STUDY AND ENJOYMENT

1. Sir William Osler (pronounced ŏs′ler) was a great man as well as a great doctor. Pick out a sentence that seems to give the secret of Osler's greatness.

2. *Faculty*, the teachers in an educational institution; *thesis*, a long essay written by a university student as part of the requirements for an advanced degree; *Regius Professor of Medicine*, a position founded at Oxford University, England, by King Henry VIII in 1546—the word "regius" means "royal" and comes from the Latin word *rex* meaning "king."

SANTA FILOMENA

During the Crimean War (1854-1856) more soldiers died in the wretched hospitals than on the battlefield. Florence Nightingale went to the Crimea and saved the lives of many men. Before reading this poem, it will be helpful to know the story of this English nurse—"The Lady of the Lamp."

> Whene'er a noble deed is wrought,
> Whene'er is spoken a noble thought,
>   Our hearts in glad surprise
>   To higher levels rise.

The tidal wave of deeper souls
Into our inmost being rolls,
  And lifts us unawares
  Out of all meaner cares.

Honour to those whose words or deeds
Thus help us in our daily needs,
  And by their overflow
  Raise us from what is low!

Thus thought I, as by night I read
Of the great army of the dead
  —The trenches cold and damp,
  The starved and frozen camp,—

The wounded from the battle-plain,
In dreary hospitals of pain,
  The cheerless corridors,
  The cold and stony floors.

Lo!   In that house of misery
A lady with a lamp I see
  Pass through the glimmering gloom
  And flit from room to room.

And slow, as in a dream of bliss,
The speechless sufferer turns to kiss
  Her shadow, as it falls
  Upon the darkening walls.

As if a door in heaven should be
Opened and then close suddenly,
  The vision came and went,
  The light shone and was spent.

On England's annals, through the long
Hereafter of her speech and song,
 That light its rays shall cast
 From portals of the past.

A Lady with a Lamp shall stand
In the great history of the land,
 A noble type of good
 Heroic womanhood.

Nor even shall be wanting here
The palm, the lily, and the spear,
 The symbols that of yore
 Saint Filomena bore.

—Henry Wadsworth Longfellow

STUDY AND ENJOYMENT

1. How did one wounded soldier show how much he appreciated the service of Florence Nightingale?

2. What stanzas of this poem give the poet's central thought? Express this idea in your own words. Which stanzas describe one who wrought a noble deed?

3. Santa Filomena (Säntä Fē-lō-mä-nä), a young Roman Christian, was martyred for her faith early in the fourth century. At Pisa, Italy, in the Church of San Francisco (St. Francis), there is a chapel dedicated to her. "Over the altar is a picture representing the saint . . . floating down from heaven . . . and beneath in the foreground the sick and the maimed, who are healed by her intercession." (Longfellow). Not only is Florence Nightingale thus linked with Santa Filomena in healing, but the very word *filomena*, in Italian, means nightingale.

4. *The symbols that of yore Saint Filomena bore.* In the altar painting at Pisa, angels attend Santa Filomena, bearing palm, lily, and spear. The palm stands for victory over death; the lily, purity; and the spear, martyrdom.

5. When nurses complete their training courses in hospitals, they usually repeat the "Nightingale Pledge" as part of their graduation exercises. Some pupil who has a relative who is a nurse might secure the wording of the pledge for the class.

MARIE HÉBERT: A MOTHER OF NEW FRANCE

In the royal household of France, when Catherine de Médici was queen, an interested audience always gathered to listen to the great explorers who came to the Court to tell of their strange adventures in the country they called "New France." Among the great ladies and courtiers in their silks and laces and ribbons there was nearly always to be found a small boy, who crept near and listened with absorbed interest to these tales of danger amid strange people and queer customs. The boy's name was Louis Hébert; and he was the son of the queen's apothecary, or physician. The stories he heard about the "new world" gripped his imagination; and he determined that when he was old enough, he would go with the explorers to see these strange things for himself.

When he grew up he became an apothecary like his father, and practised his profession in Paris. But he had not forgotten his boyhood dream; and when an opportunity came for him to accompany a fur-trading expedition to New France as ship's doctor, he accepted with great joy. It was on March 7, 1604, that he met on the docks at Hâvre-de-Grace the little band of adventurers who were off to seek their fortunes in New France. The leader of the expedition was the Sieur de Monts, an experienced fur-trader; associated with him were the Sieur de Poutrincourt and the Sieur de Pont-Gravé, and in the company was the famous Samuel de Champlain, the royal geographer.

After two months at sea, De Monts and Pont-Gravé both brought their ships safely to shore at Cap de la Hève, on the shores of what is now Nova Scotia. De Monts decided to make his settlement on the island of Ste. Croix, and the workmen immediately began to clear the land and build log huts, as well as a small mill. Champlain went off cruising along the coasts, drawing maps, making friends with the Indians, and finding out from them about their country. Sometimes Louis Hébert went with Champlain, and collected roots and herbs and vines for his garden, for he had been appointed chief gardener, and was to make experiments to see how things would grow in this new land. If it seems strange that the doctor of the expedition should be put in charge of the gardening, it must be remembered that a doctor's learning in those days was largely a matter of how to grow herbs and make them into medicines.

That first winter was a time of appalling hardships. Everything the colonists possessed froze in the frightful winds which swept over the little island. It was impossible to keep warm or to sleep soundly, and they had no fresh meat or good drinking water, so that nearly all of them were ill, and half of their number died. The miserable little handful who were left had determined to sail back to France, when Pont-Gravé, who had gone back to France before the winter, appeared with a ship full of supplies and more colonists; so with fresh courage they decided to stay on. The summer was spent in moving the settlement from

Ste. Croix across to Port Royal (now Annapolis Royal), which was a much more healthy and sheltered spot. All summer and autumn the settlers worked hard and cheerfully, making their huts warm, and cultivating their gardens.

The third winter, the leaders, remembering the experiences of previous years, determined to fight illness by providing better food, and encouraging exercise and cheerfulness among the men. On Champlain's suggestion they formed a little society called "The Order of Good Cheer," the rules of which were solemnly observed. This is how Lescarbot described it at the time.

"To this Order each man of the said table was appointed Chief Steward in his turn, which came round once a fortnight. Now, this person had the duty of taking care that we were all well and honourably provided for. For there was no one who, two days before his turn came, failed to go hunting or fishing, and to bring back some delicacy in addition to our ordinary fare. So well was this carried out that never at breakfast did we lack some savoury meat of flesh or fish, and still less at our midday or evening meals; for that was our chief banquet, at which the ruler of the feast or chief butler, whom the savages called Atoctegic, having had everything prepared by the cook, marched in, napkin on shoulder, wand of office in hand, and around his neck the collar of the Order, which was worth more than four crowns; after him all the members of the Order, carrying each a dish. The same was repeated at dessert, though not always with so much pomp. And at night, before giving thanks to God, he handed over to his successor in the charge the collar of the Order, with a cup of wine, and they drank to each other."

After such a successful winter, it was very disappointing when a ship arrived in the early summer with the news that De Monts had lost his permission to trade for furs, and that the settlement was therefore to be abandoned. Louis Hébert was one of the most sorrowful. He loved his garden in the "new world," and had made up his mind to make his home there. When he returned to France, it is probable that Hébert went with Poutrincourt to the Court, to tell their tale of adventure, and to describe the country and show the strange things that had brought back with them. The next year, in 1608, Poutrincourt received permission to equip two ships to sail again to Acadia, and his son was sent in command. He himself set sail with his wife and two other sons on February 25, 1610, and with him went also Louis Hébert and his wife. Madame de Poutrincourt and Marie Rollet, Hébert's young wife, were the first two women to settle in New France.

They lived happily and comfortably in Port Royal until the year 1613, when an English buccaneer sailed up from Virginia and captured and burnt the settlement. In a few hours the courageous French people saw all they had laboured so long to accomplish destroyed by fire. Louis Hébert and his wife went sadly back to France, opened up the little chemist shop in Paris, and lived there quietly for four years. But in the narrow little street of Paris they thought longingly of the beautiful country across the sea; and the swish of paddles on the water and the crackling of camp-fires under the skies were sounds they could not forget.

One day in 1617, into the dark little house in Paris strode a man who stirred up all their memories of their adventures, an old fellow-traveller—Samuel de Champlain. Louis Hébert ran forward.

"Ah, Sieur," he cried, "do you bring news from across the seas?"

"I have come to take you back with me again," replied the great explorer. "You and your good wife and your children. And if you will come with me, I will give you lands to farm, and tools and cattle, and the Company will pay you two hundred crowns a year for three years."

Louis Hébert called to his wife in great excitement, and together they listened to Champlain's tales of the country they had learned to love. He told them how he had, in 1608, founded a new fur-trading post at a place called

Quebec, on the great River St. Lawrence, and had built a fort there, and winter quarters, and that the Indians had been friendly to him. And now, he said, he wanted to take back with him some good, honest people, whom he could trust to live there contentedly, and grow food, and be kind to the Indians when he was away.

It did not take the Héberts long to decide to go. This time the apothecary sold all his belongings, and bought supplies to take with him; and on April 11, 1617, he and his wife and their three children set sail once again from Honfleur to New France.

The voyage to Quebec took thirteen long weeks, and even the bravest gave up hope of ever seeing land again. As well as the terrors of the sea, they had to face death from starvation, since they had not brought with them enough food and water to last for so long a voyage. During the worst storm the priest gave his blessing to all on board, thinking that they could not hope to escape being wrecked; and he wrote afterwards, "we were all touched with compassion when Dame Hébert held up in her arms her youngest child to receive, with the others, God's blessing."

The land that Champlain gave to Louis Hébert was about ten acres on the top of the cliff, which is now one of the busiest parts of the upper town of Quebec. But when Louis Hébert first gazed upon it, how his heart must have sunk! For before him stretched mile upon mile of huge trees and burnt stumps, and all these had to be cleared away before a single grain of corn could be planted. That first night he and his family simply curled themselves up on the ground under a great oak tree; and even now they will show you in Quebec the place where this tree stood.

Immediately the brave doctor and his wife and family set to work to make a home for themselves, and they worked so hard that before long they had a little space cleared, and then they began to build a house. This was the first house in the country to be built of stone, instead of logs, and to have fitted doors and windows, and a chimney for the smoke to escape. It was only thirty-eight feet long and nineteen feet wide, but it must have seemed like a mansion, when Madame Hébert set out the furnishings she had brought from Paris, and placed her pretty dishes on the rough shelves, and hung her great brass kettle over the log fire.

When Champlain returned to Quebec in 1620 he brought with him his wife, Helène Boulé, who was only twenty-two years old. Since his own wooden house had tumbled down in his absence, it is probable that he took his wife to enjoy the cheery hospitality of Madame Hébert's house. There were at this time only four women in Quebec, and so one can imagine how happy they were to welcome another of their countrywomen.

A few years later, on February 4, 1623, Hébert was granted free holding of the land he had farmed, and it was called the seigneurie of Sault au Matelot. The following year he was given another grant of land on the River St. Charles, and also the title of Sieur d'Espinay. In fact, Hébert became, except for Champlain himself, the leading citizen of the settlement; and when, in the year 1621, Champlain established the first Court of Justice in New France, Louis Hébert was made King's Procurator.

Early in 1627, misfortune befell both the Hébert family and the whole community. In the very beginning of the year Louis Hébert had a serious fall, and was so badly injured that he died on January 25th. His death was mourned by everyone in the settlement, both Indians and Frenchmen. The priests, who used to write letters, or *Relations*, to their superiors in France, all spoke of him in the highest terms. "The death of the Sieur Hébert," wrote Father Sagard, "was a calamity to all of us, not only the French, but also the savages, for they lost in him a true father, a good friend, and a man always zealous for their conversion."

In 1627 also, the supply boats from France, on which

the colony still had to depend largely for its food, and entirely for its clothing and supplies, were all wrecked on their way to Quebec. When this happened, Champlain decided to send back to France as many of his people as his ships could carry. The women and children and some of the missionaries were sent away, and many of the men threw themselves on the mercy of the Indians and went off with them for the winter. Madame Hébert and her children who had married, decided to stay in the homes they had built, and to trust to the food they had saved, and to their hunting and fishing. After a winter of suffering and hunger, their enemies, the English, under command of the Kirke brothers, sailed up to Quebec, and demanded its surrender. Starved and ill, the few remaining French people could offer no resistance. The English formally raised the British flag, but they did not turn the settlers out of their homes. In fact, they did their best to induce them to remain and go on with their farming. Champlain and some of his men went back to France, but Madame Hébert and her children remained in the country which had been their home for twelve years. The English trusted them, and treated them well; but it was with great joy that, three years later, the French people saw ships sail into Quebec, with the white flag of the King of France floating from their masts, and learned that Quebec once more belonged to their mother country.

In the end Quebec finally passed into the hands of the British, in 1763. But the population of Quebec today is largely composed of the descendants of these first settlers. In 1621 Marie Hébert's second daughter, Marie-Guillemette, was married to Guillaume Couillard, a fine young carpenter who had been in Quebec a year or so longer than Hébert; and through them the blood of Marie Hébert flows in the veins of many of the most famous families of French Canada. Her descendants have been explorers, statesmen, archbishops, authors and artists; and, just as old New

England families point with pride to their descent from the Pilgrim Fathers who came out to America in the *Mayflower*, so many a French-Canadian today takes pride in tracing his descent to the first Canadian farmer, Louis Hébert, and his brave wife Marie.

—Julia Jarvis

STUDY AND ENJOYMENT

1. *Louis Hébert*, pronounced loo-ē' ā-bair'. *Medicis*, pronounced mä-dē-sēs'.
2. From this selection, find events one for each, that occurred in the following years: 1604; 1607; 1610; 1613; 1617; 1620; 1623; 1627; 1629; 1632. In some cases the year is definitely mentioned; in others it may be found from information given. Arrange the dates in a column, and after each, write one sentence summarizing the event.
3 Why is this selection entitled "Marie Hébert" instead of "Louis Hébert"?
4. What qualities in Louis Hébert won for him a place in the story of Canada?

ALEXANDER MACKENZIE

The conflict between the French and the English, for supremacy on the North American continent, at last came to an end. By the treaty made in Paris, in 1763, England received that territory which has since become the Maritime Provinces, Quebec, and Ontario. The "gentlemen adventurers of England trading into the Hudson's Bay" held a charter for what is now the Canadian North-West. Strange to relate, no one had ever crossed the future Dominion of Canada, although it was a dream at the heart of many a voyageur.

Two years after the treaty of Paris, a boy was born at Stornoway, in the Hebrides, whose name was destined to live for ever in the annals of romance and discovery. Every boy dreams that sometime he may come first, and win the approval of men. And no doubt young Alexander Mackenzie, as he watched the ships sailing out to the broad seas beyond, longed for the time when he too might go sailing down the main.

Sixteen short years passed and Mackenzie found himself in the New World, attached to a trading company at Montreal. If one desired adventure, there was no quicker way to find it than in such a calling. And so it happened! After learning the rudiments of the game of bartering with the Indians, he was sent west to Lake Athabaska, there to establish a trading post in opposition to the rival Hudson's Bay and North-West fur companies. As the Indians brought in their rich loads of peltries, Mackenzie drew from them what information he could regarding the unexplored regions beyond. One persistent rumour told of a great river which flowed northward. But where? Could it, by any chance, be the long-sought North-West Passage, connecting the Atlantic Ocean with the Pacific, thereby opening up a highway for the ships of Europe to reach Asia? He wondered.

Alexander Mackenzie must have felt very much as Ulysses did after his return from the Trojan wars. What idle and unprofitable business to be handling furs, and bickering about, when just beyond the horizon there was adventure, and perhaps fame! There, at any rate, gleamed the untravelled world—"How dull it is to pause and make an end!"

It rarely fails! The man with a dream in the heart makes that dream come true. It usually happens that, when we make a great decision, the gods take their places at our sides in pledge of victory, for events seem to shape themselves to our purpose. So it was with Mackenzie. No sooner had he determined to follow the course of that mysterious river, than a way was opened for him to fit out an expedition.

Day after day the little party paddled farther and farther Northward from Fort Chipewyan—Lake Athabaska, Great Slave Lake, then past the mouth of the river leading to Great Bear Lake. The Indian guides were almost useless; dangers lurked everywhere; the discomforts were enough to discourage the bravest, but the little company pushed on. At last they reached the land of the midnight sun, and then one morning they saw whales frolicking in the waters below them. Here they stood, at last, upon the shores of the Arctic Sea!

EVERY HOUR TEEMED WITH DANGER

Upon his return to Fort Chipewyan, Mackenzie decided that, before he set out to discover the great river flowing westward into the great ocean, many tales of which he had heard from the Indians in the North, he would return to England and perfect himself in astronomy. After a year's absence, he once more made the Fort the point of departure for his new romance.

Early in the year of 1793, Alexander Mackenzie set out with his party of ten in a great canoe, and headed up the Peace River. Their course led into the mountains; the river rushed headlong between the sky-sweeping, snow-capped hills, and every hour teemed with danger. Lodges of unfriendly Indians lay along the river banks; these they must somehow make their friends. Fortunately, Mackenzie had an ample stock of trinkets, and other things dear to the heart of the Indian, for by this means he not only· relieved their fear or melted their anger, but also secured from them details of the country through which he wished to pass. It was one of these new acquaintances who, after a great deal of coaxing and many gifts, at last guided the party to the head-waters of the Peace River, and showed them the river that led down the western slope to the Stinking Lake, that is, the Ocean.

Dangerous as had been the course up the waterway to the Arctic, and the ascent of the Peace River, this downward course exceeded both in thrilling escapes from instant death. When the canoe went to pieces in a rapid, even the Indians "sat down and gave vent to their tears." It was only the splendid leadership of Mackenzie, his power to cheer, his infinite patience and good judgment, that guided the little party over the Rocky Mountains, and down to the great ocean beyond. Their sufferings were almost beyond belief.

At last, their goal was reached. Westward stretched the Pacific, the crowning glory of Mackenzie's dreams. Upon a flat rock he painted with vermilion mixed in grease these words:

ALEXANDER MACKENZIE, FROM CANADA BY LAND,
THE TWENTY-SECOND OF JULY,
ONE THOUSAND SEVEN HUNDRED AND
NINETY-THREE.

Then he retraced his way back to Fort Chipewyan.

Little did Mackenzie think that the tales brought to him by the coast Indians, of a white man, by them called Macubah, were true. While he was making his observations at the mouth of the Bella Coola, Captain George Vancouver, known to the Indians as *Macubah*, lay anchored just out of sight farther up the coast! One gave his name to the great river that flows into the Arctic, and inscribed his name on the roll of honour as the first white man to cross the North American continent. The other gave his name to the well-known island, and the metropolis of the coast.

Mackenzie finally returned to England, and received a knighthood. When the Duke of Kent, father of Queen Victoria, was sent to Canada, Alexander Mackenzie also accompanied him as a companion. His journal, entitled, *Voyages from Montreal Through the Continent of North America to the Frozen and Pacific Oceans*, was published in England in 1801. Napoleon Bonaparte, and his general, Bernadotte, later King of Sweden, once pored over this remarkable volume, planning a way of taking Canada. The Earl of Selkirk was kindled by it to establish a settlement upon the banks of the Red River—historic Kildonan. Out of this venture grew Winnipeg, and thereby hangs another thrilling tale.

—Selected

STUDY AND ENJOYMENT

1. Draw a sketch map of north-western Canada, marking Lake Athabaska, Great Slave Lake, Great Bear Lake, and the following rivers: Slave, Mackenzie, Peace, Parsnip, Bad, Fraser, Blackwater, Dean, Bella Coola. Mark Burke Channel, also, as it was near the mouth of that inlet that Mackenzie placed the inscription on the rock. With help from books from the school library, trace Mackenzie's two great exploring trips.

2. Like Mackenzie, men of the twentieth century have had their dreams for the Canadian North-West. In recent years, three great engineering projects have been undertaken in that area—the Alaska Highway, the Alaska Airway, and the oil pipe-line from Norman Wells to Whitehorse. What information can you find in the library regarding each of these feats?

3. How do you account for the fact that the heroes and heroines of war-times are more highly honoured than those of times of peace? Is this as it should be? Why?

HE GAVE WINGS TO WORDS

Here is another story of a man "with a dream in his heart."

One day, in 1870, a young man twenty-three years of age and in delicate health stood in the consulting room of a physician in Edinburgh, Scotland. "You are far from well," said the doctor, "there is only one hope for you. If you seek a climate less severe than this one, and live out-doors, you may regain your health."

The young man was Alexander Graham Bell. Not long before this two of his brothers had died of tuberculosis and it seemed as if he also were to become a victim of the disease. His father was determined to give his boy every possible chance. "I will take him to Canada," he said. "He can live in the clear air there and help around the farm. Perhaps he may become healthy."

The Bells moved to a farm near Brantford, Ontario, and soon Alexander's health was greatly improved. Many hours each day he spent out in the fields, ploughing and planting, and his father was especially delighted at the improvement in his health. Alexander himself was contented and whistled as he worked.

Before he left Scotland, Alexander Bell had become greatly interested in efforts being made to help deaf people understand what others were saying by watching their lip movements. His mother was deaf and his father, who was a fine elocutionist, had begun a method of teaching the deaf and dumb to read what was called "visible speech."

Before he could read a note of music Alexander Bell would often sit at the piano and play well by ear, so well, indeed, that many thought him an accomplished musician. This quick ear for sound was destined to be of great value to him later on. Several years before he left his home in Scotland he was experimenting with the laws of sound.

One day, when listening to the sound made by the vibration of a tuning fork, he asked himself why sound could not be made to travel along a copper wire and be heard at a considerable distance away. At first he thought only of making musical notes travel; the idea of having the human voice carried along the wires came to him later.

While Alexander worked on the farm in Ontario his father had been asked to give some lessons at a school for deaf and dumb children in Boston. The authorities were delighted with his work and pressed him to remain. "I cannot accept your offer," he said, "but I have a son in

Ontario who understands my methods and can teach these children as well as I can."

An offer was made to Alexander which he promptly accepted, and he began to teach in the Boston school at a salary of five hundred dollars a year. His success with the deaf mutes greatly astonished the school authorities and news of what he was doing spread through the whole countryside.

One day a great man visited Boston. This was Dom Pedro, Emperor of Brazil, who was visiting the United States in order to learn all he could about whatever he thought would help his people. He was greatly interested in what Alexander Bell was doing for the deaf mutes and spent a considerable time with him, asking a great many questions and freely expressing his admiration. Meanwhile Alexander Bell kept working away at his invention every spare moment he had. He firmly believed that it was possible to make sound travel along wires and he was determined to find out how to do it.

A man named Sanders, who lived at Salem, near Boston, brought a five-year-old boy, who was deaf and dumb, to Bell with the pathetic request that something be done to help him. Mr. Sanders suggested that Alexander Bell should live in their home in exchange for giving the boy lessons and Bell accepted the offer. This man was greatly interested in the efforts of the young inventor and let him have the use of his cellar for experimenting. So hour after hour he laboured, trying to make sound travel. Sometimes he seemed on the verge of discovery, then a difficulty would arise which might have discouraged him had he not been so patient and determined. He stretched wire from the house to the barn and tried to send messages. Whenever he noticed any improvement he would become greatly excited and, as Mr. Sanders said, "He leaped like an Indian in a war dance."

One day a Boston lawyer named Hubbard brought his fifteen-year-old girl, Mabel, who was quite deaf, to Bell and asked him to teach her. Like Mr. Sanders, this man became greatly interested in Bell's attempts to make sound travel and the two men supplied him with money in order that he might work at his invention. These two were very kind and generous to Bell, but sometimes they thought he was only a dreamer and that his ideas were not very practical. However, they did give him considerable encouragement and this meant a great deal to Bell, as most people who knew what he was trying to do said frankly that he was wasting both time and money; that his hopes were doomed to utter failure. But day after day he went on experimenting, evidently believing in himself and not discouraged by ridicule or opposition.

A friend of his who was an ear specialist secured for him the ear of a dead person, and after many careful experiments he succeeded in making the sound of his voice travel from the drum of his ear along a delicate straw. He said to himself: "Why could not a very fine, sensitive iron plate take the place of this eardrum, and why could not copper wire take the place of this straw?"

At this time Mr. Sanders and Mr. Hubbard became persuaded that the invention was impossible and refused to give him any further help. This was a severe blow to Bell, as he was almost penniless. The outlook seemed dark indeed. He had applied to Washington for a patent for his invention and he received a letter summoning him there. Mr. Sanders loaned him enough to pay his fare, and off Bell went. While in Washington he called upon a distinguished scientist and electrician, Professor Joseph Henry, and showed him the instrument he had so far developed. Very carefully the old scientist examined the instrument while the young inventor awaited the verdict with his heart in his mouth. At last the professor spoke: "You have made a beginning of a marvellous invention," he said. "Do not stop until it is finished." These words gave Bell, who was just twenty-eight years old, a tremendous thrill. "I will never give up," he said. When Mr.

Sanders and Mr. Hubbard heard what the scientist had said, they were greatly pleased and agreed to supply him with the money to continue his experiments.

In order to get certain delicate instruments made, Bell went to an electrical shop where he formed an acquaintance with a young man named Thomas Watson. This man was keenly interested in Bell's invention, and the two spent a great many hours together, as Watson's electrical knowledge was useful to the inventor. Bell did succeed in making sound travel over wire, but for many months there was nothing distinct; there were simply noises. Over and over he tried, each time using instruments more delicate and sensitive. He perfected the diaphragm, using gold-beater's skin, which is very much like the human ear. Opposite to it he set up an electromagnet through which the electric current passed over the wire. Then, one day in June, 1875, he managed to pass the twang of a watch spring over the wire, and he was wild with excitement. Still there was much yet to be done, and more months of tremendous concentration and hard work were necessary. Then came a never-to-be-forgotten day.

It was March 10, 1876. Bell was in one room with his instrument and Watson was at the end of the wire in another room. Suddenly Watson heard Bell's voice over the wire say distinctly: "*Mr. Watson, please come here, I want you.*" The telephone had been discovered. True, it was by no means perfect, and even simple sentences had often to be repeated five or six times before the meaning could be understood. But the beginning was made, and one of the most useful and marvellous inventions of all time was born.

Alexander Bell was granted the patent for his wonderful invention on his twenty-ninth birthday, but it was some considerable time before its value was recognized. In 1876 there was a great Centennial Exposition in Philadelphia; substantial prizes were being given for new inventions, and many remarkable things, such as the first electric light, the first reaper and binder, and other things were on view and competition was keen. Bell was anxious that his "Baby Telephone" should be considered by the judges. He was, however, unfortunate in not being able to secure a good position. While other inventions were displayed to advantage, the best Bell could do was to have a small table in a corner, and it looked as if the judges would never even see his telephone. All day these men passed from one place to another, carefully considering each invention in turn. It was seven o'clock in the evening before they passed near Bell, and they were impatient to be through. He was given a chance to explain his device, but they were bored. Some of them openly laughed at his idea of making the human voice travel. But Dom Pedro, Emperor of Brazil, was with the judges, and he spoke up and told of Bell's great success with deaf mutes. This secured from him a better hearing. Bell spoke to the Emperor: "Put your ear to this receiver," he said. Dom Pedro did so and Bell went to the far end of the room and began to talk over the wire. Astonishment, then amazement, spread over Dom Pedro's face. "My God! It talks!" he fairly shouted. Then Professor Henry, who had encouraged Bell some time before, took up the receiver and he was equally astonished. The judges now changed their attitude and stayed for hours examining the new discovery. The next day they gave their decision that the telephone was the most wonderful of all the exhibits. Many people were hard to convince and insisted that there was a trick somewhere and that the invention was a fraud, but at last even this criticism disappeared.

Soon afterward the Bell Telephone Company was organized, and in the first eight years paid dividends amounting to over four million dollars. The telephone spread to other lands and in less than twenty-five years it was being used in nearly every civilized country in the world.

Alexander Bell became a wealthy man. He married Mabel Hubbard, the deaf mute of whose education he had charge for many years when she was a girl.

For many years he continued to perfect his invention, and he lived to see his discovery made a means of blessing to millions. He used to spend his summers in Cape Breton, Nova Scotia, and there he died in 1922, having given to the world a priceless means of communication.

—Archer Wallace

From *Heroes of Peace*

STUDY AND ENJOYMENT

1. What difficulties and what discouragements did Alexander Graham Bell face in making his dream a reality?
2. Name five people who helped Bell, and tell in what way each gave assistance.
3. What quality, besides brilliance, did Bell need to reach success?
4. In tracing the story of communication "from runner to radio," how important a place should we give to the telephone? What additional information can you obtain about this invention in the library?

THE FIRST KNIGHTS OF THE AIR

In June, 1919, two English aviators, Alcock and Brown, made the first non-stop flight across the Atlantic Ocean. A week later, this editorial appeared in an English newspaper.

When Sir Francis Drake, the first Englishman to circumnavigate the world, then a very big and mysterious place, reached Deptford, Queen Elizabeth went down in state and knighted him on the deck of the *Golden Hind*. It was her habit to distinguish prowess and virtue without over-much regard to the wealth or position of the persons who received her favours. The Queen also gave Drake an elaborate crest, depicting on a globe a ship trained about with hawsers by a hand issuing out of the clouds, the motto being *Auxilio Divino*, but the pioneer navigator preferred a simpler device, an eagle displayed, emblematic of power and speed. We stand face to face with an

achievement which may fittingly be set side by side in the
pages of history with that of the great seaman of the
sixteenth century, and the King, so Mr. Winston Churchill
announced yesterday, has decided to confer knighthoods
on the two men who have flown the Atlantic—the two eagles
of this new century.   They will become, and very fittingly,
Knights Commander of the Order of the British Empire.
Today they will travel down to Windsor to be received
by His Majesty.   Throughout this country and the
Empire satisfaction will be expressed that the King should,
in this Elizabethan manner, have set the seal of pride of
the British people on an exploit which, apart from its
romantic appeal to the imagination, marks the conquest of
the air by man and the opening of a new era in the means of
communication between the Old World and the New,
separated by the broad expanse of the Atlantic.   The very
success of these two knights of the air—the very absence
of misfortune—has somewhat tended to conceal the
magnitude of their triumph.   We can only obtain an
adequate conception of what their landing in Ireland
signifies in human endurance and skill and engineering
perfection if we look back, seeking for a vantage-point of
observation.   As they rose from St. John's to explore the
upper world of cloud and fog and sleet, they might have
contrasted their experience with that of the discoverer of
this, the oldest Dominion of the British Empire.   The
first journey to Newfoundland was undertaken by Sir
Humphrey Gilbert.   He set out from Plymouth in the
Delight, with four other little ships, on 11th June, 1583,
and considered himself the happiest of mortals when on
30th July, after buffeting the winds and seas for seven
weeks, he sighted the northern shores of the land of his
adventurous quest.   Now the leagues of ocean separating
Ireland from Newfoundland have been covered—not by
sea, but by air—in less than sixteen hours.   The two
airmen put out on their journey a week ago, after tea-time,
and they landed in Ireland for breakfast the next morning.

of foolscap covered with unparagraphed long-hand, with the hope that this bunch was O.K." The result was a book, *Sixty Below*, from which this passage is taken.

It's Christmas, and as I gaze into the crimson and golden glow of the fire, I think of other Christmases. That one at Fort Norman, for instance.

For days before the great day, dog bells have been ringing, jangling, echoing, not only at the Fort, but along the trails, which, from every outlying part, converge on the little community of tents and shacks that lie so contentedly in the deep, sparkling snow. Since August the trappers have been out on their lines, alone with their husky-dogs, and now they are returning just for the Christmas festival. If you happen to be one of the early arrivals at the Fort you might stand on the river bank and look down on the mighty Mackenzie River, and there you'll see a string of dog-teams two miles long, like a black snake, over the ice, with their bells and many coloured tassels and little flags fluttering. The dogs themselves seem to know that they are in for a holiday. For some of these people it is the end of two weeks' travelling. They have come hundreds of miles from their trapping grounds. A trapper will make the journey by himself until he passes some other cabin on the trail, where he will be joined by the trapper who belongs there, so that as they go on, man after man, white, half-breed, Indian, and their families and squealing kids, will hitch on with their sleighs to the procession. This is the first time in many moons most of us have had any human being to speak a word to. You can guess how we have looked forward to our Christmas. We wouldn't miss it for all the gold in the North.

At the Fort itself hand-shaking is going on, everybody is welcoming everybody and exchanging news, and wishing a merry Christmas all round. The whole place has come to life, as though it had been a graveyard. Before Christmas Eve, for months, the only people living there are the Mission Father and the Anglican preacher, the wireless man

EVERYBODY IS WELCOMING EVERYBODY

and the "Mountie" of the Mounted Police, and a couple of traders. Just a handful. But now it has suddenly become a buzzing hive of activity. Up go new tents. People are digging their shacks out of the snow, tamping it down to make a smooth floor. You see them drifting up to the trading post. They carry bundles of furs on their backs or under their arms. They are taking them to trade with. They are our currency. In return we are supplied with the little necessities and luxuries that we have been without— tea and sugar, maybe a clean shirt and socks, and, last but not. least, razor-blades. Oh, yes, we have been looking forward to our Christmas clean-up!

Darkness falls early in the North on Christmas Eve, at about two o'clock in the afternoon. But there are still teams drifting in, the stragglers. The last one to come just unloads himself on you until he has got his own place fixed up and, of course, you gladly give him tea and whatever meal has been quickly prepared from the canned goods obtained at the post. Overhead a finger of smoke will be rising straight up from the shacks into the cold, breathless air. Fifteen feet high a finger of smoke will show in the Arctic where the temperature is fifty below.

Across the snow bright candles are beginning to flicker in the tents, and the lights shine cosily over the snow. And then comes the most seasonable light of all, the lamps and candles shining in the log-house church, where Midnight Mass draws everybody, man, woman and child, Catholic and Protestant alike.

The priest greets his flock one by one. Then the service starts, and he preaches in English, French and Indian. Instead of cash the congregation give furs. It is a lovely offering: all kinds of fox, white, black, and silver; martens; minks; wolverines; lynx—not many lynx though; we like to hang on to them for they are valuable and too big to carry to the service. The same, or nearly the same, method is used at the Anglican Church next morning, when practically the same crowd makes up the congregation. The two Churches are very friendly to each other out there.

After church the people begin to limber up a bit. . . . A tea dance starts up in the trader's warehouse or in a big tent pitched especially for the purpose, and everybody is dressed up in their finery, beads and silkwork flashing in the light of many candles. An old fiddler squats in a corner, playing a French-Canadian quadrille, and the fun goes on and on right through Christmas Day, and sometimes the day after. We take time off for eating and sleeping if we feel like it, but there's always someone to keep the show going.

But we don't forget Santa Claus. He came three or four weeks ago on a plane. Along with the Christmas mail and the turkeys, the toys have arrived for the little Indian children and the few white children. The Indians always choose a blonde doll, just the opposite to what they are themselves, with nice pink cheeks and flashing white teeth. They are fascinated by anything blonde or fair. One of the Hudson's Bay men had a child like that, and the Indian children would approach her shyly and touch her cheeks and curls. Then they would go off and discuss the wonder among themselves. "*Nee cha, na zon, nee cha na zon,*" was their verdict—"Good, very good."

During Christmas morning the dancing stops for a brief while as the men and women and children form a procession and move along from shack to shack, tent to tent, greeting the occupants and gathering them into the procession so that by the time the last shack is reached the whole settlement is on the move. The Indians fire off their guns just to make a noise, everybody chatters and laughs, everybody is happy. We finish up at the two missions, where the priest and minister give the children presents of sweets. . . .

And so on to Christmas dinner. A good many of us have had frozen turkey flown in, and anyone who is alone— as we white trappers are—will take it round to the home of a half-breed for roasting, and she and her family share the meal. Those who have no turkey and don't expect one usually save a fat lynx for Christmas. It's good stuff, and personally I prefer it to turkey because it is delicious white meat and there's more of it. The day finishes with the children playing among their new toys and the grown-ups dancing. . . .

Bells; children; dancing and the snow; Christmas; Fort Norman on the Mackenzie River. . . .

—*Tony Onraet*
From *Sixty Below*

STUDY AND ENJOYMENT

1. "You can guess how we looked forward to our Christmas." List some of the pleasures to which the trappers looked forward.

2. Tony Onraet brings his scenes to life by his mention of common objects— the dog bells, the shacks, the ice, and the snow. What other "things" do you find mentioned? In addition to sights, he describes sounds— jangling bells, squealing children. What other sounds are heard in the selection?

3. What details show that the people of the north are friendly? are generous?

I WILL LIFT UP MINE EYES
[*Psalm 121*]

I will lift up mine eyes unto the hills, from whence cometh my help.

My help cometh from the Lord, which made heaven and earth.

He will not suffer thy foot to be moved: he that keepeth thee will not slumber.

Behold, he that keepeth Israel shall neither slumber nor sleep.

The Lord is thy keeper: the Lord is thy shade upon thy right hand.

The sun shall not smite thee by day, nor the moon by night.

The Lord shall preserve thee from all evil: he shall preserve thy soul.

The Lord shall preserve thy going out and thy coming in from this time forth, and even for evermore.

—The Bible

READ A BOOK

Modern Aladdins. By Rush and Winslow. Little, Brown. A very readable book on everyday things and how they are made.

One Hundred Stories for Boys. By Archer Wallace. Ryerson. Human interest stories to strengthen a boy's character.

Within the Circle. By Evelyn Stefansson. Scribner. Life north of the Arctic Circle.

Drina. By Marion F. Flexner. Coward McCann. The early days of Queen Victoria's life, until her marriage.

Why the Chimes Rang. By Raymond M. Alden. Bobbs, Merrill. Allegorical stories, with a moral, charmingly told.

Nansen. By Hall. Viking. Nansen's travels to the Polar regions.

Map Makers and *Heroes of Science.* By Cottler and Jaffe. Ryerson. A stimulating account of the lives of the great men who discovered the secrets of the earth and of science.

X

With Glowing Hearts

O CANADA!

O Canada! Our home and native land!
True patriot-love in all thy sons command.
With glowing hearts we see thee rise
The True North strong and free;
And stand on guard, O Canada,
We stand on guard for thee.

Chorus

O Canada, glorious and free!
 We stand on guard, we stand on guard for thee!
O Canada, we stand on guard for thee.

O Canada! Where pines and maples grow,
Great prairies spread and lordly rivers flow.
How dear to us thy broad domain,
From East to Western Sea!
Thou land of hope for all who toil!
Thou True North strong and free.

O Canada! Beneath thy shining skies
May stalwart sons and gentle maidens rise
To keep thee steadfast through the years
From East to Western Sea,
Our own beloved native land,
Our True North strong and free!

Ruler supreme Who hearest humble prayer,
Hold our Dominion in Thy loving care.

Help us to find, O God, in Thee
A lasting rich reward,
As waiting for the better day,
We ever stand on guard.

—*R. Stanley Weir*

STUDY AND ENJOYMENT

1. The title for this section of your Reader is taken from this Canadian national song. We have two national songs—"God Save the King," which is not only ours but belongs also to every country in the British Commonwealth of Nations, and "O Canada!" which belongs to us alone. All Canadians should know this song by heart, and be able to sing it "with glowing hearts."
2. Robert Stanley Weir (1856-1926) was born at Hamilton, Ontario. A lawyer by profession, he practised in Montreal. Besides a number of legal books, he wrote some poetry, including this version of "O Canada!"

THE MOUNTIES

Just as John Bull represents England, and Uncle Sam the United States, so might the stalwart Mountie stand for Canada. He suggests the romance, the daring, and the rugged strength of our Dominion. The Northwest Mounted Police were organized in 1873 to establish law and order on the western plains. The word "Royal" was added to their title in 1904, and the word "Canadian" replaced "Northwest" in 1920. Now the activities of the Force extend across the whole of our country.

You have seen them, perhaps, doing sentry on Ottawa's Parliament Hill. Their Stetsons are tilted at a jaunty angle. Every button on their scarlet tunics catches and tosses back the sunbeams. Brown riding-boots and Sam Browne belts gleam with all the lustre that polish and rubbing can lend. Astride quiescent horses burnished with grooming they might be mistaken for equestrian statues, except that bronze or marble could never reproduce their colour, their vigour, their zest for life.

You may have seen them on escort duty, touring Canada with our King and Queen, with a prince, a duke, a governor-

general.　Possibly you were among the cheering crowds at
an exhibition in Vancouver, in Halifax—oh! in any one of
our cities—or in New York's Madison Square Garden,
when their musical ride has stolen the show.　And as you
thrilled to the surge of applause, you told yourself with a
catch in your throat: "They are Canada's!　*They're ours!*"

Such is the glamorous phase of the life of the Royal
Canadian Mounted Police—the phase played up in Holly-
wood films, in romances of the legendary West.　It is the
show-window of the Corps.　But for every exciting hour
they spend dreary days of drudgery.　For every parade
past admiring throngs there are lonely patrols across
blizzard-swept plains or over the icy wastes of the North.
Yet it is upon the drab day-by-day routine that the Force
has built its record.　The tedium of everyday duties is the
final test of their ability to live up to the motto: *Maintiens
le droit!—Uphold the Right!*

You know them by an assortment of names—names
borrowed from a score of books, a hundred newspaper
articles: The Scarlet Riders; The Silent Force; The Frontier
Constabulary; The Riders of the Plains; The Red-Coated
Troopers—to quote but a handful.　But in common with
the rest of the world you call them "The Mounties."

You have, of course, heard the slogan: *They get their man!*
To you and me and the rest of us that slogan tags the Force.
Many, in fact, believe that *Get Your Man* is their motto and
refuse to be convinced that it is not.　But be warned: Never
use the expression within earshot of the Mounted Police
themselves; it enrages them for they abhor swagger.
Nonetheless, it is an amazingly accurate label.

II

In a twenty-eight-months' voyage the Mounted Police
have recently added a final episode to the saga of exploration
which began in the days of Columbus.　Their exploit was
the cruise of the North-West Passage, but in reverse.

In their eighty-ton R.C.M.P. patrol ship, *St. Roch*, with Danish-born Sergeant Henry Larsen as skipper, they sailed from Vancouver in June, 1940, on their west-to-east voyage across the roof of the world.

The steamer followed the route known to the whalers, past the mist-shrouded Aleutians, through Bering Straits, around Point Barrow to Herschel Island, and eastward from there.

The first winter they were marooned off the west coast of Victoria Land, while blizzards wailed their constant dirge and the mercury in the thermometers froze. Through the eerie gloom of the northern night the Mounties went game-hunting. Also, they ranged the district to take a census of the blue-eyed Copper (or "Blond") Eskimos—a ponderous task, in view of the natives' whimsical habit of changing their names, and of dating events by "the year of the deep snows," or "the summer we built the big kayak."

On snow-shoes or with dog-sleds they trekked to native villages and lonely igloos, seeking possible news of strange visitors, mysterious ships, or aeroplanes that might have been lurking about; for it was known that a German agent with sham credentials had penetrated to the heart of rocky Baffin Land, in search of a springboard from which to take off on an attack upon Canada.

Onward the boat squirmed between churning ice-floes, past sleet-lashed shores where famished Eskimos had at times turned to cannibalism, through glacial waters strewn with the battered hulls of ships and skeletons of men lost in the centuries-old effort to find the legendary north-west route to the Pacific.

The second winter caught them close to the magnetic pole and two days' sail from King William's Land. There Constable Chartrand, worn out by the hardships of the trip, was buried sadly on the windy shore of Peasley Bay, with a cairn to mark his grave.

With spring the sturdy iron-shod craft shouldered its way into the last lap of the journey. Through the Arctic fog the crew could see the spectral hull of Captain Ross's *Victory*, stranded for more than one hundred years.

When the *St. Roch's* ice-scarred prow entered Pond Inlet on the northern shore of Baffin Land, loud cheers hailed the conquest—for the first time—of the west-to-east course of the fateful passage.

There, with Constable Doyle to replace Chartrand, the *St. Roch* swung southward on the final three thousand miles of her record voyage. And when, in the misty dusk of an October day the little steamer anchored in the Sydney Harbour, Nova Scotia, these sea-going men of the Force had completed the chore of generations of explorers, traders, and navigators, who had spent their lives in a search for the highway that spans the crest of the world.

—Anne I. Grierson
From *The Mounties*

STUDY AND ENJOYMENT

1. How did the slogan *They get their man!* come to be connected with the R.C.M.P.? Why should you not use that expression in the presence of the Mounties? In what way is their real motto better?

2. The scarlet tunic is no longer worn except on dress occasions. What colour is the Mountie's ordinary tunic?

3. Describe in your own words the appearance of the Mounties as pictured in the first paragraph of the selection. *Stetsons*, slouch hats; *quiescent*, silent and motionless; *equestrian statue*, the moulded figure of a person on a horse.

4. You remember the long and perilous search for the North-West Passage, a route by water through the land masses of the far north. Look up the story of Sir John Franklin (1786-1847) in a reference book. His two ships, the *Erebus* and *Terror*, vanished into the Arctic seas in July, 1845, never to be seen again. Amundsen, a Norwegian, was the first navigator to succeed in taking a ship from the Atlantic to the Pacific by way of Bering Strait. His voyage was made in 1904.

5. The North Magnetic Pole was discovered by Sir James Clark Ross in 1831. His observations placed it at Cape Adelaide on the west coast of Boothia Peninsula. For three years Ross remained on Boothia, his ship *Victory* being fast in the ice. Finally, he and his men abandoned the ship, took to smaller boats, and finally reached a whaler which carried them home.

6. Trace the route of the *St. Roch* on a map of Canada.

7. You may read more of the work and adventures of the R.C.M.P. in the book from which this selection was taken—*The Mounties*, by Miss Anne I. Grierson.

THE CAMP FIRE

Joyce Hamilton, aged sixteen, is spending a summer with the David-
sons at their camp, Ken-jockety, on Georgian Bay. Professor Davidson
(Uncle Graeme) and his neighbour, Dr. Benson (Uncle Ben), organize a
three-day canoe trip, taking with them Drew and Christine Davidson;
Judy Benson and her friend, Nancy Nairn; and Joyce herself. On the
second day of the trip, camp is struck at Two Pines, where the party is to
be joined by Nancy's brother, Jack, and his friend Tom, who have paddled
from Bala in Muskoka. As Joyce and Christine prepare supper, they are
looking for the return of a red canoe bearing three fishermen—Uncle
Graeme, Uncle Ben, and Drew.

There was no red canoe on the beach when Joyce and
Christine landed at Two Pines. They got to work at once,
and the fire was just burning well and the potatoes almost
ready for the pot, when Drew's piercing whistle was heard.

"Judy and Nancy are waiting for the boys," called
Christine as soon as the canoe was within earshot. "Show
us your minnows, Drew."

Drew went through a pantomime of disgust and disappointment, and then, unable to wait till they landed, picked up a fish from the basket at his feet and held it up with pardonable pride.

"Ohhhh!" said Christine and Joyce together. "What a dandy!"

Uncle Ben was beaming. For once his fisherman's soul was satisfied. It had been a great day!

"Izaak Walton had nothing to beat this," he declared solemnly as he lifted out the catch to Drew who had landed first. "I used to think of him with envy, but now I'm sorry for him. He never fished for a gamey black bass in Canada, poor fellow! Cricky, that big one gave me a fight—I thought he was off a dozen times at least. Ah, there comes Judy now—with two strange young men. I'd better wash my hands before she introduces me as her respected parent. Christine, is the part in my hair straight? Do you think they will like my complexion? Don't giggle, girl, advise me."

The newcomers proved to be two khaki-clad, well-tanned youths with the same springy carriage and alert keen eyes as Drew.

"How terrible if my johnnycake were not light and fluffy!" thought Joyce as she hurried up to the fire again. Of course she had made it exactly as she did for breakfast at Ken-jockety—but one never knew. She hovered about the fire anxiously poking in little bits of sticks where they seemed needed in order to get an even heat.

Uncle Ben and Drew performed miracles of speed in getting the fish ready for the pan, and luck was with Joyce, for her cake came out fluffy and light and browned to a most desirable tint. She put the pan on one side of the fire to keep hot until the fish was ready to serve, and helped with the blueberry salad. The boys had brought a little bucketful of late raspberries from Muskoka, and as these were rarely found about Georgian Bay, Christine decided they would make them go as far as possible by mixing them with the blueberries they had picked that morning.

It was the jolliest of meals. Anything would have tasted good eaten in such good company, and seasoned with that best of sauces, a keen out-of-doors appetite. The cooks were complimented upon their success, and the johnnycake received especial praise. When the dishes were washed and put away, Drew and Jack built a bonfire down on the point, and the whole party adjourned there to watch the sunset.

"It's going to be absolutely gorgeous," said Christine happily. "There are enough clouds to make it beautiful; it's lovely now, but wait till the afterglow! If *only* we had some music for the songs!"

The sun had almost disappeared, but long bars of colour banded the horizon: orange and rose, violet and palest primrose, blended at last in an exquisitely lovely shade of pale green.

The little company sat quietly watching, while the sun dropped down behind the low clouds on the horizon; the pine-trees on the banks were etched in startling contrast against the glowing sky; a star appeared, shining like a jewel set in the green jade band.

"'And o'er the crested pine shall hang one star,'" quoted Professor Davidson.

"I'd be perfectly happy," murmured Christine, "if Mother were here to sing to us."

"Those colours are doing their best for you," said Judith. "They really *are* a harmony, aren't they? Though I wish we *could* have some music."

"To Judith, who may command me, Anything," parodied Jack cleverly—

"Bid me to live, and I will live
Thy musicker to be."

He was sitting with Drew a little apart from the rest of the group, and, as Judith turned to smile at the compliment, a tiny thread of thin elfin-like music seemed to trickle from his left hand. Everyone turned in astonishment. Was this sleight-of-hand, or magic, or what? Some one, or *something* was undeniably humming, "Drink to me only with Thine Eyes."

Nancy was the first to solve the puzzle.

"Your ukulele!" she said. "You've hidden it very nicely, but you needn't be so modest. Now we can have a sing-song. It's what we've all been wanting today. Next time I go on a camping trip I'm going to bring a whistle or a mouth-organ, even if I have to leave my tooth-brush behind."

And sing they did with a right good will; "Swanee River," and "Ole Black Joe," "A la Claire Fontaine," and "John Peel."

Then came requests for special favourites. Tom surprised every one by his "Annie Laurie": then Nancy must sing "Might' Lak A Rose," which she did delightfully.

"Now, it's your turn, Uncle Graeme," suggested Judith. "Please let us have 'The Cruise of the Bugaboo.'"

"The Bugaboo" was applauded, and Jack followed by request with

> "Under the greenwood tree,
>   Who loves to lie with me,
>   And tune his merry note,
>   Unto the sweet bird's throat,
>   Come hither, come hither, come hither."

Jack, like Nancy, had a very pleasing voice. He broke off after the first stanza of the quaint old-fashioned song to say meditatively, "I wonder, now, if Will Shakespeare would have enjoyed this sort of thing?"

"Of course he would," said Christine promptly. "He'd have been a first-rate paddler and sailor, and swimmer and fisherman, and—oh, I know!—he'd have written something like 'Johnnie Courteau.' Let's have 'Johnnie Courteau,' please, Uncle Ben. We *couldn't* go camping without hearing 'Johnnie Courteau.' I wonder if Dr. Drummond composed it on a trip like this—seems as if he must have."

"Johnnie Courteau!" said the others in chorus.

Uncle Ben was whittling a whistle, and had arrived at a critical point in its creation. Would it blow or would it not? He tried! It would not!

"*Eh bien!*" he grunted—

> "'You bad leetle boy not moche you care
>   How busy you're kipin your poor grand pere.'

That's 'Leetle Bateese,' *n'est-ce pas?* Somebody start me!"

> "Johnnie Courteau of de mountain,
>   Johnnie Courteau of de hill,"

Christine prompted.

"*Mais oui*," said the doctor. "I have heem."

> "Johnnie Courteau of de mountain,
>   Johnnie Courteau of de hill,
>   Dat was de boy can shoot de gun,
>   Dat was de boy can jomp an' run,
>   An' it's not very offen you ketch heem still,
>   Johnnie Courteau.

> "Ax dem along de reever,
>   Ax dem along the shore,
>   Who was de mos' bes' fightin' man
>   From Managanee to Shaw-in-i-gan?
>   De place w'ere de great beeg rapide roar,
>   Johnnie Courteau!

> "Sam' t'ing on ev'ry shantee
>   Up on de Mekinac,
>   Who was de man can walk de log,
>   W'en w'ole of de reever she's black wit' fog
>   An' carry de beeges' load on hees back?
>   Johnnie Courteau!"

The colours in the sky had deepened and softened; there were more stars glittering now in the soft green in the west and in the deep blue overhead; behind them the woods were dark.

Drew put another log on the fire, and for a few moments

nobody spoke; every one sat looking contentedly into the dancing flames or into the soft loveliness of the sky.

"My turn now," said Drew. "Judy, will you please stand up on that high rock just behind you and say Pauline Johnson's 'Song My Paddle Sings'?"

"Oh," groaned Judith. "Must I move, Drew? I'm so comfy here. What's the idea?"

"Picture," said Drew. "Pine-tree to your right, after-glow behind, admiring audience at your feet!"

Judith apparently couldn't resist such an appeal, for she obediently climbed the rock. She gave a little cry of delight.

"Picture!—I should say it is: sunset, and the canoes down there on the shore;—the fire here, and those lovely pines—thank you, Drew."

Then, quite simply, but with an appreciation of its beauty which she passed on to her hearers, she recited the Indian princess's lovely lyric.

> "August is laughing across the sky,
>   Laughing while paddle, canoe and I,
>   Drift, drift,
>   Where the hills uplift
>   On either side of the current swift.
>
> "The river rolls in its rocky bed,
>   My paddle is plying its way ahead;
>   Dip, dip,
>   While the waters flip
>   In foam as over their breast we slip."

Judith looked down to where through the trees she could see the little river and the white foam of its rapids; unconsciously she spoke more quickly as she described the journey through the seething waters in the frail little craft. Then:

> "We've raced the rapid, we're far ahead!
>   The river slips through its silent bed.
>   Sway, sway,
>   As the bubbles spray
>   And fall in tinkling tunes away.

"And up on the hills against the sky,
A fir-tree rocking its lullaby,
Swings, swings,
Its emerald wings,
Swelling the song that my paddle sings."

There was a moment's silence as Judith finished, a silence which was broken by a slight but unmistakable snore.

"Oh, shameless one," said Jack, shaking Tom who lay beside him comfortably propped against a fallen tree, "have you *no* soul for poetry and beauty?"

"What's the row?" inquired Tom sleepily amid the laughter of the others.

"Row's the right word," said Jack severely. "And as you made it—"

"I expect we're all sleepy," said Professor Graeme; "all good campers go to bed early."

"Good-night, ladies," tinkled the ukulele. "Good-night ladies," boomed Uncle Ben's bass and Drew's tenor. And "Good-night ladies," they all sang together, just for the pleasure of singing once more.

—*Ethel Hume Bennett*

From *Camp Ken-jockety*

STUDY AND ENJOYMENT

1. Name four activities enjoyed by the campers. Which of these would you like best?

2. *Izaak Walton* (1593-1683), the author of *The Compleat Angler*, a famous book on fishing; *Muskoka*, a favourite district in Ontario for holidaying; *n'est-ce pas?* isn't it?; *eh bien*, oh well; *mais oui*, literally "but yes," translated "yes."

3. A parody is a humorous imitation of a poem or a piece of prose. Jack's parody, "To Judith who may command me Anything," is based on a poem by Robert Herrick (1591-1674), which has for its title, "To Anthea, who may command him Anything."

4. "Leetle Bateese," "Johnnie Courteau," and "The Song My Paddle Sings" may all be found in this Reader. A stanza of "A la Claire Fontaine" is quoted in "Johnnie Courteau."

5. Judith and her friends took pleasure from the songs and poems they knew by heart. In memorizing poems you will find these suggestions helpful:

   (i) Be sure that you understand the meaning of the poem as fully as possible.

(ii) Learn by wholes as much as possible—that is, repeat the whole poem each time in the learning stage. The little child who recites "Twinkle, twinkle little star," and has to be prompted at the beginning of each line, has learned the poem a line at a time instead of learning it as a whole. If a poem is too long to be learned as a whole, divide it into several sections, and learn a section at a time.

(iii) Distribute repetitions of the poem over several days. Five repetitions each day for three days will help more than fifteen repetitions on one day.

(iv) Let the rhythm of the poem help you. While you will not wish to recite the poem in sing-song fashion, you may emphasize the beat of the rhythm as you learn it.

(v) If you need prompting at one place several times, stop and think of a plan to link the words or ideas in your mind.

(vi) When you have the poem committed to memory, fix it there by repeating it once each day for several days, and occasionally thereafter.

TOM THOMSON

I

Tom's home was at Claremont, Ontario, not far from the beautiful Georgian Bay country. There was always plenty to do and see on the Thomson farm; but from the beginning Tom preferred to roam the countryside, either through the thick woods of elm, beech, birch and pine, or by the streams, where he soon learned to catch and clean his own fish, and cook them over an open fire.

Then there was the Bay itself, with its fishermen who brought back, with their fine catches of fish, exciting stories of adventure on the stormy waters of the Great Lakes. Tom felt he would like to be a sailor, and he went out on fishing trips with old Joe Clôture, a French-Canadian fisherman who had a two-masted sailing boat that was said to be the fastest on the Bay.

Now Tom was a resourceful fellow, and Joe's sailing boat soon gave him an idea. The Thomsons had an old rowboat of their own. Tom persuaded his father to let him fix it up with mast and sails. The first day there was a good stiff breeze blowing offshore, Tom and his friend, David, put out into the open water of the Bay, and soon caught sight of Joe Clôture doing a bit of leisurely trolling. The boys' spirits rose, and they tacked until they came alongside Joe's boat—then they skimmed past him, with excited shouts and wavings, and boasts about the superiority of their home-made craft!   This episode called for a glowing account afterwards of how they had outsailed the two-master.   Tom was more than ever determined now to be a sailor, and own a fishing boat.

When he left school, Tom faced a problem that troubles most young people—what career should he take up?   He knew what he *didn't* want to do, but not what he *did* want. Not till he was twenty-one did Tom get himself a job, and then it didn't last.   With the help of a small legacy from his grandfather, he apprenticed himself in a machine-shop. He liked learning to handle tools and machines, but couldn't get on with the foreman.   So he left, and took up a business course, thinking he might settle down to office life.   But this didn't suit his out-of-doors tastes at all, and he soon gave it up.

It was about this time that he found a job that really interested him—working on a new method of reproducing illustrations, called photo-engraving.   Tom studied photo-engraving and learned how to use the method in reproducing advertisements.   Lettering and titles had still to be added by hand to the metal plate, and Tom became specially skilled in this branch of the work, and by it earned enough money to keep himself.   Also, as he became more interested in art, he began, in his spare time, to make his first sketches in crayons and in water colours.

In 1905 Tom returned to Eastern Canada and settled in Toronto, where he worked for an engraver, took a few art lessons, and learned to paint in oils.   But he never thought of selling his sketches, and usually gave them away to his brothers and sisters.

One day he had a disagreement with his employer, and decided to find a new job.   By good luck, he applied to a well-known commercial art agency, whose manager, Albert

Robson, was a good judge of character and talent. When Tom—tall, good-looking, but very modest—walked into his office, Robson saw at once that there was something unusual about him, and offered him a job on his staff. And here, for the first time, Tom found himself in a circle of artists who seemed to have a purpose beyond merely making a living. They were training themselves to go out and explore their native Province, and paint pictures which would express its beauty to the people of Canada.

II

One summer evening, after the day's work at the office, a friend called to see Tom Thomson at his room in Wellesley Street. He found him sitting by an open window, carefully painting what he could see across the street.

"That's not much of a subject!" remarked the friend. "Only a corner drugstore, and a boy with a dog loafing outside."

"Never mind," replied Tom. "Look at these!"—and he showed his friend a whole sheaf of sketches he had made of the same street-scene. "I mean to go on painting this scene till I've mastered it," he explained. "Then I'll know I can tackle *any* subject, and in time make something out of *it* too."

But it was in the wilds, not in the city, that Tom wanted to turn his skill to account. In the summer of 1911 he made friends with a young English artist who was visiting Toronto, and wanted to try canoeing and camping in the North. They took two months' canoeing down the River Mississauga to Georgian Bay, and on the way had various adventures. First, they met Grey Owl, the strange Englishman who had turned himself into an Indian. Tom made a great many sketches on this trip, but most of them were lost when the canoe upset in the rapids near the river's mouth.

However, about twenty sketches were saved, and Tom brought them back with him to Toronto. They were drawings of river scenes, reedy swamps, and mist-clad lakes. When Tom's artist-friends looked at them, they noticed that they were different from the ordinary type of landscape.

"Tom," they told him, impressed, "this is something new. You've caught the spirit of the North country in a way no one else has yet. You must go there again."

Tom hardly needed this advice. He waited only till the next summer. He had a strong taste for living by himself in the woods, making his own tools and tackle, building his own shack, catching and cooking his own food—being independent of his fellow-men, in short. Algonquin Park seemed just the place for this. Indeed, it became Tom's second home. As the years passed, he tried to spend more and more time up there, and regretted having to return to earn his living in the city.

III

Sketching had now become, not a reason for going up north, but a result of living there for part at least of every year. Tom was in love with the wilderness, and his sketches were a way of expressing this. When he came back to Toronto in the fall of each year, he would bring with him a bundle of sketches, and leave them with friends, not bothering whether they were sold or not.

After his first visit to Algonquin Park, Albert Robson persuaded Tom to paint one of his sketches on a fullsize canvas—the first big picture he had ever done. It was called "Northern Lake" and showed waves lashed by a storm, beating on a distant shore. Robson sent this picture in to the Ontario Society of Artists, where it was exhibited and much admired.

Soon afterward Robson came into the office where Tom was working at his desk, walked over and said to him, "Tom, your picture has been sold!"

For a few seconds Tom said nothing. Perhaps he thought he was having his leg pulled. Then a red flush slowly spread over his face, as he quietly commented, "What fool did that?"

Tom was too modest to believe anyone would *buy* a picture of his. But it was true. The Ontario Government had bought "Northern Lake," awarding it a prize of $300— a large sum in those days for a work by a Canadian artist.

Seeing that Tom was encouraged by this success, his friends urged him to give up commercial work, and spend all his time painting. He knew the North now so well that he could tell the truth about it, in paint. Tom moved into an old cabinet-maker's workshop, and had it fixed up to look exactly like a northern shack. He lined it with beaverboard, fitted it with a bunk, and made a window opening east, to face the dawn. Here Tom, sleeping in blankets and cooking his own meals, could imagine himself away up north, and so be inspired to go on painting.

Because Tom lived so much in the wilds, he was able to paint many sides of nature that most of us never see. He could catch the melting snow under the young birches in spring, and the crimson and scarlet leaves whirling down the swollen streams in fall. He knew when the wild ducks would begin their flight south, and when to expect their return after the winter. Often he would spend whole nights alone in his canoe out on some lake, painting under the stars, or at dawn.

On a July day, in 1917, Tom set out on one of his usual fishing trips in his canoe. Time passed, and he did not return. Discovering his upturned canoe floating on the lake his friends became alarmed, and searched. When they found Tom's body it appeared that he had fallen into the water and been drowned. But how this had happened none could tell. Nature, in her own mysterious way, had taken him out of life.

Tom's friends afterward put up a stone cairn at Canoe Lake, with a sign on it bearing words written by another great Canadian artist, J. E. H. MacDonald:

> To the memory of Tom Thomson, Artist, Woodsman and Guide, who was drowned in Canoe Lake, July 8th, 1917. He lived humbly but passionately with the wild. It made him brother to all untamed things in nature. It drew him apart and revealed itself wonderfully to him. It sent him out from the woods only to show these revelations, and it took him to itself at last.

—Richard S. Lambert
From *The Adventure of Canadian Painting*

STUDY AND ENJOYMENT

Inexpensive reproductions in colour of a number of Tom Thomson's paintings may be purchased either from The National Gallery, Ottawa, Ontario, or from The Art Gallery of Toronto, Toronto, Ontario. Among the prints available are: *The Jack Pine, Spring Ice, Northern River, The Artist's Hut,* and *West Wind.*

CHAPDELAINE MAKES LAND

The novel, *Maria Chapdelaine,* from which this selection is taken, was written about a frontier farmer who lived in a lonely part of northern Quebec. His single desire in life was to clear land and carve out a little farm from the untamed forest. Whenever settlement came near him, he moved farther away.

After a few chilly days, June suddenly brought veritable spring weather. A blazing sun warmed field and forest, the lingering patches of snow vanished even in the deep shade of the woods; the Peribonka rose and rose between its rocky banks until the alders and the roots of the near spruces were drowned; in the roads the mud was incredibly deep. The Canadian soil rid itself of the last traces of winter with a semblance of mad haste, as though in dread of another winter already on the way.

Chapdelaine, his three sons and man, proceeded then to "make land." The forest still pressed hard upon the

buildings they had put up a few years earlier: the little
square house, the barn of planks that gaped apart, the
stable built of blackened logs and chinked with rags and
earth. Between the scanty fields of their clearing and the
darkly encircling woods lay a broad stretch which the axe
had but half-heartedly attacked. A few living trees had
been cut for timber, and the dead ones, sawn and split,
fed the great stove for a whole winter; but the place was a
rough tangle of stumps and interlacing roots, of fallen
trees too far rotted to burn, of others dead but still erect
amid the alder scrub.

Thither the five men made their way one morning
and set to work at once, without a word, for every man's
task had been settled beforehand.

The father and Da'Bé took their stand face to face on
either side of a tree, and their axes, helved with birch,
began to swing in rhythm. At first each hewed a deep
notch, chopping steadily at the same spot for some seconds,
then the axe rose swiftly and fell obliquely in the trunk a
foot higher up; at every stroke a great chip flew, thick as
the hand, splitting away with the grain. When the cuts
were nearly meeting, one stopped and the other slowed
down, leaving his axe in the wood for a moment at every
blow; the mere strip, by some miracle, still holding the
tree erect, yielded at last; it began to lean and the two
axemen stepped back a pace and watched it fall, shouting
at the same instant a warning of the danger.

It was then the turn of Edwige Légaré and Esdras;
when the tree was not too heavy, each took an end, clasping
their strong hands beneath the trunk, and then raised
themselves—backs straining, arms cracking under the
stress—and carried it to the nearest heap with short
unsteady steps, getting over the fallen trees with stumbling
effort. When the burden seemed too heavy, Tit'Bé came
forward leading Charles Eugene dragging a tug-bar with a
strong chain; this was passed round the trunk and fastened,

THE TWO AXEMEN STEPPED BACK A PACE AND WATCHED IT FALL

the horse bent his back, and with the muscles of his hindquarters standing out, hauled away the tree, which scraped
along the stumps and crushed the young alders to the
ground.

At noon Maria came out to the doorstep and gave a
long call to tell them that dinner was ready. Slowly they
straightened up among the stumps, wiping away with the
backs of their hands the drops of sweat that ran into their
eyes, and made their way to the house.

Already the pea-soup smoked in the plates. The five
men set themselves at table without haste, as if sensation
were somewhat dulled by the heavy work; but as they
caught their breath a great hunger awoke, and soon they
began to eat with keen appetite. The two women waited
upon them, filling the empty plates, carrying about the
great dish of pork and boiled potatoes, pouring out the
hot tea. When the meat had vanished, the diners filled
their saucers with molasses in which they soaked large
pieces of bread; hunger was quickly appeased, because they
had eaten fast and without a word, and then plates were
pushed back and chairs tilted with sighs of satisfaction,
while hands were thrust into pockets for their pipes, and
the pigs' bladders bulging with tobacco.

Edwige Légaré, seating himself upon the doorstep,
proclaimed two or three times:—"I have dined well. . . .
I have dined well. . . ." with the air of a judge who
renders an impartial decision. The elder Chapdelaine
sank deeper and deeper into his chair, and ended by falling
asleep; the others smoked and chatted about their work.

"If there is anything," said the mother, "which could
reconcile me to living so far away in the woods, it is seeing
my men-folk make a nice bit of land—a nice bit of land
that was full of trees and stumps and roots, which one
beholds in a fortnight as bare as the back of your hand,
ready for the plough; surely nothing in the world can be

more pleasing or better worth doing." The rest gave
assent with nods, and were silent for awhile, admiring the
picture. Soon, however, Chapdelaine awoke, refreshed by
his sleep and ready for work; then all arose and went out
together.

The sun dipped toward the horizon, disappeared; the
sky took on softer hues above the forest's dark edge, and
the hour of supper brought to the house five men of the
colour of the soil.

While waiting upon them Madame Chapdelaine asked
a hundred questions about the day's work, and when the
vision arose before her of this patch of land they had
cleared, superbly bare, lying ready for the plough, her
spirit was possessed with something of a mystic's rapture.

With hands upon her hips, refusing to seat herself at
table, she extolled the beauty of the world as it existed for
her: not the beauty wherein human beings have no hand,
which the townsman makes such an ado about with his
unreal ecstasies, but the quiet, unaffected loveliness of the
level fields, finding its charm in the regularity of the long
furrow, and the sweetly flowing stream—the naked fields
courting with willing abandon the fervent embraces of
the sun.

She sang the great deeds of the four Chapdelaines and
Edwige Légaré, their struggle against the savagery of
nature, their triumph of the day. She awarded praises
and displayed her own proper pride, albeit the five men
smoked their wooden or clay pipes in silence, motionless
as images after their long task; images of earthly hue,
hollow-eyed with fatigue.

"The stumps are hard to get out," at length said the
elder Chapdelaine, "the roots have not rotted in the
earth so much as I should have imagined. I calculate
that we shall not be through for three weeks." He glanced
questioningly at Légaré who gravely confirmed him.

"Three weeks. . . . Yes, confound it! That is what I think, too."

They fell silent again, patient and determined, like men who face a long war.

The five men worked on unceasingly, while from day to day the clearing extended its borders by a little; deep wounds in the uncovered soil showed the richness of it.

Maria went forth one morning to carry them water. The father and Tit'Bé were cutting alders, Da'Bé and Esdras piling the cut trees. Edwige Légaré was attacking a stump by himself; a hand against the trunk, he had grasped a root with the other, as one seizes the leg of some gigantic adversary in a struggle, and he was fighting the combined forces of wood and earth like a man furious at the resistance of an enemy. Suddenly the stump yielded and lay upon the ground; he passed a hand over his forehead and sat down upon the root, running with sweat, overcome by the exertion. When Maria came near him with her pail half full of water, the others having drunk, he was still seated, breathing deeply and saying in a bewildered way:—"I am done for. . . . Ah, I am done for." But he pulled himself together on seeing her, and roared out:—"Cold water! Perdition! Give me cold water."

Seizing the bucket he drank half its contents and poured the rest over his head and neck; still dripping, he threw himself afresh upon the vanquished stump and began to roll it towards a pile as one carries off a prize.

Maria stayed for a few moments looking at the work of the men and the progress they had made, each day more evident, then hied her back to the house swinging the empty bucket, happy to feel herself alive and well under the bright sun, dreaming of all the joys that were to be hers, nor could be long delayed if only she were earnest and patient enough in her prayers.

Even at a distance the voices of the men came to her across the ground baked by the heat; Esdras, his hands

beneath a young jack pine, was saying in his quiet tones:—
"Gently . . . together now!"

Légaré was wrestling with some new inert foe. "Perdition! I'll make you stir, so I will." His gasps were nearly as audible as the words. Taking breath for a second, he rushed once more into the fray, arms straining, wrenching with his great back. And yet again his voice was raised: "I tell you that I'll have you. . . . Oh, you rascal! Isn't it hot? . . . I'm pretty nearly finished. . . ." His complaints ripened into one mighty cry:—"Boss! We are going to kill ourselves making land."

Old Chapdelaine's voice was husky but still cheerful as he answered: "Tough! Edwige, tough! The pea soup will soon be ready."

And in truth it was not long before Maria, once more on the doorstep, shaping her hands to carry the sound, sent forth the ringing call to dinner.

Toward evening a breeze arose and a delicious coolness fell upon the earth like a pardon. But the sky remained cloudless.

"If the fine weather lasts," said Mother Chapdelaine, "the blueberries will be ripe for the feast of Ste. Anne."

—Louis Hémon
From *Maria Chapdelaine*
Translated by W. H. Blake

STUDY AND ENJOYMENT

Louis Hémon (1880-1913) was born in France, and came from Breton stock as did Jacques Cartier. He had written two or three books, when he came to Canada and hired out on a French Canadian frontier farm near Peribonka, Quebec. No one there suspected this quiet young man of being a writer. After he left, his novel, *Maria Chapdelaine*, appeared, and the old habitant cottage in the woods, the farmer, his wife and daughter all became famous. In this story the life and spirit of Quebec have been made known round the world. Hémon died suddenly in Northern Ontario.

1. Madame and Samuel Chapdelaine have three sons—Da'Bé, Tit'Bé, and Esdras—and one daughter, Maria, the heroine of the novel. Edwige Légaré is the hired man, and Charles Eugene is the horse.

2. How did Chapdelaine "make land"?
3. From this selection what do you learn of the appearance of a frontier farm, its buildings and land? Could you draw a picture of it?
4. Describe how the Chapdelaines cut down large trees.
5. From this account, select five sentences, each from a different paragraph, that help us to realize—almost to feel—how hard the men worked in clearing the land.
6. Read aloud the lines in which Légaré speaks to the trees.

THE CANADIAN YEAR:

Some people like to go south every winter. Most young people like the changing year in Canada, where each season brings its beauties and its pleasures. Here are four selections, each by a Canadian writer, and each describing a different season. Which do you like the best?

Now the Lilac Tree's in Bud

Now the lilac tree's in bud,
And the morning birds are loud.
Now a stirring in the blood
Moves the heart of every crowd.

Word has gone abroad somewhere
Of a great impending change.
There's a message in the air
Of an import glad and strange.

Not an idler in the street,
But is better off today.
Not a traveller you meet,
But has something wise to say.

Now there's not a road too long,
Not a day that is not good,
Not a mile but hears a song
Lifted from the misty wood.

Down along the Silvermine[1]
That's the blackbird's cheerful note!
You can see him flash and shine
With the scarlet on his coat.

Now the winds are soft with rain,
And the twilight has a spell,
Who from gladness could refrain
Or with olden sorrows dwell?

—Bliss Carman

STUDY AND ENJOYMENT

1. Read two lines from this poem, each describing a pleasant sight in spring-time. Read two lines each describing a pleasant sound. Gladness sings through all the poem, but read the stanza that sounds the happiest to you.

2. Carman not only describes the sights and sounds of spring, but he tells us how spring makes people feel. Find lines or stanzas in which he does this.

3. The atmosphere of spring—in the woods, in the winds, and in the twilight—is caught very beautifully in the poem. Can you find the phrases?

4. What lines in Wordsworth's "Daffodils" echo the thought,

"Who from gladness could refrain
Or with olden sorrows dwell?"

5. Alfred Noyes, author of "To the R.A.F." and "Old Grey Squirrel," has written a long poem, "The Barrel Organ," in which the refrain is, "Come Down to Kew in Lilac Time." Perhaps a pupil might find the poem, and read the "lilac time" stanzas to the class.

HEAT

From plains that reel to southward, dim,
    The road runs by me white and bare;
Up the steep hill it seems to swim
    Beyond, and melt into the glare.
Upward half-way, or it may be
    Nearer the summit, slowly steals
A hay-cart, moving dustily
    With idly clacking wheels.

[1] A lovely eastern brook near which the poet lived.

By his cart's side the wagoner
  Is slouching slowly at his ease,
Half-hidden in the windless blur
  Of white dust puffing to his knees.
This wagon on the height above,
  From sky to sky on either hand,
Is the sole thing that seems to move
  In all the heat-held land.

Beyond me in the fields the sun
  Soaks in the grass and hath his will;
I count the marguerites one by one;
  Even the buttercups are still.
On the brook yonder not a breath
  Disturbs the spider or the midge.
The water-bugs draw close beneath
  The cool gloom of the bridge.

Where the far elm-tree shadows flood
  Dark patches in the burning grass,
The cows, each with her peaceful cud,
  Lie waiting for the heat to pass.
From somewhere on the slope near by
  Into the pale depth of the noon
A wandering thrush slides leisurely
  His thin revolving tune.

In intervals of dreams I hear
  The cricket from the droughty ground;
The grasshoppers spin into mine ear
  A small innumerable sound.
I lift mine eyes sometimes to gaze:
  The burning sky-line blinds my sight:
The woods far off are blue with haze:
  The hills are drenched in light.

And yet to me not this or that
   Is always sharp or always sweet;
In the sloped shadow of my hat
   I lean at rest, and drain the heat;
Nay more, I think some blessèd power
   Hath brought me wandering idly here:
In the full furnace of this hour
   My thoughts grow keen and clear.

              —*Archibald Lampman*

STUDY AND ENJOYMENT

Archibald Lampman has been called "the most pictorial of Canadian poets." In "A Thunderstorm" on page 175 of this Reader, the leaf-still calm gives way so violently to roaring winds, white lightning, and pelting rain, that the changing view could only be recorded by a moving-picture camera. In "Heat," however, the scene is quiet enough for snapshot photography. What is the one thing that moves "in all the heat-held land"?

1. This poem gives us a number of pictures of a hot summer day. Which picture do you like best? Which picture makes you *feel* the heat most?

2. Where is the poet resting? How does the heat affect him?

3. Select words and phrases that bring out the idea of intense heat.

4. Two places are mentioned where there is relief from the heat. Can you locate them?

VAGABOND SONG

There is something in the Autumn that is native to my blood,
Touch of manner, hint of mood,
And my heart is like a rhyme
With the yellow and the purple and the crimson keeping
    time.

The scarlet of the maples can shake me like a cry
Of bugles going by,
And my lonely spirit thrills
To see the frosty asters like smoke upon the hills.

There is something in October sets the gipsy blood astir,
We must rise and follow her,
When from every hill of flame
She calls and calls each vagabond by name.

—Bliss Carman

STUDY AND ENJOYMENT

1. What autumn colours are mentioned in this poem?
2. What exciting words and phrases are used "to stir the blood"?
3. Lampman's "Heat" dealt with the fields, the woods, the stream, the wagoner, the birds, and the insects—with many sharply drawn pictures. What pictures do you find in Carman's poem? How does he differ from Lampman in his way of describing what he sees and what he feels?

WINTER

Yesterday the last leaves tugged at the branches, and soon all the branches were bare. The wind was from the north.

They looked up from the stable yard on the prairies, saw the slate-grey sky, and knew that it had come. The cattle wandered dolefully, picking at the dried grass, and the long autumn hair of the horses was ruffled in the wind. The fishermen along the Nova Scotia coast battened down their boats and ran for shore. In the Hope Mountains of British Columbia, Bill Robinson denned up in his cabin, twenty-five miles from other human life, hoping his radio battery would keep going until spring.

Today it came, the Canadian winter. Snow eddying across the prairies until a woman peering through the windows could not see the neighbour's house and knew she was a prisoner until April. Snow sifting through the streets of Winnipeg and everyone hurrying to get anti-freeze in his radiator, a heater on the windshield; and the vacant lots flooded for the kids' skating rinks. Winter marching eastward over the badlands, placing a puff of snow carefully on every tiny Christmas tree. Winter tiptoeing into an

Ontario village by night and all the children awaking with a whoop to get out sleighs and skis and hockey sticks, and the black squirrel in the garden taking one look and disappearing for good. . . .

In Quebec the big stoves crammed with wood and the habitant out in the back yard with axe and saw, eyeing the wood pile with careful calculation. In the kitchen the pot bubbling with pea soup. In the silent woods, the sleighs brought out, with jingle of bells, to carry logs to the river.

In the Maritimes the fisherman hauls up his boat. Snow smudges out the harbour of Halifax and ships move through it vaguely. The liners come into port from the North Atlantic, their shapes distorted with ice, like layers of glass, rigging turned solid, sailors' faces pinched and blue.

Now Winter turns westward at his leisure. The valleys of the Rockies can be filled up quickly with snow, and more slides off the hills, carrying trees and rocks with it. Every drip and trickle of water has long since seized up, the rivers drop, and over them grows the winter skin, save where the water breaks it with fierce bubbling and then plunges again under the dumb ice. On the untouched smoothness of the snow there is a single track of moose, or the light touch of weasel or rabbit, or perhaps the smooth path of a ski. Every spruce tree and cedar bears an incredible burden, all the branches borne down, and the snow lies on the bare twigs of tamarack like cotton carefully glued there.

It is time now for Winter to make his annual holiday trip to the Pacific Coast. By December he has settled down in Vancouver, in a cottage by the sea, but he is a changed man. He puffs out a few billows of fog, ties up the traffic for a day or two, forces the coastwise captains to navigate entirely by the echoes of their whistles against the shore and then, after turning on the shower bath, Winter forgets to turn it off. Apart from that, he is a considerate guest. Even the last weary roses escape his touch until January when, as a matter of form, he makes a brief show of anger. Then the Victoria golfers are outraged to miss their eighteen holes even for a day and sadly the gardener cuts down the last frozen chrysanthemum. But the snowdrops are out already, and the first crocus opens its brave cup of gold to show the drop of sunshine inside, the first faint wink of Spring.

—Bruce Hutchison
From *The Unknown Country*

STUDY AND ENJOYMENT

1. Although this selection is written in prose, it is very like poetry in its choice of words. Here are a few examples— *marching, tiptoeing, smudges.* What other examples can you find?
2. Winter is pictured in every province. Where is it the loneliest? Where is it the most beautiful?
3. What is the winter "skin"? Why is the ice "dumb"?
4. Where does winter remain the shortest time? Quote sentences to support your answer.
5. Which paragraph of this description do you like best? Point out the pictures, or the words and phrases in it, that appeal to you.
6. Look at the first and last sentences of this selection. Why is the one a good beginning, and the other a good ending, for the description?

THE VOICE OF CANADA
[*A Radio Play*]

This selection should be read chorally. Study it carefully, and decide just how each part should be read.

NARRATOR: I listened for the voice of Canada—

FULL CHORUS   (*rhythmically*):
               I listened at the busy intersection;
               I listened to the roar of the machine and
                  the shop,
               To the tread of a million feet,

GIRLS: To the quiet tale of the bedtime hour,

BOY: And the strident call of the loud speaker.

NARRATOR: I heard a voice—

FULL CHORUS: Selfish voices that said—

GIRL: I want pretty clothes,
                      I want popularity;
                      Others have everything. Why should I
                          sacrifice?

BOY: I want to get on in the world,
                      To make money and gain power.
                      I am much too busy getting to have time to
                          give at all.

ANOTHER BOY: I once had a star to steer by, but I have lost
                          my course.

GIRL: Life is so dull and lonely that I might as well
                          be dead.

FULL CHORUS (*slowly*):
                      Are these, are these the voices of Canada?

BOYS: Out of the darkness came this cry:

VOICE: "Where there is no vision, the people
                          perish."

NARRATOR: Then the Voice of the Past called to me,

BOYS: The pioneers, the Builders of Empire,

FULL CHORUS: A hundred mighty voices rolled into one and
                          calling, "O Canada,

GIRLS: We nurtured you.

BOYS: We loved you.
                      We fought for you.

FULL CHORUS: We founded you to be great.

BOYS: To be strong,

FULL CHORUS: To be free,
                      To be free to obey God!"

NARRATOR: I said, "Is this Canada?"
                      And the Voice of the Present answered me,

Boys: "We are the millions who toil and fight for you,

We work night and day; we offer our lives,

We long for a purpose to strive for, a future,

A hope that is more than bread."

Narrator: And I said, "Is this Canada?"

The Voice of the Future answered me,

Girls: "I see a people striving, rising, building,

Boys: I see a nation waking, stirring, changing,

Full Chorus: Working together, humbly triumphant, its races united,

Fulfilling the hopes of its founders,

Girls: The dreams of its people,

Full Chorus: The plan of its God."

Narrator: And I said, "Is this Canada?"

Boys: And the mountains said, "Yes!"

And the seas said, "Yes!"

Girls: "Yes! Yes!" cried the lakes.

Full Chorus: And a million, million voices—

[*Single voice for each place*:

From city and farm,

From factory and workshop,

From the shore and the plain,

From the Arctic to the broad St. Lawrence,

Full Chorus: Joined in one crashing, resounding, solemn affirmation—

"CANADA!"

Adapted from "The Voice of Canada", the Moral Re-armament Revue "Pull Together Canada!"

STUDY AND ENJOYMENT

1. It takes all kinds of people to make a country. What kinds of people are mentioned in this selection?
2. Where does the author listen for the Voice? Mention other places where he might have listened.
3. Which is the true Voice of Canada? How do you know that the author agrees with you?

THE FUGITIVE

William Lyon Mackenzie led a rebellion in 1837 against the ruling class of Upper Canada. After his defeat, he escaped, with the help of friendly settlers, to the United States. That incident forms the basis of the story—partly fact and partly fiction—from Emily Weaver's historical novel, *The Only Girl*.

The Lydgates live on a lonely farm in the woods near Toronto. Peggy Lydgate has gone to their neighbours', the Cranes', to seek news of her brother Jim, who has disappeared. Ellen Crane accompanies Peggy home, as the woods are full of soldiers searching for William Lyon Mackenzie.

After a prolonged farewell, rather suspiciously over-cheerful on both sides, Peggy and Ellen set out through the woods, along the edge of the ravine, at the bottom of which the swollen Creek was racing towards the Lake. They were in the wood, still some distance above Dundas Street, when Peggy said suddenly, "I hope we shall not be stopped. Do you hear that? I'm sure there are soldiers guarding the bridge."

"We have no reason to be afraid of loyal soldiers," said Ellen valiantly, "and our men with the King's force."

"We don't know who is holding the bridge," said Peggy, rather emphatically. "It would be delightful if our own boys were there, only I think they'd rather the rebels had a chance to run. At any rate, there's one thing I'm sure of, none of them will be wanting to gain those rewards. A curse would rest on money so earned."

"I bless you for that word," exclaimed an agitated voice, apparently coming from the ground at her feet.

Peggy jumped and Ellen fled—a yard or two from the track but stood still when a little man rose from behind a log and grasped at Peggy's hand. That was more than she had bargained for. She put both hands behind her. "I am a Loyalist," she said.

"And he whose hand you now refuse to take is none

other than William Mackenzie, arch-enemy of all those traitors to the community who under the name of Loyalists enrich themselves at the expense of the poor and the ignorant, but true friend and brother to the misguided sufferers (by whatever name they call themselves) preyed upon by the wolves and the scorners. Whither are you going, girl?"

"Home," replied Peggy, somewhat disturbed when another and a taller shadow arose out of the confusion and wild growth behind her.

"By which road?"

"Dundas Street. We can't cross the Creek tonight except by the bridge."

"You cannot go by that road, girl. I do not distrust your will; but how could you women withstand soldiers bound to win the thousand pounds set on the head of the rebel Mackenzie? With such a prize in view they would stop at nothing to force confession from your lips."

"Why didn't you rest quiet and let us pass?" demanded Peggy in perplexity. Then she was seized with a great, a brilliant idea. "If you had not shown yourselves we could and would have said we had seen no one answering to your description as we came through the woods. Now, the utmost we can do is to refuse to speak."

"Then—again I say—you shall not go forward," said the little man resolutely. "Be still. Make no noise, or our blood will be upon your heads just as surely as if you sold our lives for money."

"Wait a moment," commanded Peggy with severity. "Mr. Mackenzie, I'm not quite certain that your blood is altogether innocent. If we cry out you are lost. Now I wish to tell you frankly, sir, that in our house, though we know that this country has many wrongs to be righted, we believe you have only added to our troubles by taking up arms, and father thinks some day you will feel the same."

"Never, never," said the rebel leader.

"Well, I hope you will change your mind," said Peggy.

She was really trying to persuade herself that she was justified in giving the rebel another chance; but she also wanted to make a bargain with him. "I believe I can show you a good hiding-place, where you can rest awhile; but I am of the opinion that one good turn deserves another—"

"Surely. But had we not better be walking on?"

"In one moment. Listen. A dear brother of mine, Jim Lydgate, was taking a lady to town last Tuesday, when he was fallen upon and carried off by some of the people who call themselves your followers."

"It was an act of justice and of self-preservation on their part. I know something of that boy. He came to several of our meetings, but is one of those who put their hands to the plough and turned back, unless, as some believed, he was spying upon us from the first."

"That is not true. At first, poor boy, he was sure that you were a very Joshua to lead us into a new Land of Promise; but later he saw that you would only bring misery and bloodshed upon us and he promised my father that he would not join you."

"Well, well, I will look into the thing as soon as may be, and if injustice has been done—"

"We cannot wait. Tell me this instant, where he is and in whose keeping, and give me an order in writing that he is to be set free."

"Girl, there is no time—"

"There *is* time. Where is my brother? It is life for life with me. Speak quickly or I shall cry out to the soldiers."

"The lad was not seized by my orders. But you don't know all. He had purloined and concealed documents of immense importance. They are holding him only till he will tell what he has done with these papers."

"Purloined indeed! Jim Lydgate is no thief. But now— yes or no—will you tell me where he is?"

"Hush, speak softly. He is in the keeping of Daniel Craig, as I understand, or his man Dixon. Somewhere on

Craig's farm or the old Saxby place. On my honour, I
know no more. I will write the order to Craig as soon as I
can find a scrap of paper. Will that satisfy you, woman?"

"It will," replied Peggy, taking Ellen by the arm.
"Come. Follow me as quietly as possible."

*Peggy led the men swiftly through the woods and hid them
temporarily in the Crane's barn. Then, with the help of Frank
Hurd, she went in search of a better hiding place in the ruins of an
old, old smuggler's hideout. In the garret of an old cottage near
the ruins she found her brother very ill. Frank returned to guide
the fugitives to this new hiding-place, while Peggy watched over Jim.*

As Peggy sat watching her delirious brother, she began
to feel as if she were part of a horrible dream. The little
draughty room under the roof was patched up with all kinds
of spoil from the ruins and, in the flickering light from her
lantern, the beams in the ceiling seemed to waver and the
ugly stains and patches on the partition walls, as she gazed,
seemed to turn into uncanny shapes and shadows.

Presently Jim too grew quieter, and his sister, crouching
on the floor beside him, stiff and chilled to the bone, almost
lost the sense of where she was and what she was doing.
Suddenly she heard steps on the rickety ladder and thought,
with a sigh of relief, "Frank at last!"

But it was not he. Peggy stared in astonishment at a
grotesque figure in the doorway, clad in a very hideous
cotton sunbonnet and a ragged homespun gown.
Thoroughly mystified, Peggy continued to gaze, till the
thing bent over the bed and muttered hoarsely, "Wake up,
Jim Lydgate. Wake, I say!"

Jim made not the slightest response, but the harsh, too-
carrying voice effectively roused his guardian. "Stop, stop,
don't wake him," she exclaimed angrily. "Who are you?
What do you want?"

The intruder turned towards her, saying, with solemnity,
"Peggy Lydgate, I must know what the boy has done with

the green carpet bag. If it falls into wrong hands, it will mean ruin to many."

She flashed her lantern full on the face framed in the sunbonnet and knew it for that of the rebel whom she had spared—almost against her conscience.

"He is past telling you anything," she answered passionately. "Go. If he dies it is you who have to answer for his death."

"I must wake him. Jim! Jim Lydgate!" and Mackenzie laid his hand heavily on the sleeper. "I tell you, girl, those papers are of more importance than any ordinary life."

"Go. Go," insisted Peggy, clutching his arm.

He tried to shake her off.

"Listen," she muttered. "The soldiers! Are you mad? I hear them, I tell you. Leave this room instantly. I will not save you a second time. Go, or I will call out to them."

Mackenzie straightened himself, pushing up the sunbonnet on one side that he might hear the better. For a moment he had thought Peggy's cry of "The soldiers!" just a bluff, but now he realized that the pursuers were on his track.

"Call out from the window," he said with a grimace. "If I am to be taken, why shouldn't you get the thousand pounds as well as another?"

"You are mad," cried Peggy, in a rage. "As if I would touch that money! There are lots of holes and corners in this crazy place. Crawl in somewhere. Why did you come to trouble us again?"

"Those papers," said Mackenzie, "and someone put temptation in my way in the shape of this disguise. Shall I risk trying its virtues on those fellows below?"

Peggy stamped her foot. "Don't be foolish," she cried, and holding her lantern now high, now low, she scanned every possibility of hiding in the patched-up little room. "There, there," and she pointed to a spot, almost at the

level of the floor, against which the porch of the original
cottage broke out into a fancy gable, leaving a small
triangular recess. Across this a few rough boards had been
carelessly nailed. "Come here," she said imperiously.
"Help me to pull off this lower board, then you can crawl
in there. Be quick, they are poking about the ruins now."

Between them they pulled off the board. It gave way
with a disconcerting snap, and with difficulty, Mackenzie
crept into the recess. Peggy put the board back in place....

A thundering rap on the old door just beneath him gave
warning that his pursuers had not wearied of the search.
The rap was repeated and a loud voice shouted, "Open, in
the King's name."

The noise provoked an answering hubbub within, but to
Peggy's terror, Jim paid no attention to the outcry. He
neither spoke nor moved. His sister was in despair till it
suddenly occurred to her—this was the help he so sorely
needed. Jim was suffering for his loyalty, and Loyalists
would take him to safety.

She hastily descended the ladder to find the kitchen
full of armed men, trying to extract information from the
terrified widow and children. But Peggy did not wait for
the militia captain, whose face was half familiar, to speak to
her. She confronted him and plunged headlong into her
tale.

"Please, sir, help me. I have found my brother here
wounded. We could get no news of him after he left home
on Tuesday to try to get our cousin back to her family in
Toronto. That American, Craig, shot at him and kept him
here a prisoner in a garret where he will get his death of cold.
Please, please help me to take him away. You know me,
don't you, Captain Anderson?" Peggy had suddenly
remembered the name of the burly Hannahsville farmer;
but he found it difficult to follow the flow of her eloquence.

"What's this you say? Who are you, Miss?"

"Peggy Lydgate! Lesley Lydgate's daughter. We
live just across the Creek from here." More slowly she

told her tale again, and the facts of it began to shape themselves into a sort of meaning in the captain's mind. But, before he could answer, one of his men, whom the others called Mick, and who was especially eager to make sure of the promised reward for the capture of the rebel leader, said roughly, "Let the girl wait. While she talks, Mackenzie may escape us after all."

Under the circumstances, Peggy had a particular objection to being questioned, so she played a bold game and again besought the captain to come up and see her wounded brother.

"Where is he?" asked Anderson.

She led the way up to the garret and, as she expected, several of the militiamen followed. She guessed, however, that most of them were not more eager than herself to see the fugitive captured.

The captain looked intently at the wounded boy, saying, "Hallo, do any of you fellows know where the doctor is? This lad is in a pretty bad way, I'm thinking."

One of the men answered, "He's on the hunt with the rest, somewhere about the old place. Shall I find him?"

"Do," replied Anderson. Then he turned to the others. "See any sign hereabouts of the old fox, lads?"

At that instant Jim began to moan and toss about, and Peggy, rearranging the ragged quilts, lest he should be chilled, made as if she was unaware of the movements of the men in the tiny room. Yet somehow she knew perfectly well that Mick was on his knees behind her glaring into the triangular recess; and she could hardly refrain from turning round to see what was happening. But she was afraid to face the light lest someone should read the secret in her eyes.

Every moment she expected to hear Mackenzie cough or fidget, for she had small opinion of his discretion. Finally she was convinced she could hear his breathing, and she almost laughed with sheer relief, when a newly arrived Englishman said, "What's the trouble, Mick? You are puffing like one of them new-fangled steam-engines they are using in England to save coach-horses. Think you've got him?"

"Reminds me of a dog with his nose in a rat-hole," observed another. "Are you going to stick there on your knees all night, man? Mackenzie may be a little bit of a fellow, but he's got a fine big head on him, and he couldn't get in between those cracks no-how."

Mick rose with a disappointed air. "No, I suppose not," he admitted.

He lurched down the ladder, just as the doctor (turned soldier for the time) came to see Jim. He made a hasty examination, and said, "He's in bad shape to move, but we must get him out of this, or he'll die of cold," and to Peggy's satisfaction he speedily made arrangements to take the still-unconscious lad to the Cranes'.

Just as they were leaving Dixon's cottage, Frank, who had been pressed into service to carry a message for Anderson, joined the party, and contrived to tell Peggy what had kept him and to hear her story. Afterwards, when the coast was clear, he guided Mackenzie and his younger comrade through the bitterly cold waters of the neighbouring stream, now thick with drifting ice, to the house of a friendly Scotch farmer, who gave them a meal and dry clothing and volunteered to lead them to a spot where the Twelve Mile Creek could be crossed on a fallen tree.

We can follow the fortunes of the rebel leader no farther, except to say that, owing to the faithfulness of many friends and the generosity of not a few political opponents, he succeeded in effecting his escape to the United States. There he spent a dozen years in exile and poverty. He was then suffered to return to Canada; and lived long enough to see the dawn of a new era of liberty and fair government in the country which (whatever his mistakes) he had loved much and had sincerely tried to serve.

—*Emily P. Weaver*
From *The Only Girl*

WHOSO LOSETH HIS LIFE

The Victoria Cross stands above all other British awards for bravery.
In the Second World War, 1939-1945, Canadians won sixteen Victoria
Crosses, eight of these being awarded after death (posthumously). Here
we read of a Canadian hero of the air.

"Hey, fellows, look what I've found! A four-leafed
clover!" called "Andy" Mynarski to his seven·comrades
in Air Force blue.

"I'll bet you stuck the fourth leaf on, then," teased
George Brophy, rolling over the grass to see what Andy held.

"O.K., wise guy, I'll give it to you, then, just to prove
my heart's in the right place," laughed Andy, tossing the
bit of green into his friend's lap.

The eight Canadians made up the crew of a Lancaster
heavy bomber, flying with the famous Moose Squadron of
the R.C.A.F. Andy, whose home was in Winnipeg,
Manitoba, was then Warrant Officer Mynarski, later to be
Pilot Officer Mynarski. He was mid-upper gunner on the
bomber. His friend George, from Port Arthur, Ontario,
was Flying Officer Brophy. He was the rear-gunner, whose
dangerous duty post was in the turret at the tail of the
plane. Besides these two chums, there were Flying Officer
Arthur de Breyne, pilot; Flying Officer Arthur Body,
Navigator; Pilot Officer John Friday, Air-Bomber; Pilot
Officer William Kelly, Wireless Operator—all men of the
Royal Canadian Air Force—and Flight Sergeant Roy
Vigars, of the Royal Air Force, as Flight Engineer.

On this warm evening of June 12, 1944, the boys were
sitting on the grass in the shadow of the huge bomber.
It was just six days after the historic D-Day of the war,
which marked the Allied invasion of German strongholds
along the coast of Europe. Day and night, bombers
roared over enemy targets. Tonight, this particular crew
had been given their orders for the night raid, and were
waiting now for the hour to take-off.

As they sat or lay on the cool grass, they talked and

laughed together, more like schoolboys waiting for the school bell than men on the brink of a perilous mission. But it was not that they failed to realize the danger, or belittle it. Simply, they knew well their duty, and faced it with stout and courageous hearts, like many thousands of their comrades in arms.

Soon the waiting was over. The bomber showed signs of life. The men climbed aboard. Half an hour later, the giant craft rose slowly from the earth, and soared away into the darkening sky.

The night was clear, although a light mist hovered close to the ground. De Breyne took the plane high over the English Channel, and each man gave all his attention to his particular duty.

With its great heart throbbing steadily, the big bomber rode through the night, drawing nearer and nearer to the target, which was the railway yards at Cambrai. Looking earthward, the airmen saw flames licking wickedly through the town, showing up their target in the darkness. Through the clouds the dim shapes of other Allied bombers were visible, and the watchful gunners in the Lancaster saw a German night fighter shoot out of the shadows to attack a bomber above them.

About fifteen minutes after midnight, Friday, the bomb aimer passed word over the "inter-com." to the navigator that the time had come to bomb the railway yards. Each man settled grimly to his allotted duty. The plane went into its bombing run. But the bombs were not dropped on the target. For, just then, George, from his position in the rear turret, glimpsed a Nazi night fighter heading after them in the dark sky.

"Enemy fighter behind. Guess he's picking us up," called George over the inter-com. to the pilot.

Instantly, de Breyne took evasive action to dodge the fighter. For a moment, it seemed the trick had worked, as the Nazi disappeared in the clouds. All too soon, however, the rear-gunner saw it had failed. The fighter plane came swiftly into view again, this time directly below the Lancaster.

"We've had it," said each man to himself.

But there was no time to think about it. Just as the crew of the bomber realized their deadly danger, the guns of the Nazi plane blazed. The Lancaster rocked and shuddered and orange flames burst from its fuselage. Both starboard engines were disabled. It was no longer possible to hope to keep the craft in the air.

"Abandon ship," came the order as the flames crackled through the body of the bomber.

Each man looked to his parachute gear and began to make his way to the nearest escape hatch. Andy, coming from his post in the mid-gun turret, looked through the mounting flames for his pal George. To his horror, he saw that the rear turret was cut off by fire from any escape hatch. The levers that swung this turret to right or left, so opening or closing the door into the main body of the bomber, were damaged beyond use. George was hopelessly trapped in the blazing tail of the doomed aircraft.

Turning without hesitation from the path to safety, Andy beat his way through the smoke and flame of the pitching bomber. Frantically, he tugged at the jammed levers. Inside the turret, George struggled for his very life. But the levers would not move. The turret door remained blocked. The fire licked eagerly at Andy's flying boots; his clothing began to catch fire.

"Go back, Andy! Bail out! It's no use," cried George. But Andy still worked at the twisted mechanism. One by one the other crew members jumped from the blazing plane.

"Get going, Andy! You're on fire, and you can't help me anyway," shouted George, despairingly motioning his loyal friend to leave him to his fate.

By this time, all the other crew members, except the pilot, had jumped. Andy seemed to realize at last how hopeless was his task. He turned from his vain struggling. Staggering through the swirling, choking smoke and searing flames, he reached the escape hatch. By this time, much of his clothing and even his parachute were ablaze.

For a second he straightened, with his back to the escape hatch, facing his trapped friend. Outlined in his burning clothes, he stood motionless, lifted his right hand to his brow in salute, then turned and swung out into the night.

The pilot, seeing that all his crew, except the ill-fated rear-gunner, had bailed out, and knowing nothing more could be done, followed his men through the front hatch.

He and three of his crew were picked up and helped to safety by the French underground. Two others were taken prisoner and were released at the end of the war.

But the trapped gunner did not die after all. As the blazing bomber crashed to earth, it burst apart in the mighty impact, throwing him clear of the wreckage.

Half an hour after he had hopelessly waved his chum away, George was lying alone and alive in a French field.

No such miracle saved the life of brave Andy Mynarski, however. In another French field, some distance away, the gallant airman reached the ground in a mass of flames. French workers beat out the fire and did their best for him, but five minutes afterwards Andrew Charles Mynarski "laid down his life for his friend."

Many months later, the Victoria Cross was awarded posthumously to Pilot Officer Mynarski.

In the official story of this award, there are these words:

Pilot Officer Mynarski must have been fully aware that in trying to free the rear-gunner he was almost certain to lose his own life. . . . Willingly accepting the danger, Pilot Officer Mynarski lost his life. . . .

—Mabel Tinkiss Good
From *Men of Valour*

PRINCESS ELIZABETH SPEAKS

Princess Elizabeth, the elder daughter of King George VI, broadcast this moving message to the British Empire from Capetown, South Africa, on her twenty-first birthday, April 21, 1947. Princess Elizabeth pledged, to devote her life to the service of the British Commonwealth and urged the youth of the Empire to help her ease the burden of the older generation which bore the responsibilities of the Second Great War.

On my 21st birthday, I welcome the opportunity to speak to all the peoples of the British Commonwealth and Empire, wherever they live, whatever race they come from and whatever language they speak.

Let me begin by saying "thank you" to all the thousands of kind people who have sent me messages of goodwill. This is a happy day for me, but it is also one that brings serious thoughts—thoughts of life looming ahead with all its challenges and with all its opportunity.

. . . .

At such a time it is a great help to know that there are multitudes of friends all round the world who are thinking of me and who wish me well. I am grateful, and I am deeply moved.

As I speak to you today from Capetown I am 6,000 miles from the country where I was born, but I am certainly not 6,000 miles from home. Everywhere I have travelled in these lovely lands of South Africa and Rhodesia my parents, my sister and I have been taken to the heart of their people and made to feel that we are just as much at home here as if we had lived among them all our lives.

That is the great privilege belonging to our place in the world-wide Commonwealth—that there are homes ready to welcome us in every continent of the earth. Before I am much older I hope I shall come to know many of them.

Although there is none of my father's subjects from the oldest to the youngest whom I do not wish to greet, I am thinking especially today of all the young men and women who were born about the same time as myself and have grown up like me in the terrible and glorious years of the Second Great War. Will you, the youth of the British family of nations, let me speak on my birthday as your representative?

.   .   .   .

Now that we are coming to manhood and womanhood, it is surely a great joy to us all to think we shall be able to take some of the burden off the shoulders of our elders who have fought and worked and suffered to protect our childhood.

We must not be daunted by the anxieties and hardships that the war has left behind for every nation of our Commonwealth. We know that these things are the price we cheerfully undertook to pay for the high honour of standing alone seven years ago in defense of the liberty of the world.

Let us say with Rupert Brooke, "Now God be thanked who has matched us with His hour."

I am sure that you will see our difficulties in the light that I see them, the great opportunity for you and me. Most of you have read in the history books the proud saying of William Pitt that England had saved herself by her exertions and would save Europe by her example. But in our time we may say that the British Empire has saved the world first, and has now to save herself after the battle is won.

I think that is an even finer thing than was done in the days of the past, and it is for us who have grown up in these years of danger and glory to see that it is accomplished in the long years of peace that we all hope stretch ahead.

If we all go forward with an unwavering faith, a high courage and a quiet heart, we shall be able to make of this ancient Commonwealth which we all love dearly an even grander thing—more free, more prosperous, more happy and a more powerful influence for good in the world—than it has been in the greatest days of our forefathers. To accomplish that we must give nothing less than the whole of ourselves.

. . . .

There is a motto which has been borne by many of my ancestors—a noble motto, "I serve." Those words were an inspiration to many bygone heirs to the throne when they made their knightly dedication as they came to manhood.

I cannot do quite as they did, but through the inventions of science I can do what was not possible for any of them, I can make my solemn act of dedication with a whole Empire listening.

I should like to make that dedication now. It is very simple.

I declare before you all that my whole life, whether it be long or short, shall be devoted to your service and the service of our great imperial family to which we all belong, but I shall not have strength to carry out this resolution alone unless you join in it with me, as I now invite you to do.

I know that your support will be unfailingly given.

God help me to make good my vow and God bless all of you who are willing to share in it.

READ A BOOK

Canadian Painters. By Richard S. Lambert. McClelland and Stewart. Short biographies of famous painters of Canada.

When Canada was New France. By George H. Locke. Dent. The founding of Canada by the French.

Canada and Her Neighbours. By Griffith Taylor. Ginn. A modern geography of our country.

The Only Girl. By Emily P. Weaver. Macmillan. Pioneer life in Ontario in the days of the MacKenzie rebellion.

By Paddle and Saddle. By Olive Knox. Macmillan. The travels by stage coach of a young Scottish lad in western Canada in the early nineteenth century.

Hill-Top Tales. By Don McCowan. Macmillan. Tales of fearless voyagers and trail-blazers of early days, in which animals of all kinds play their parts.